68000, 68010 and 68020 Primer

Stan Kelly-Bootle and Bob Fowler

Howard W. Sams & Co., Inc.
A Subsidiary of Macmillan, Inc.
4300 West 62nd Street, Indianapolis, Indiana 46268 U.S.A.

FIRST EDITION
FIRST PRINTING—1985

International Standard Book Number: 067-22405-4
Library of Congress Catalog Card Number: 85-61636

Typography by Walker Graphics
Printed in the United States of America

To my childers everywhere:
Edmund Paul, Michèle Rose,
Carol Ann, David Russell
and rather late, alas,
Anna Clare

—Stan Kelly-Bootle

To Guruprem Singh Khalsa,
whose encouragement, inspiration,
and vision over the years have helped
to prepare me for this task

—B.F.

Acknowledgments

We were tempted for a while to break with tradition, and claim that this book was entirely our own work, conceived, written and produced with no outside help whatsoever! Honesty and chivalry, though, combined with threats from certain quarters, finally convinced us that we should pay our respects in the customary manner.

First, we must thank Motorola's MOS Integrated Circuit Group without whom (as they say) our primer would undoubtedly be devoted to a less interesting and rewarding family of chips. In particular, we are grateful to James J. Farrell III, Technical Communications Manager, and Margaret Dickie at Motorola Inc., Austin, Texas for their courteous help with permissions, pictures and diagrams.

Our debt to writers on the M68000 and 16/32 bit micros in general is enormous and must here be condensed to a simple, nonexhaustive enumeration: Stritter, Treddenick, Scanlon, Starnes, Kane, Hawkins, Leventhal, Alexandridis, Waite, Morgan.

Editorially, we received encouragement from James Rounds of Howard W. Sams & Co., helpful advice from Dr. Roger C. Gledhill of International Micro Technologies, Inc., and much-needed cajolery from Mitch Waite and Jerry Volpe of The Waite Group.

On the production side, we would like to thank Lynella Cordell and her staff at The Waite Group, who together with Marla Rabinowitz and Walter Lynam resolved the many typographical and stylistic problems created by our keystrokes.

Our program examples were derived from work on the Alpha Microsystems Am-100/L™ using their M68 Assembler. The authors wish to thank Alpha Microsystems and the San Francisco Chapter of AMUS (Alphamicro Users' Society) for their technical assistance. We also benefited from many informal discussions with Dr. Michael Godfrey of ICL, London and Bob Toxen of Stratus Computer, Inc., Boston. Nevertheless, we accept full responsibility for any residual bugs and welcome your polite corrections.

Stan Kelly-Bootle proclaims his everlasting devotion to his wife Iwonka and step-daughter Natasha Leof for their love and support throughout the project.

Contents

Introduction

This primer is intended for the growing number of programmers and hobbyists, both novice and experienced, who want to understand the powerful **instruction set** of the Motorola M68000 family of 16/32-bit microprocessors. The instruction set represents the language built into the chip, and ultimately, all programs written for the M68000, whether in ADA, BASIC, C language, assembly language, or whatever, need to be translated "down" to this level.

With 8-bit micros it was tricky but possible to hand code at the machine level without assemblers. With 16-bit instruction words (up to seven of them per instruction) hand coding is strictly for masochists too tight to buy an assembler. So the M68000 instruction set will usually be studied in the context of an assembler.

The authors' attempts to master M68000 assemblers revealed a monstrous, horrifying gap in the literature. There was no patient elementary introduction even to those basic instructions and addressing modes that are common to all M68000 models. More understandably, there were no popular expositions of the exciting extensions available on the MC68010 virtual machine chip and the full-32-bit mainframe-micro MC68020. This primer is our selfless attempt to fill both gaps.

You can view the book as a painless "first pass" for all those who wish to gain fluency in any of the many fine M68000 assemblers and cross-assemblers now available (see Appendix E).

Assembly language documentation can be pretty daunting unless you already understand how the op codes work, and many of the manuals are less than clear on which addressing modes are legal with which instruction. Beyond that you face the hurdles of directives, macros, conditionals, libraries, linkers, overlays, monitor calls, and so on — all of which can vary from assembler to assembler.

Yet the rewards are great. Quite apart from the obvious advantages — speed and compactness (notice how often advertisements for software boast,

"Written in tight, fast assembly language!"), we know of no greater joy in computing than successfully running one's own first sizeable chunk of assembled code. There is a feeling of, "Wow, we did it – the 68000 and me!"

Our book should also be useful for those wanting to experiment with the various M68000 educational single board kits and systems.

We have purposely avoided a detailed exploration of the M68000 microelectronics and IC technology. Our bird's eye view of the M68000 hardware is a simple "black-box" approach, but sufficient, we hope, to reveal the subtle interplay of hardware and software as realized by the Motorola design team. If you want to delve deeper (and in the field of computers there is no bottom layer beyond possible delving) this book will help you tackle the vast technical literature on M68000 architecture and timing, support chips, I/O, coprocessors and systems integration.

Success breeds success — a maxim which is compounded in the microcomputer industry. All semiconductor prices fall dramatically as fabrication volume and yield increase, so successful chips like the M68000, especially the economy MC68008 version, are inevitably finding their way into the low-cost entry-level personal and home computer market. The basic MC68000, now available for around $50 each in small quantities, can already be found playing diverse roles in graphics workstations and multiuser business systems — not only on the main CPU (central processing unit) board, but also powering intelligent device drivers and I/O (input/output) preprocessors. Even the more expensive MC68010 is found lurking inside peripherals, such as the Apple laser printer.

The MC68020 chip, currently selling for $500 in small quantities, seems certain to fall in price to the MC68000 level over the next few years. The impact on personal and office computing will be staggering!

The Apple Macintosh has already given us a glimpse of what can be done with the power of a basic 16/32-bit MC68000. The user-friendliness we associate with crisp, bit-mapped screens, icons, windows, and mouse-controlled pulldown menus puts heavy demands on CPU and memory.

The MC68020's extra speed (16.67 MHz, with fast RAM to match), lower power consumption (1.5 watts), built-in coprocessor interface for economical multiprocessing and number-crunching support, and increased memory addressing space (over 4 billion bytes) — will allow bigger and friendlier operating systems, more complex color graphics (including animation), and less unnatural high-level query languages providing easier access to large databases.

An added bonus will be the ability to offer several operating systems on the same machine, solving many of the present compatibility quirks ("what runs on what?") and ending once and for all those tiresome medieval disputes such as "UNIX versus AMOS" or "CP/M versus PC-DOS." Our book will prepare you for this revolution!

All members of the M68000 family share the same basic instruction set, with each enhanced model building up from the previous simpler model. This concept of **upwards compatibility** at the object code level provides vital insurance for all software developers, both the individual "hacker" and the major software houses. For as fast as hardware prices shrink, the cost of programming escalates. The M68000 was designed with ease of programming and debugging in mind, and further, with the assurance that whatever advances might occur in IC techniques, programs will run without change on all future models. We will all undoubtedly have new things to learn as the revolution unrolls apace, but readers should be happy to know that little in this book will have to be *unlearned*.

PREREQUISITES

Exactly how much prior knowledge should be assumed is a problem faced by all computer book authors. We have veered in the direction of assuming less rather than more exposure to computer basics, and we rely on your own judgment to skip any familiar material.

Chapter 1, for example, is a quick summary of some essential microprocessor concepts that you are invited to bypass at your own discretion.

Our strategy was conditioned by the fact that a new generation of programmers, the class of '85, is entering the field with little or no prior exposure to the previous (dying?) generation of 8-bit micros. If you have done any assembly language programming on the Intel™ 8080™, Zilog Z80™ or Motorola M6800, for instance, many of the M68000 op codes will be old friends (at least functionally), and you will be able to concentrate on the subtleties introduced by the richer set of addressing modes. But for those new to the world of op codes, we have tried to explain both the function and the motivation for each instruction, with lots of simple examples. We have carefully chosen the order in which the instructions are introduced, grouping together those which share some fundamental property.

There are four appendices (A – D) that list the op codes and addressing modes in different ways, plus a pullout reference card.

BOOK PLAN

After the optional basic concepts in Chapter 1 (we dismissed the corny notion of calling this Chapter 0), Chapter 2 gives some historical and design perspectives and lists the features distinguishing the five M68000 models currently available. Chapter 3 explains the chip from a software perspective (memory organization and register disposition). The instructions and addressing modes are then progressively described with examples, starting with the most common and useful in Chapter 4, accelerating gently to more advanced op codes in Chapter 5. Chapter 6 deals with the remaining instructions. Chapter 7 explains the VM concept in relation to the MC68010. Finally, Chapter 8 discusses the many enhancements found in the new full-32-bit MC68020.

M68000 RESOURCES

If, as we hope, you are encouraged to explore the M68000 scene in more depth, we have listed some sources for hardware and software in Appendix E. Be warned that no such list can claim to be complete or entirely accurate by the time you come to read it. Prices and telephone numbers are especially volatile.

As you can see, the M68000 has been implemented in an incredibly wide variety of microcomputer systems, ranging from the under-$500 home computers, through the sophisticated $1,500-$3,000 personal computer bracket (highlighted by the ubiquitous Apple® Macintosh™), on through the professional $5,000+ UNIX™ workstations (from over 20 different manufacturers at our last count) — the IBM® 9000 laboratory system, multiuser business systems from AlphaMicro, Stride, Cromemco — the list grows daily.

From $200 to $200,000, they all use **MOVE.z Dm,Dn**! When you reach Chapter 4, you'll know why.

1

Basic Microprocessor Concepts

Inasmuch as the completed device will be a general-purpose computing machine it should contain certain main organs relating to arithmetic, memory storage, control, and connection with the human operator.

— A. W. Burkes, H. H. Goldstine, and J. von Neumann, *Preliminary Discussion of the Logical Design of an Electronic Computing Instrument* (1946)

This chapter presents a number of useful basic ideas that you will need to better understand the M68000 family. Primers, by definition, cannot assume too much prior knowledge, so we will warn you, up front, that we plan to cover such fundamentals as bits, bytes, binary arithmetic, and busses which are essential for later chapters.

MICROPROCESSORS

On first hearing the word *microprocessor* one immediately senses that we are talking of something small, and it is indeed a physically small computing component on a silicon chip (*micro* is a common prefix in science standing for a millionth part, as in microsecond).

The MPU (MicroProcessing Unit) is just one element, or resource, in a computer **system**. Figures 1-1 and 1-2 show typical computer systems. The MPU chip, when mounted on a circuit board with other essential supporting chips, is often referred to as a microcomputer or an MPS (MicroProcessing System) or a CPU (Central Processing Unit).

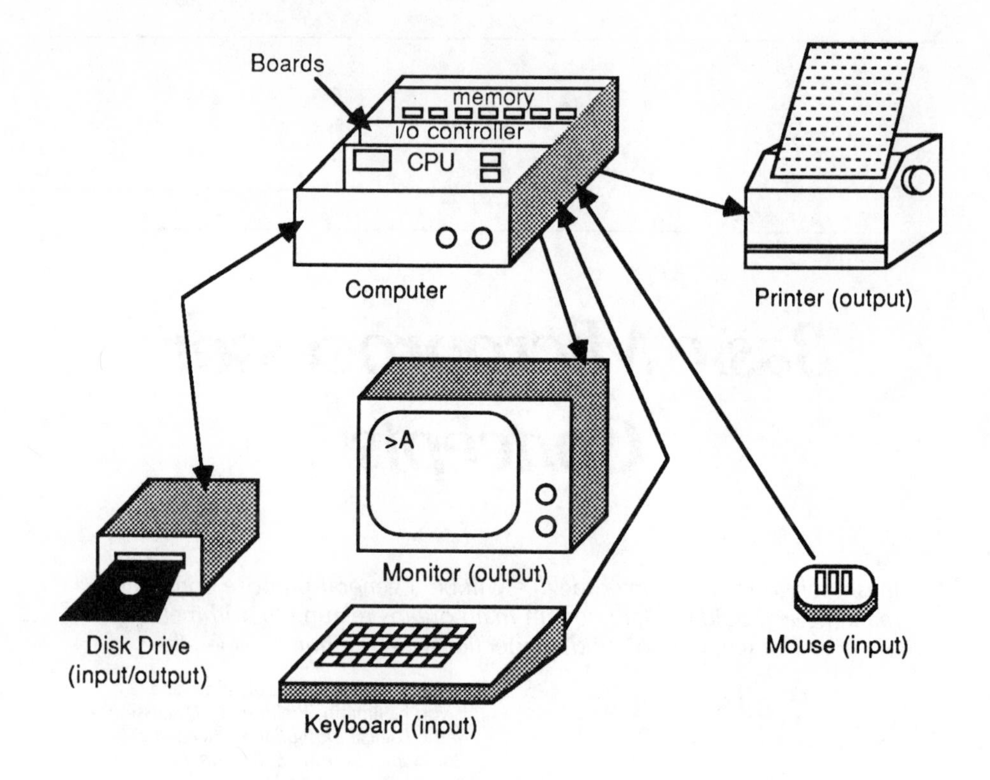

Fig. 1-1 Typical Small Computer System

The MPU is often called the brains of the system, the resource with programmable intelligence that coordinates all the other dumb elements connected to it. MPUs have logical and arithmetical abilities, and they make decisions and exert control in many ways. You will see, however, that all this occurs in a predetermined way, set up by **programs** (sequences of precise instructions).

MPUs are no longer the most expensive component in the system, and several MPUs may be found in the one system (which is then labeled a multiprocessor system). Quite often there is one **master** MPU with several **slave** MPUs assigned to particular duties; sometimes each MPU is an independent source of intelligence that can be called on to process any job.

PROCESSING WHAT?

But what and why are you processing? Cuisinarts process food, and sewage plants process sewage, but microprocessors process **data** and (with the help of many attached gadgets and carefully detailed programs) they produce **information**.

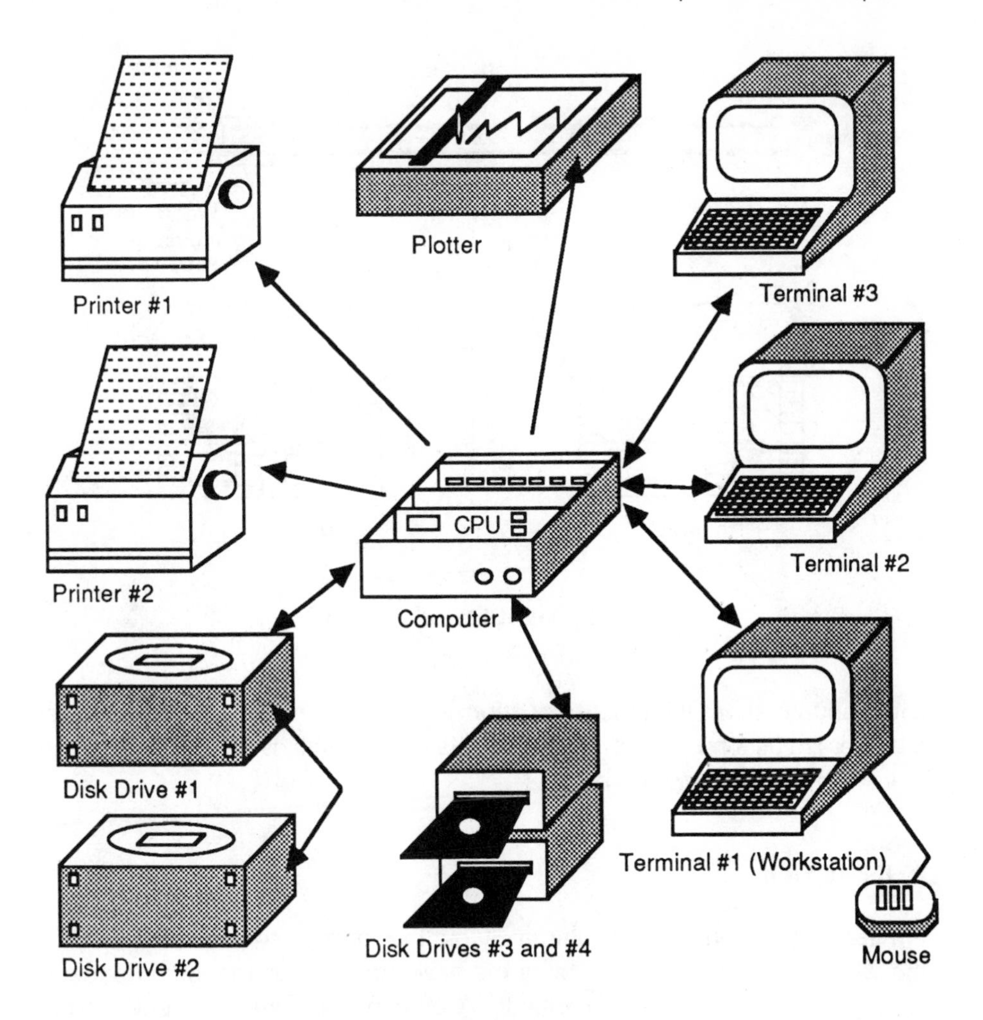

Fig. 1-2 Typical Multiuser System

If this sounds abstract and intangible, well, in a sense, it is. The computer is a very general-purpose, blind manipulator of symbols — it is you, the user, who gives meaning and purpose to its processes.

Throughout the following discussions, we will use the word data as a singular, collective noun.

Information and Data

Information, in everyday usage, is a strange something that reduces uncertainty. In the 1940s Claude E. Shannon of Bell Labs refined this vague idea into a whole new branch of mathematics, known as **information theory**. He showed

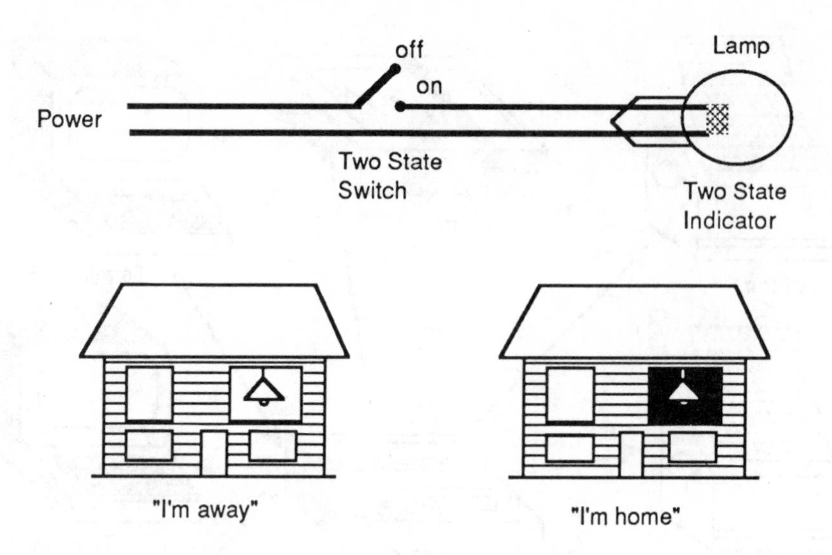

Fig. 1-3 Light Switch as a Bit

that in many situations the amount of information in a message can be measured and expressed as a number of **binary digits** or **bits**. Milk is traded in pints, but you order information by the bit.

BITS IN ACTION

The miracle of computing rests ultimately on this concept — one of the simplest in the whole of mathematics. A bit is the basic unit of information, capable of resolving a single yes or no uncertainty. A bit can therefore represent just one of two values, usually given the symbols "0" and "1", but that can be interpreted in many ways: on and off, black and white, true and false, yes and no, but note that the bit is incapable of indicating any shades in between, like gray or maybe or perhaps.

It turns out that many physical devices, such as the familiar household electric switch, have this same on-or-off property and can therefore be used to store one bit of information.

Devices like switches which have a limited number of states are called **discrete** devices, as opposed to devices like rotary volume controls which can vary continuously through an infinite number of states.

In Figure 1-3, the state of the switch is indicated by the state of the lamp, on or off.

The information you could signal from your window using this simple one-bit device might be "Yes, I am here" or "No, I'm out of town." Ah-ha, but which is which? "Lamp-on" could signal your absence, perhaps. The message of the lamp requires a prearranged code between you and the intended receiver of the message. There are only two possibilities:

Code A	*Code B*
Lamp on = at home	Lamp on = away
Lamp off = away	Lamp off = at home

The main point is that the bit as a bearer of information is meaningless without some prior coding agreement between sender (encoder) and receiver (decoder).

Shannon defined the bit as the amount of information that would make something twice as definite! Two equally likely outcomes share a probability of 1/2 (a 50/50 chance of each), so one bit will completely resolve this amount of uncertainty, but no more. For more useful information storage you need to increase the number of bits, and at the same time devise methods for rapidly storing, accessing, changing, sending, and decoding the information.

Each bit you add to your store doubles the amount of information. For example, with two lamps in your window, you can devise a code to represent four distinct messages:

Lamp 2	*Lamp 1*	*Message*
off	off	Leave no milk today
off	on	Leave one pint
on	off	Leave two pints
on	on	Leave three pints

Once again you must ensure that the decoder (milkperson, in this case) knows the code, and especially, which lamp is which. If the lamps are not marked or distinguishable in some way, you can see that only three possible messages can be encoded. So, in order to extract the maximum benefit from our 2 bits, they must be ordered in a prearranged manner. With this proviso, there is a simple rule relating the number of bits to the number of possible encoded messages:

1 bit can encode 2 (2^1) messages
2 bits can encode $2 \times 2 = 4$ (2^2) messages
3 bits can encode $2 \times 2 \times 2 = 8$ (2^3) messages
N bits can encode $2 \times 2 \times \ldots \times 2$ (2^n) messages

For this reason, powers of 2 play a fundamental role in information theory and computing.

The case of N=10 is also important, since $2^{10} = 1,024$, which is widely abbreviated to K (as in kilo). So when you read of a 32K memory, this means 32 x 1,024 = 32,768 rather than 32,000.

The messages you encode can be anything you like — instructions, symbols, numbers, names, or perhaps even nothing at all (a perfectly valid message might be "ignore this message"). Some combinations of bits may be specially earmarked as errors. Often there are more bit patterns available than messages to be decoded. This redundancy can be exploited to detect and possibly correct transmission or storage errors.

BINARY ARITHMETIC

There is a natural way of relating these bits to familiar decimal numbers — we call it **binary arithmetic** because it uses powers of 2 with the two symbols 0 and 1, rather than powers of 10 with the ten symbols 0 through 9. Nearly all computer calculations are performed internally in binary arithmetic, even if the final results are needed in decimal form. Our two-lamp code for ordering milk has already given a hint of how this works. Given the following code:

Lamp on = 1   Lamp off = 0
Lamp 2 = 2   Lamp 1 = 1

these would be the results:

Lamp 2	*Lamp 1*	*of pints*
0	0	0
0	1	1
1	0	2
1	1	3

The decoding rule is:

pints = (2 x Lamp 2) + (1 x Lamp 1)

With three lamps we can extend our order to 7 pints as follows:

Lamp 3	*Lamp 2*	*Lamp 1*	*of pints*
0	0	0	0
0	0	1	1
0	1	0	2
0	1	1	3
1	0	0	4
1	0	1	5
1	1	0	6
1	1	1	7

Lamp 3 now carries the value 4 = (2 x 2) and we decode as follows:

pints = (4 x lamp 3) + (2 x lamp 2) + (1 x lamp 1)

You can already recognize the similarities between our usual decimal notation and this binary system. Treating the lamps as column positions, each column represents a power of 2. When you write, say, 2379 in decimal, you are using a shorthand for

2 thousands 3 hundreds 7 tens 9 units
$2 \times (10 \times 10 \times 10)$ plus $3 \times (10 \times 10)$ plus 7×10 plus $9 \times 1 = 2379$

where each column represents a power of 10. The units column may not look like a power of 10, but in fact it represents 10^0 which equals 1.

In the same way, the binary number 1101, is evaluated as:

1 eight 1 four 0 twos 1 unit
$1 \times (2 \times 2 \times 2)$ plus $1 \times (2 \times 2)$ plus 0×2 plus $1 \times 1 = 13$

We can therefore establish a straightforward correspondence between bit patterns, binary numbers, and decimal numbers. This is just one of many encoding schemes and must be agreed upon in advance as in any scheme for sending information.

To stress the role of the bit let's look again at our 3-lamp signals to the milkperson. Initially, the number of pints needed is uncertain to the extent that it lies anywhere in the range 0 through 7 (8 possibilities). Lamp 1 reduces this uncertainty as follows:

Lamp 1 on = number of pints must be 1, 3, 5 or 7
Lamp 1 off = number of pints must be 0, 2, 4 or 6

The uncertainty is now down to four possibilies, so it has effectively been halved.
Lamp 2 and Lamp 3 each independently halve the uncertainty:

Lamp 2 on = number of pints must be 2, 3, 6 or 7
Lamp 2 off = number of pints must be 0, 1, 4 or 5
Lamp 3 on = number of pints must be 4, 5, 6 or 7
Lamp 3 off = number of pints must be 0, 1, 2 or 3

All three bits (lamps) in parallel completely remove the uncertainty — just one of the eight possible messages is indicated.

The modern computer uses exactly these principles in sending and decoding messages and data. The switches and lamps are replaced by large numbers of high-speed two-state electronic devices such as transistors built into silicon chips.

SUMMARY OF BITS AND MESSAGES

With an ordered group of N bits you can encode up to 2^N distinct messages. A common encoding system relates these to the 2^N binary numbers running from 0 through $2^N - 1$. Since binary numbers can be easily stored electronically in the form of on-off switches (or gates), computers perform all their basic arithmetical and logical operations in binary.

Special Groups of Bits

Groups of 4, 8, 16, and 32 bits are so commonly encountered that they have their own names:

- A nibble = 4 bits, which can store 16 messages
- A byte = 8 bits, which can store 256 messages
- A word = 16 bits, which can store 65,536 messages
- A longword = 32 bits, which can store 4,294,967,296 messages!

These names and their associated "ranges", will crop up repeatedly because, for excellent reasons to be explained, the M68000 is designed to operate on these groups of bits.

Notice in Figure 1-4 how the bits are numbered from right to left, starting with bit 0, called the LSB (least significant bit). The highest, leftmost bit is called the MSB (most significant bit); because of a commonly used method of encoding negative numbers, the MSB is also called the **sign bit** (more on this later).

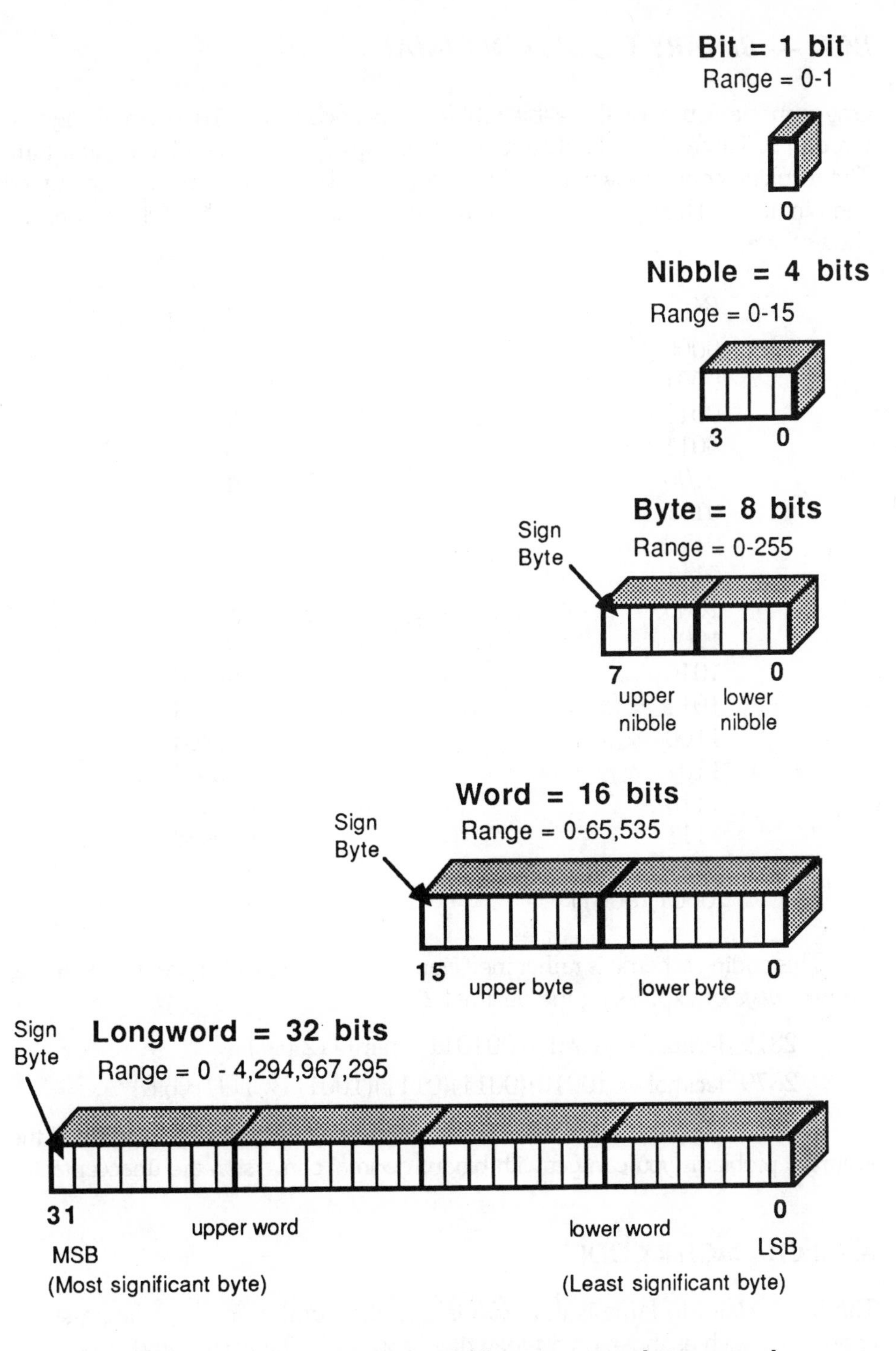

Fig. 1-4 Groups of Bits: Nibble, Byte, Word, Longword

BCD — BINARY CODED DECIMAL

One important use of the 4-bit nibble is to encode the 10 decimal digits 0 through 9. Three bits will only encode 0 through 7, so four bits is the minimum. The resulting code, known as BCD (binary coded decimal), has five unassigned combinations. They, and the binary codes for decimals 0 through eleven, are shown here:

BCD	*Decimal*
0000	0
0001	1
0010	2
0011	3
0100	4
0101	5
0110	6
0111	7
1000	8
1001	9
1010	unused
1011	unused
1100	unused
1101	unused
1110	unused
1111	unused
(0001)(0000)	10
(0001)(0001)	11

This coding scheme is rather inefficient, space-wise. Compare, for example, the two ways of expressing the decimal 2379:

2379 decimal = 100101001011 binary (12 bits)

2379 decimal = (0010)(0011)(0111)(1001) BCD (16 bits)

The main application of BCD is in financial calculations where some of the accuracy problems you can get with binary-decimal conversion are unacceptable.

ASCII CHARACTER CODE

The byte's claim to fame is that 256 is a useful number for encoding a set of characters, such as those on a typewriter keyboard. The upper- and lower-case

Table 1-1 Decimal Interpretation of 4-Bit Binary

Binary	1's Complement Mode	2's Complement Mode	Unsigned Mode
0111	7	7	7
0110	6	6	6
0101	5	5	5
0100	4	4	4
0011	3	3	3
0010	2	2	2
0001	1	1	1
0000	0	0	0
1111	−0	−1	15
1110	−1	−2	14
1101	−2	−3	13
1100	−3	−4	12
1011	−4	−5	11
1010	−5	−6	10
1001	−6	−7	9
1000	−7	−8	8

letters plus the usual crop of punctuation symbols and controls (carriage return, backspace, etc.) take up only 128 combinations (encodable in 7 bits) but since the 8-bit byte offers 256, we have lots of spares for graphics. There is a standard called ASCII (American Standard Code for Information Interchange) which assigns a symbol for each 8-bit pattern. Apart from a few variants for foreign scripts, ASCII is pretty constant around the world.

HOME ON THE RANGE

The byte can only store numbers in the unsigned range 0 through 255, so for most mathematical operations we need more than 8 bits. The situation is even worse because in order to handle negative numbers, we must steal a bit to indicate the sign (0 for plus and 1 for minus).

Under what is known as 2's complement notation (see Table 1-1) a nibble can store a number in the range −8 through +7 (still a total of 16 distinct numbers) and a byte can store a number in the range −128 through +127 (note that we are still encoding a total of 256 distinct numbers).

The bits in a byte are numbered 0 through 7 from right to left (so remember the first bit on the right is bit 0). In 2's complement form bit 7 (the leftmost) is designated the **sign-bit**.

The 16-bit **word** offers a range of 0 through 65,535 unsigned (that is, positive numbers), but if we use the sign-bit trick for negative values we can store signed (2's complement) numbers from –32,768 to +32,767.

Before the arrival of 32-bit micros, the above 16-bit data range was a restriction needing extra programming if your sums led to larger numbers. Also since 16 bits were often used to encode addresses in memory (more on this later) this resulted in a more tricky restriction on memory capacity to 65,536 different addresses (again, there were tricks in hardware and software to overcome this).

You can now guess why there is so much excitement over the arrival of 32-bit microprocessors. A 32-bit **longword** can store unsigned numbers in the range 0 through 4,294,967,295, and signed numbers in the range –2,147,483,648 through +2,147,483,647. And when you are not doing big sums, the longword can store two smaller 16-bit numbers, or four ASCII characters, or eight BCDs.

BINARY SUMS

Working with binary numbers has its good and bad aspects. On the bright side, the rules are fewer than with decimal numbers:

$1 + 0 = 1$	$1 \times 0 = 0$	$1 - 1 = 0$
$1 + 1 = 10$	$1 \times 1 = 1$	$10 - 1 = 1$

The hard part is that binary numbers are not compact; the human eye and brain suffer from reading and remembering 100101001011 compared with its decimal equivalent, 2379.

Let's add two binary numbers together manually, so you can see the rules in action:

$$
\begin{array}{rl}
10111 & = \text{decimal } 16+0+4+2+1 = 23 \\
+\ \underline{11101} & = \text{decimal } 16+8+4+0+1 = 29 \\
110100 & = \text{decimal } 32+16+0+4+0+0 = 52 \text{ (check)}
\end{array}
$$

(We proceed from the right: 1 + 1 = 10, so write 0 and carry 1, and so on.)

OCTAL AND HEXADECIMAL

We should mention here two other number notations you will encounter, both of which are easily derived from binary notation but which offer more compactness and ease of use.

The octal system uses the base 8, so that only the numbers 0 through 7 are employed, and each column represents a power of 8. Here are a few examples:

Binary	*Octal*	*Decimal*
111	7	7
1000	10	8
100000	40	32
111111	77	63

Conversion from binary to octal is very simple. The trick is to partition the binary expression into groups of 3 starting from the right. Then evaluate each group of 3 bits into decimal.

111111 = (111)(111) = (7)(7) = octal 77

100101001011 = (100)(101)(001)(011) = (4)(5)(1)(3) = octal 4513

The hexadecimal (short name **hex**) system uses a base of 16, so we need 16 distinct symbols to express numbers in hex. Our usual symbols 0 through 9 are okay for the first ten, then we borrow the letters A=10, B=11, C=12, D=13, E=14, F=15. Here are some examples:

Binary	*Octal*	*Decimal*	*Hex*
111	7	7	7
1000	10	8	8
1010	12	10	A
1111	17	15	F
100000	40	32	20
111111	77	63	3F

Once you get used to it, hex is probably the most convenient notation for 16/32-bit computer work. Each hex symbol represents a nibble, two of them make a byte, and so on. Binary-to-hex conversion can be done "at sight" using a similar trick to the binary-octal method just described. Divide the binary number into fields of 4, from the right:

111111 = (0011)(1111) = (3)(F) = hex 3F

An even easier method, if you venture into serious machine-level programming, is to buy an electronic hand calculator with instant binary, octal, decimal, and hex conversion.

Bases higher than 16 have been tried, but what you gain in compactness, you lose in legibility. The mathematician and computer pioneer, Alan M. Turing (1912-1954), was fond of the base 32. This requires, of course, 32 distinct symbols, namely 0 through 9 and the 22 letters A through V, for example. Whence: 1111111111 = 1777 (base 8) = 1023 (base 10) = 3FF (base 16) = VV (base 32). Turing's notation was even trickier since he was tied to the arbitrary 32 characters on his five-channel teleprinter (an early printer, operated from five-track paper tape).

SUMMARY OF NUMBER SYSTEMS

Numbers can be expressed using bases other than the familiar base of 10 (decimal system). Binary (base 2), octal (base 8), and hexadecimal (base 16) arise naturally in computer mathematics.

The neat thing about binary numbers is that simple and fast electronic circuits can be built that automatically perform the basic arithmetical operations (add, subtract, multiply and divide) — witness, for example, the aforementioned pocket calculator. The step from on/off switches to arithmetic requires a brief detour into logical operators and Boolean algebra.

BOOLEAN ALGEBRA

George Boole (1815-64) was the first to develop mathematical rules for logical operations, now known as Boolean algebra.

Logic deals with a particular binary situation since it labels propositions true or false. Boole therefore assigned the numeric symbols 1 for true and 0 for false, and then studied the rules for combining these using the logical operators NOT, AND and OR in place of the familiar arithmetical operators.

As in everyday "logic," if the propositions A and B are *both* true, we say that the single proposition (A AND B) is true. If either or both A and B are false, then we say (A AND B) is false. Similarly, if A is true, we say that (NOT A) is false. We commonly use the symbols

$$\wedge = \text{AND}$$
$$\vee = \text{OR}$$
$$\sim = \text{NOT}$$

Replacing true and false with 1 and 0, the rules turn out to be similar to binary arithmetic with "∧ = multiply" and "∨ = add" but there are some subtle differences:

Logic	*Boolean*	*Binary*
false OR false = false	$0 \vee 0 = 0$	$0 + 0 = 0$
true OR false = true	$1 \vee 0 = 1$	$1 + 0 = 1$
false OR true = true	$0 \vee 1 = 1$	$0 + 1 = 1$
false AND false = false	$0 \wedge 0 = 0$	$0 \times 0 = 0$
true AND true = true	$1 \wedge 1 = 1$	$1 \times 1 = 1$
true AND false = false	$1 \wedge 0 = 0$	$1 \times 0 = 0$
false AND true = false	$0 \wedge 1 = 0$	$0 \times 1 = 0$

So far, so good! But the rules diverge with:

Logic	*Boolean*	*Binary*
true OR true = true	$1 \wedge 1 = 1$	$1 + 1 = 10$
NOT(true) = false	$\sim 1 = 0$	1's complement of 1 = 0
NOT(false) = true	$\sim 0 = 1$	1's complement of 0 = 1

COMPOUND LOGICAL OPERATORS

Various compound logical operators can be defined in terms of AND, OR, and NOT. For instance NOT and AND can be combined to give NAND. The tables below (known as truth tables, since they never lie), show the compounds you'll meet in computer schematics and programming situations:

AND

A	B		A∧B
0	0	→	0
0	1	→	0
1	0	→	0
1	1	→	1

NAND (Not AND)

A	B		~(A∧B)
0	0	→	1
0	1	→	1
1	0	→	1
1	1	→	0

OR

A	B		A∨B
0	0	→	0
0	1	→	1
1	0	→	1
1	1	→	1

NOR (Not OR)

A	B		~(A∨B)
0	0	→	1
0	1	→	0
1	0	→	0
1	1	→	0

EOR (Exclusive OR)

A	B		(A∨B)∧~(A∧B)
0	0	→	0
0	1	→	1
1	0	→	1
1	1	→	0

The exclusive OR gives true when either input (but not both) is true. In normal speech we do not always distinguish between these two meanings of OR. So everyday "logic" is not always precise enough for "reasoning" with a computer.

PROGRAMMER'S LOGIC

The precision of Boolean algebra is a vital part of the programmer's life, since we are often interested in getting the system to test the outcome of a routine (true or false) and then perform different programs according to the result. An example familiar to all those who have ever tackled a tax form might be:

> If you are male, married, over 40, earning less than $10,000, or female, single, under 50 earning more than $6,000 complete line 3. Otherwise skip to line 12.

In Boolean terms this requires evaluating an expression like:

(~F x M x A>40 x SAL<10,000) + (F x ~M x A<50 x SAL>6000)

where each individual term, called a Boolean variable or expression, is set to 1 for true and 0 for false. The answer obtained by mechanically following the rules will be 1 for true (so complete line 3) or 0 for false (skip to line 12). Note that if you are male, then F ("being a female") is false = 0, while~F ("not being a female") is true = 1, and so on.

LOGIC GATES

Electronically, it is possible to build devices called **gates** that combine signals according to the rules of Boolean algebra. Figure 1-5 illustrates how these are shown in circuit diagrams. In modern micros, these gates are transistors embedded in the silicon. The MC68000, some say by coincidence, has about 68,000 such gates. (The earlier M6800 had about 6,800 transistors, so there may be some logic to Motorola's numbering scheme.) The "1" and "0" can represent any two distinct electrical states, for example "0" may mean a +5 volt signal and "1" may be 0 volts. The NOT function is called an **inverter** since it inverts 0 to 1 and 1 to 0. Gates are the basic building blocks of computers. They can be interconnected in complex patterns to perform a variety of functions, such as decoding and binary arithmetic. IC (integrated circuit) chips are available in tens of thousands of variations offering every conceivable combination of logic for the circuit designer. And if your volume is high enough, a special purpose chip may save you wiring together off-the-shelf chips.

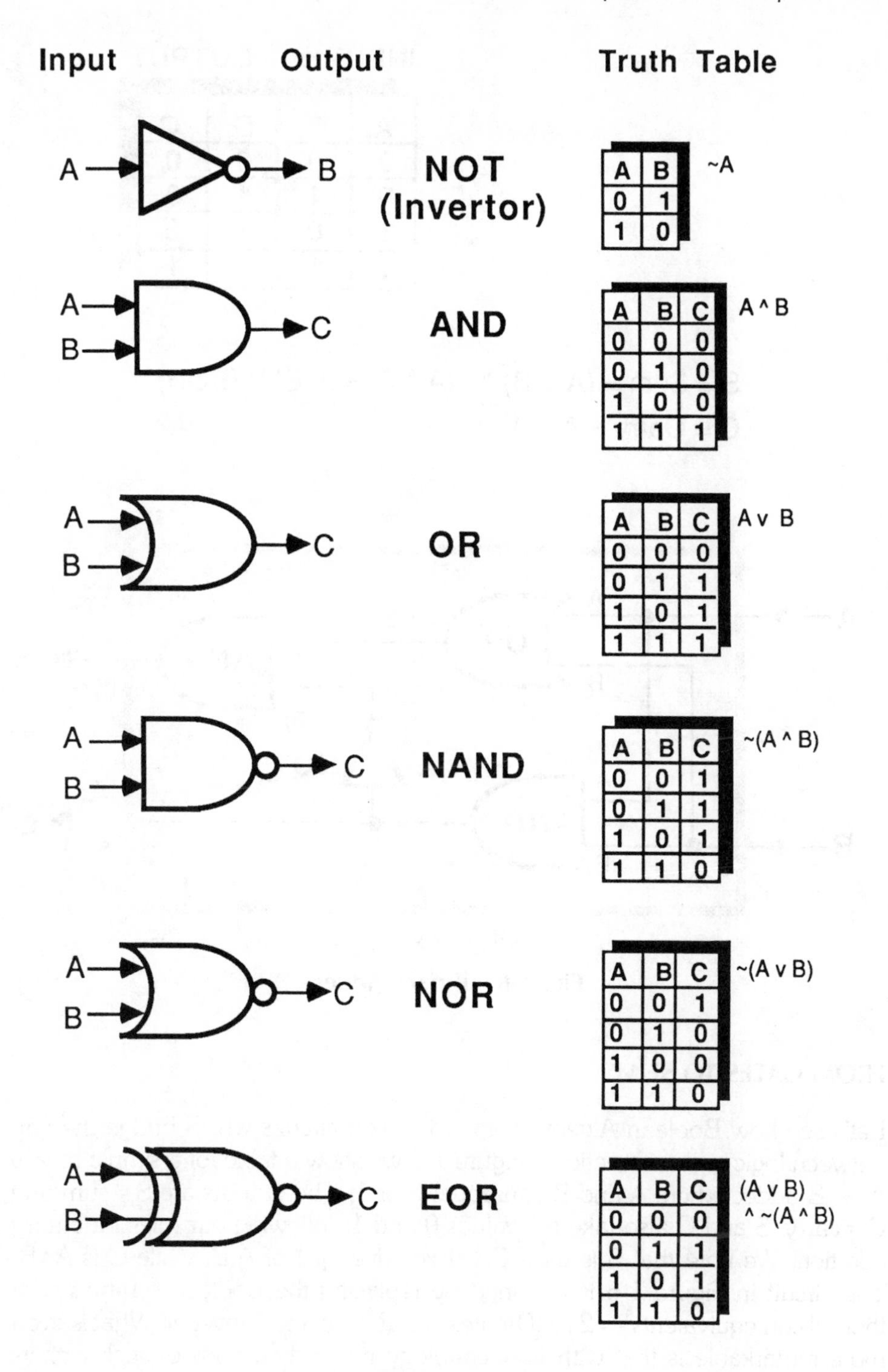

Fig. 1-5 Logic Gates

INPUT		OUTPUT	
A	B	S	C
0	0	0	0
0	1	1	0
1	0	1	0
1	1	0	1

$$S = \text{Sum} = (A \vee B) \wedge {\sim}(A \wedge B) = A \oplus B \text{ (EOR)}$$

$$C = \text{Carry} = A \wedge B$$

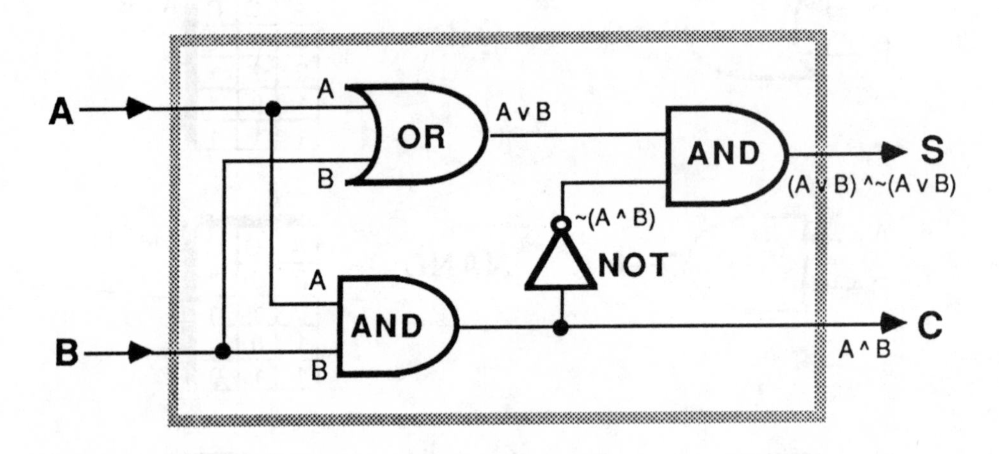

Fig. 1-6 Binary Adder

FROM GATES TO SUMS

Let's see how Boolean Algebra helps to design circuits which bridge the gap between logic and arithmetic. In Figure 1-6 we show a table for a simple binary $A + B$ adder, where A and B can equal 0 or 1. The outputs are $S = \text{sum}$ and $C = \text{carry}$. S and C also take the values 0 and 1, following our rules for binary addition. We note that S is the EOR (Exclusive OR) of A,B, while C is $A \wedge B$. The circuit in Figure 1-6 is obtained by replacing the Boolean symbols with their silicon equivalents—2 AND-gates, 1 OR-gate and 1 inverter. What is even more remarkable is that with IC technology many thousands of such circuits can be integrated into a tiny mass-produced chip.

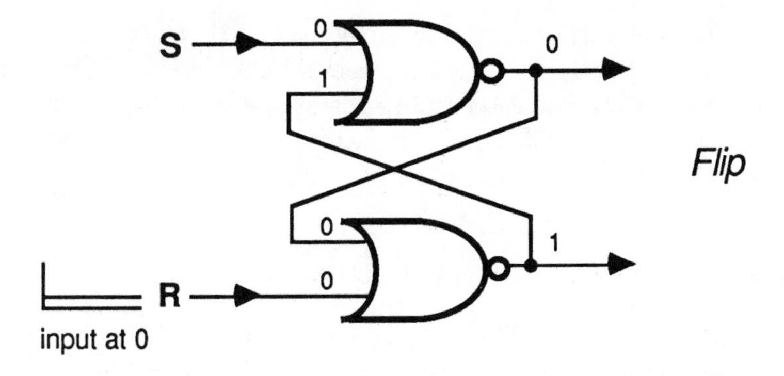

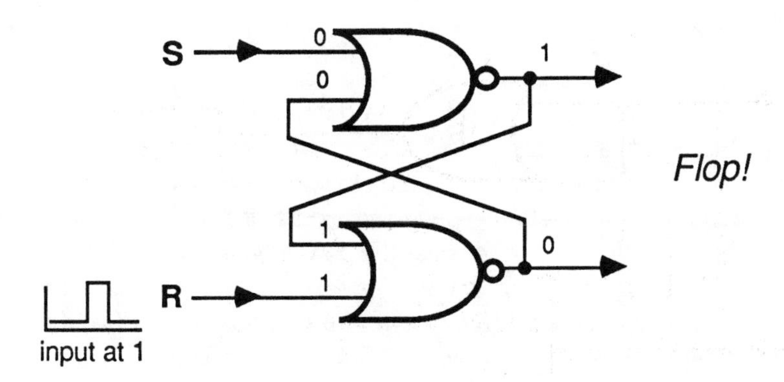

Fig. 1-7 Basic Flip-Flop

The half-adder circuit in Figure 1-6 just adds two bits together, but it is not difficult to cascade similar circuits in series to give full binary addition of 8 or 16 bits depending on the chip's architecture. A full-adder needs three inputs, since it must take in the previous "carry" bit — but the principle is as shown in Figure 1-6.

FLIP-FLOPS

Before we leave the topic of basic computer circuitry, we want to show you a clever combination of gates which indicates how data can be stored electronically. The **flip-flop** consists of two NOR-gates wired as shown in Figure 1-7. Momentarily pulsing the S (Set) and R (Reset) inputs in different ways causes the two output lines to flip-flop between 0/1 and 1/0 states. These states are remembered long after the input pulses have disappeared, so we have the basis for storing 1 bit per flip-flop, and the means of reading or writing its value. As with the binary adder, flip-flops can be wired together in wondrous ways to provide fast on-chip storage units known as **registers**.

SUMMARY OF GATES AND BINARY SUMS

We have seen, in very general terms, that the basic logical operators, AND, OR, and NOT, and their compounds NAND, NOR, and EOR, all have silicon analogues called gates. These gates can be interconnected to perform more complex functions, including binary addition and register storage.

To coordinate these networks of gates, we need another ingredient — time.

CLOCKS

The frozen-frame 1's and 0's shown as inputs A, B, S, and R in Figures 1-6 and 1-7 actually arrive as a stream of high-speed electrical pulses synchronized by a system clock. This quartz-controlled clock (which may be part of the MPU chip or a separate chip) sets the pace for a host of MPU activities. Generally speaking, the faster the clock, the faster the computer. A typical MC68000 clock would run at 8 MHz (8 million cycles per second) giving a cycle time of 125 nanoseconds (a nanosecond is a billionth of a second — 1/1,000,000,000 sec. This is the time it takes light to travel approximately 1 foot).

MICROCOMPUTERS — THE THREE COMPONENTS

We can now take a look at the overall organization of a typical microcomputer system, so we can identify the main elements prior to discussing each in detail. We will find that a microcomputer can be viewed as "three black boxes on a bus".

SYSTEM BUS

Figure 1-8 shows the system bus, a sort of wiring freeway, through which the major components, labeled **MPU**, **memory**, and **I/O** communicate with each other.

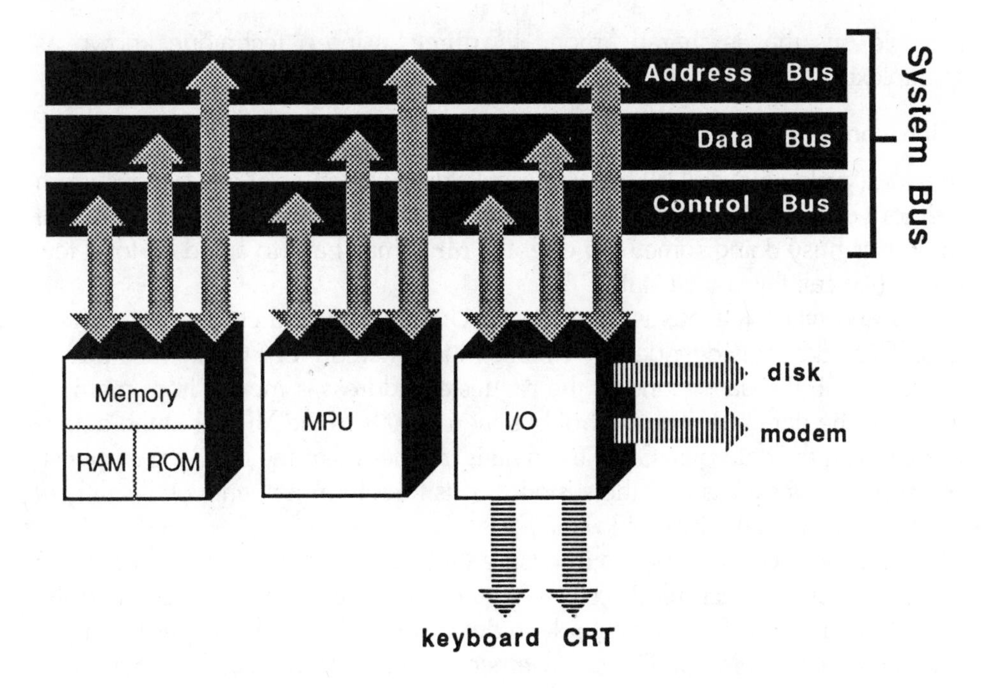

Fig. 1-8 Microcomputer System Bus

Memory

The box marked *memory*, subdivided into RAM and ROM, represents the main *immediate* storage for data and programs. Each piece of memory is assigned a unique address allowing fast, random access by the MPU. ROM is read only memory, whereas RAM (Random Access Memory) can be read from or written to.

I/O — Input/Output

The single black box marked I/O (input/output) covers a multitude of devices — disk units, user terminals, printers, modems and so on — each with its own particular interfacing hardware circuits (known as I/O controllers) supported by dedicated software such as terminal drivers. I/O is the area of most direct visibility and concern to the average user. In the midst of our microelectronic delving we must not lose sight of the average user, keying in data and printing pie charts.

The system bus carries three kinds of **signal traffic**: **data**, **address** and **control**. In some computers these three sets of signals are electrically independent (separate wires). We call these multibus systems, since one can identify a data bus, an address bus, and a control bus. Cheaper, slower systems may have a single bus that is shared among the three, using a technique known as multiplexing.

Microcomputer Operation

In a read cycle, (Figure 1-9) the MPU seeks data (numbers or instructions) from memory or I/O by sending appropriate request signals down the control bus. If the bus is busy doing something else, the MPU may have to stand by for a few cycles (we call this a *wait* state).

If and when the bus is free, the MPU places an address on the address bus. This address is decoded by circuits in the memory or I/O interface and, if all goes well, the data found at the requested address is moved from memory or I/O to the data bus. The control bus then signals to the MPU that the data is available on the data bus. Once the data is transferred to the MPU's data buffer, the control bus signals that the system bus is free. In a moment you'll see how the MPU handles the incoming data.

The width of the data bus (measured in bits) dictates how much data can be fetched during each read cycle — so the wider the better. You'll see that the size of the data bus plays a vital role in determining the flexibility, performance, and the *cost* of an MPU. The cost element stems from the fact that each bit of the data bus needs a corresponding pin on the MPU chip and associated pathways within the chip.

When people talk about 8-, 16-, and 32-bit computers without further qualification, they *should* be referring to the width of the MPU's data path. But note that some salespersons have been known to lie. Remember Gerswhin's law : "It ain't necessarily so!"

We really need four sizes to honestly characterize an MPU: data width, ALU (Arithmetic/Logic Unit) width, register width, and address width, but life is so short. Who wants to buy an 8/16/32/20-bit micro? (That's the MC68008, by the way.)

The width of the address bus determines the total number of distinct memory (including I/O) addresses that can be accessed and hence affects the maximum memory size. As with data width, the wider the better, but also the more expensive. Here we can make use of our earlier messages-per-bit theory. Most of the 8-bit MPUs have a 16-bit address bus that, as we've seen, allows a maximum of 64K memory addresses (each of which normally accesses an 8-bit byte), since $2^{16} = 65{,}536 = 64K$.

Although there are many clever ways of fitting more than 64K of memory on a 16-bit address bus, they all add overhead in time or cost. The M68000 family has address widths in the range of 20 to 32 bits, giving memory addressing spaces from 1 Mbyte to 4 Gbytes.

The write cycle (Figure 1-10) allows the MPU to send data to memory or I/O. The MPU signals its intentions (*request to write*) on the control bus, and

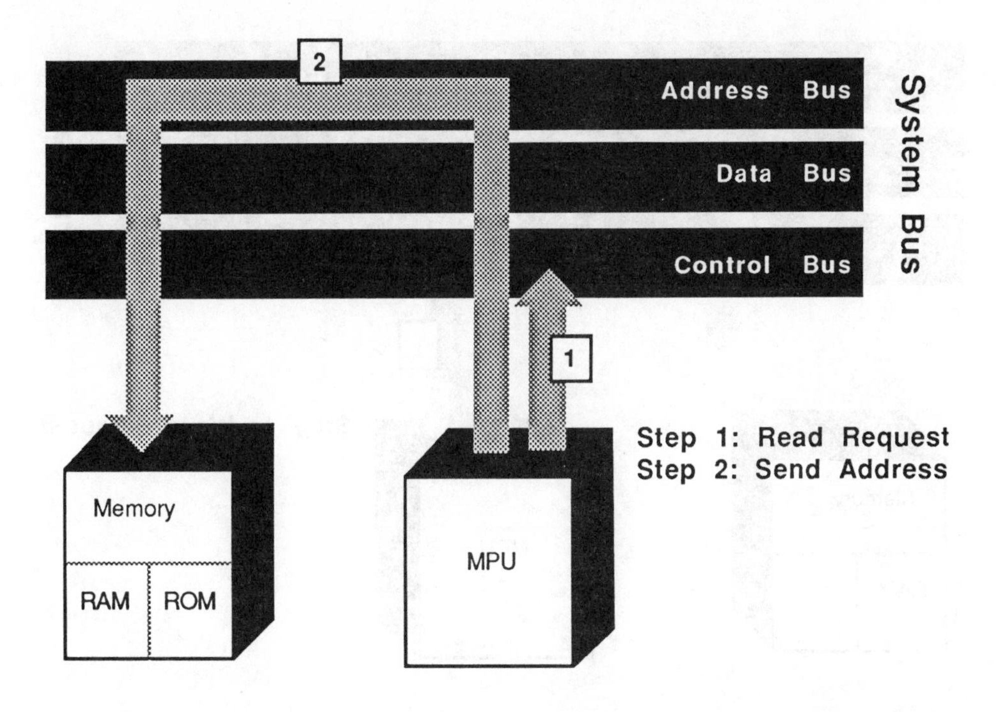

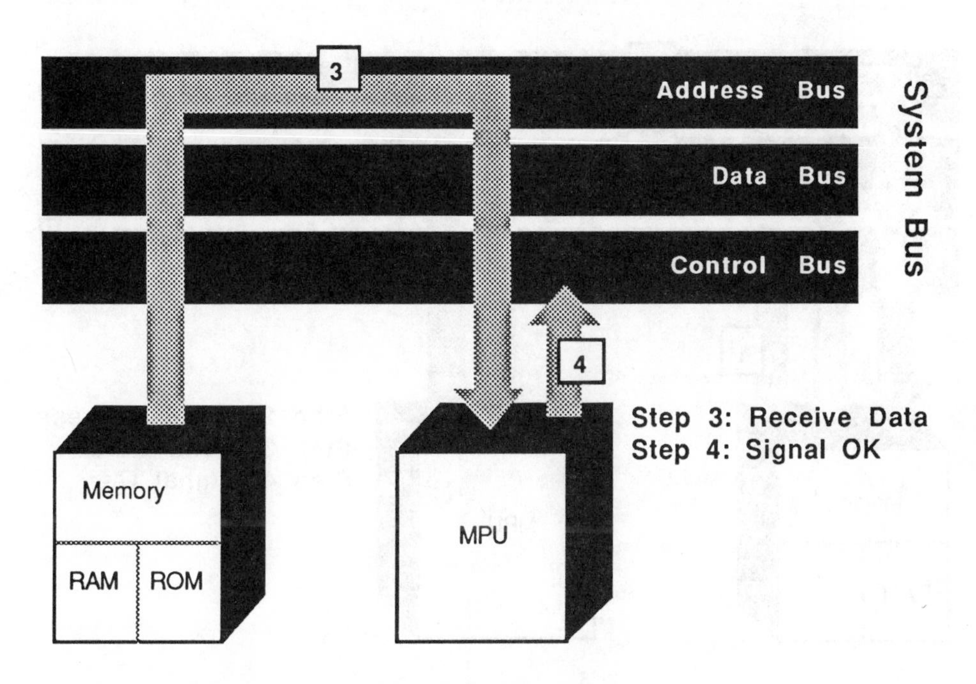

Fig. 1-9 Read Cycle

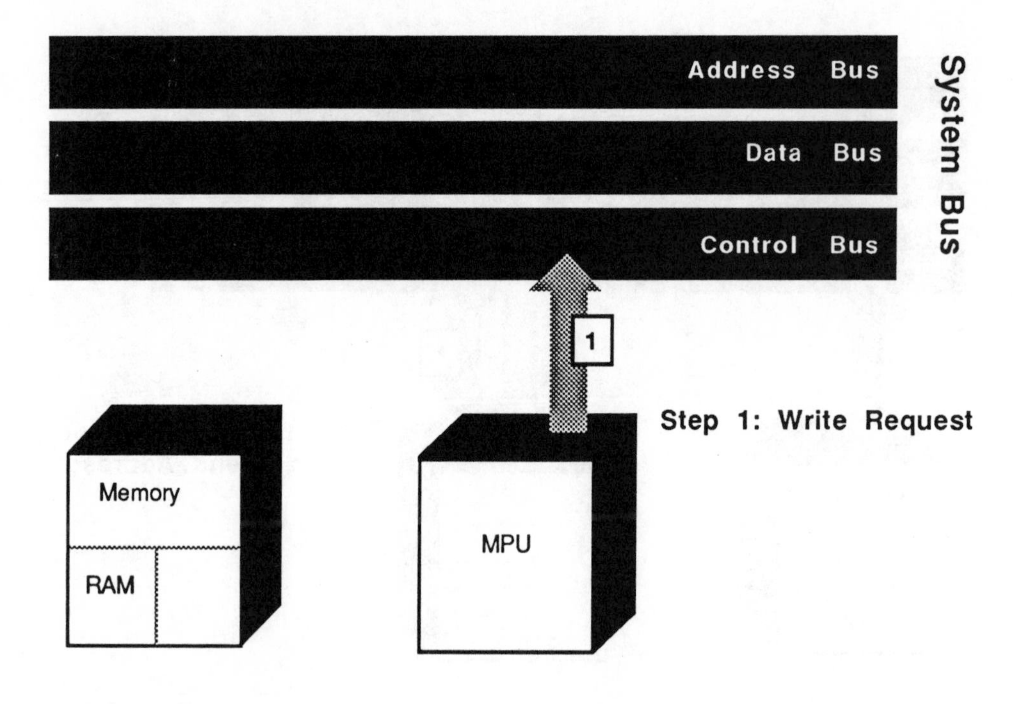

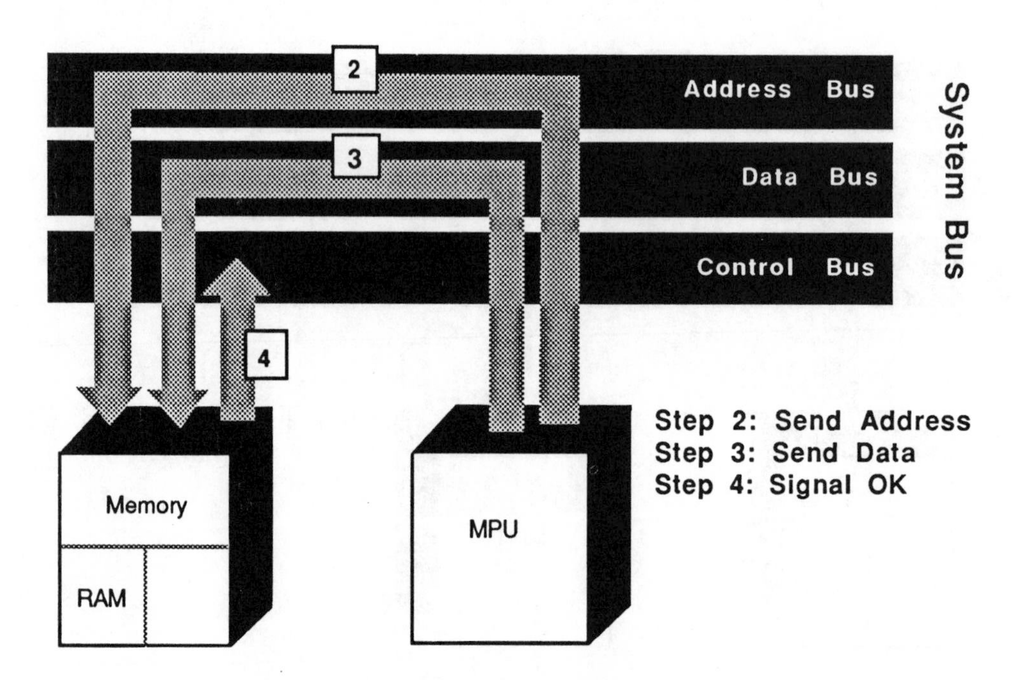

Fig. 1-10 Write Cycle

when the coast is clear, it places the data on the data bus, and the destination address on the address bus. The MPU can then carry out its next instruction.

Recall that the data being moved around is represented by fast bursts or pulses (0's and 1's) synchronized by the system clock. When we talk of read and write cycles, these are definite periods of time related to the speed of the system clock.

SUMMARY OF SYSTEM BUS

The system bus links the main units of the computer, providing an electrical path between MPU, memory and I/O. It carries three types of signals: data, address and control.

Now that you have an overall picture of how the MPU interacts with the system bus, you can look inside the MPU and see how it works. Although MPUs have evolved into myriad designs, there is a useful "generic" architecture that serves to describe them all.

INSIDE THE MPU

The first thing to notice in Figure 1-11 is that the microprocessor has three main connections to the "outside world," namely the paths to the data, address, and control busses. Note that it also has an internal bus (there can be several of these) connecting various functional units of the MPU. Within the MPU, in fact, control and data signals move along the internal bus, synchronized by the system clock — not unlike the picture we drew of the traffic on the system's bus.

Corresponding to the user programs of the computer system, the internal operation of the MPU is guided by microprograms stored in special ROM within the chip. (This is true of the M68000 and many other MPUs; other MPUs employ hard-wired control logic.)

Let's run through a typical sequence of events.

1. *Instruction Fetch:* The **program counter** (PC) is a special register that holds the memory address of the next instruction. Placing this address on the address bus and calling a read cycle will fetch this instruction over the data bus and load it into the instruction register (IR), via the internal bus. Instructions, briefly, are words (or groups of words) that represent the steps of the program stored consecutively in memory. Each instruction is encoded to perform a particular operation, such as ADD or MOVE, on one or more specified operands. For an ADD instruction, for instance, the operands would be the two numbers to be added. A MOVE instruction would specify the operand to be moved (the **source**) and the place it is to be moved to (the

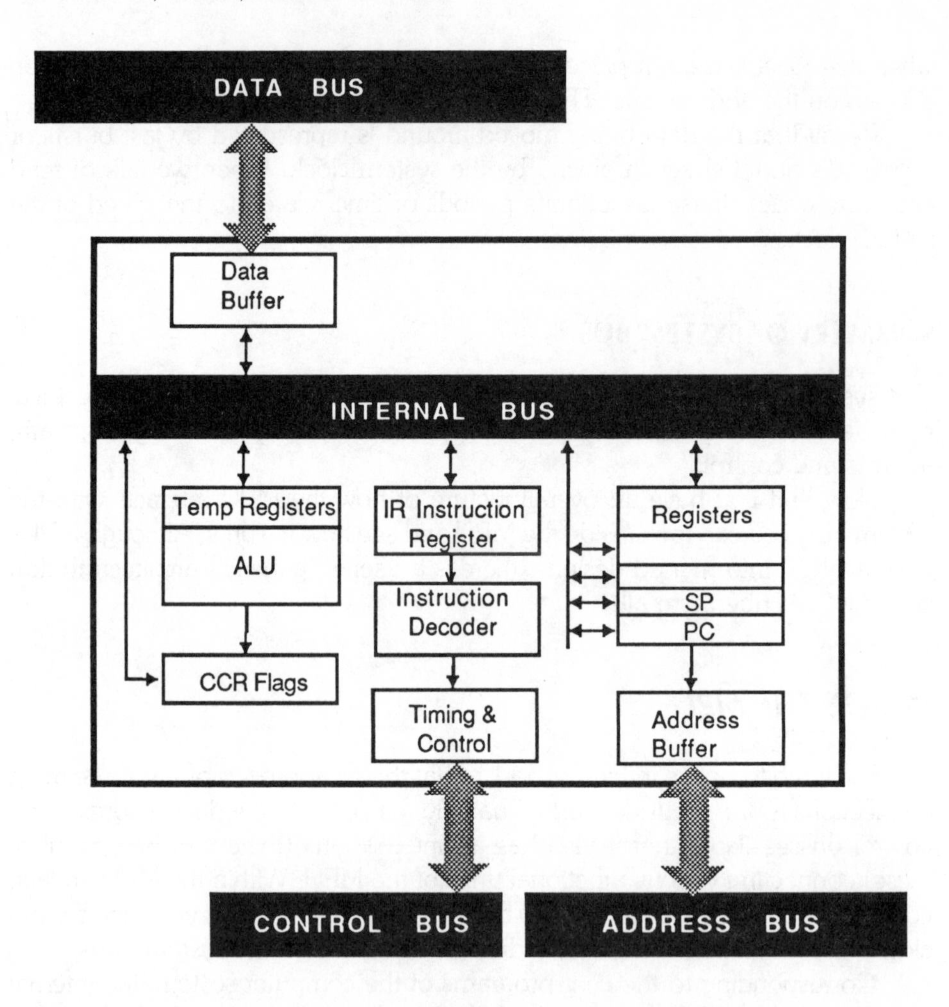

Fig. 1-11 Microprocessor Schematic

destination). Once the instruction has been fetched, the program counter is incremented so that it "points" to the next instruction in memory.

2. *Instruction Decoding:* The instruction word passes from the IR to the instruction decoder, which "decides" from the incoming bit-patterns what operation is needed. Typically, the instruction also contains addressing information for the operands, that is, which register or memory location holds the data to be operated on.
3. *Data Fetch:* Determining where the operands are often involves some arithmetic to calculate the operand addresses from the information included in the instruction. For some multiword instructions there may have to be another

instruction fetch, as in step 1 above. It may now take one or more **read cycles** to bring in the operands from memory, or to transfer them from registers. The operands will be routed along the internal bus(ses) to temporary registers.

4. *Execute Cycle:* The microprocessor is now, hopefully, ready to execute the instruction. The MPU "knows" what to do, where, and to whom. More often than not execution will involve the ALU (Arithmetic/Logic Unit). The answer will be routed via the internal bus to a register, or to the data bus buffer en route to memory. In the latter case, a **write cycle** will be initiated using the destination address specified in the instruction. The ALU also sets a **flag register** (also known as a **condition code register**) according to certain conditions arising from the operations (result negative, result zero, overflow and so on).

Having completed steps 1 through 4, the MPU is all set to do the same for the next instruction — since you saw that the PC (Program Counter) has already been increased, and therefore has the address for this next instruction. Remember that instructions are normally stored in successive memory locations.

Among the many deviations possible from the simple sequence listed above, a common one involves **branching**. In branching, some program condition arises that calls for the execution of an instruction out of normal sequence. Branching is achieved by setting a new address in the PC.

Other deviations can arise from errors, exceptions, and interrupts from other jobs. These will be covered in later chapters, since the M68000 has some unique features for handling errors and exceptions.

A rather amazing fact is the sheer *speed* with which our four basic steps take place. MPU speed is rated in MIPS (million instructions per second) — of course, not all instructions take the same time, so MIPS can be misleading. A single instruction can take from 4 to over 200 basic machine cycles. The MC68020, to give you an idea, runs at a sustained rate of 2 to 3 MIPS, with occasional bursts of 8 MIPS.

PREFETCH AND PIPELINING

If you look at our four steps — fetch instruction, decode, fetch data, execute — you can imagine a tremendous amount of bus activity, both on the main system bus and on the MPU internal bus. In the never-ending fight to squeeze more performance from a system, the designers obviously attempt to speed up each aspect of the cycle, especially by reducing the possibility of delay (wait states) arising from bus contention or a slow memory access time. But when that has reached practical limits there still remains the possibility of gaining speed by

overlapping operations — achieving what is known as **concurrency**. It turns out that several of the steps 1 through 4 can be overlapped — performed simultaneously. A typical **prefetch** strategy involves having three instructions passing through the MPU at any one time — one being executed, one being decoded, and one being fetched. In **pipelining** a greater number of instructions may be passing through. These steps often require different system resources, provided the chip has the necessary buffers and pathways. If, as will happen from time to time, there is a clash or contention, one of the steps will be held up. In Chapter 8 you will see how the instruction cache on the MC68020 further improves performance by holding a set of instructions at the ready in fast on-chip registers. In many programming situations the same loop is iterated many times; the instruction cache can reduce the fetch time considerably.

Let's review in more detail some of the main boxes in Figure 1-11, and then see how memory is organized.

ARITHMETIC/LOGIC UNIT

An area of the MPU designed specifically for arithmetic and logical operations is called an arithmetic/logic unit (ALU). Advanced MPUs like the M68000 have several independent ALUs. The width of the ALU, 16 bits for the MC68000, for example, tells you how many bits can be added together in parallel, at one time. Larger numbers, of course, can be handled by taking extra clock cycles.

You saw earlier how gates could be combined to perform binary addition. It is not too difficult to extend these to perform the other basic arithmetical operations.

Subtraction is equivalent to adding a complement (easily obtained with inverters); multiplication is repeated addition (although it is sometimes performed from preset tables); and division is repeated subtraction and testing for zero.

Hardware division, incidentally, is one of the many mainframe features now appearing as standard on the 16/32-bit micros. The alternative on most of the 8-bit micros, dividing by software, is tedious and much slower. Similarly, the M68000 offers hardware BCD (Binary Coded Decimal) arithmetic as well as a useful repertoire of shifts, rotates, and extended arithmetic. The latter involves several clever multi-precision aids for doing sums across several registers for increased accuracy.

MATH COPROCESSORS AND THE MC68881

For heavy number crunching using floating-point format, Motorola introduced the MC68881 math coprocessor, which is fully compatible with the M68000 range (indeed the MC68881 is a chip in the same range of complexity as the MC68000).

Coprocessing differs from multiprocessing in the way that the work load is shared. Any suitably interfaced MPU in the system, on decoding an instruction calling for floating point, will pass that instruction over to the MC68881 — so coprocessors actually share the same instruction stream. Multiprocessors normally do their own thing from independent programs, although they can and do interact by sharing data and passing signals (known sometimes, rather pleasantly, as semaphores) via memory.

Simply stated, you can look on the ALU as the calculating center of the chip, capable of seeking help from a math coprocessor.

Inputs to the ALU are numbers from temporary registers (or buffers) via the internal data bus together with control signals, (instructions indicating the calculation or logical operation required). Output from the ALU, the results of the calculation plus various control and routing signals, flow back to other parts of the MPU via buffers and the internal bus. An important source for ALU data input, as well as a destination for ALU data output is a special area of on-chip fast memory, organized into fixed length **registers**. Unlike the temporary registers and buffers, these are accessible to the programmer.

REGISTERS

Registers play a major role in giving an MPU its personality and programmability, and they come in all shapes, sizes, and flavors. The basic MC68000 has 17 general-purpose registers, each 32 bits wide. In Chapter 3 we will cover this aspect in depth, since the instruction set and the way the registers are organized are intimately related.

MEMORIES ARE MADE OF THIS

The normal fast immediate memory for modern computers is the RAM (Random Access Memory) chip. RAM Chips come in various sizes and are plugged into memory boards to give a total capacity per board from 16 K-bytes up to 2 M-bytes. A system may well have more than one memory board within it. The physical arrangement of memory is usually of no concern to the programmer, who is interested only in the logical addressing scheme.

You should remember, in passing, that a growing number of peripherals will have local RAM and/or ROM, outside the main MPU addressing space. Typical examples are buffers for printers, keyboards, and CRT displays.

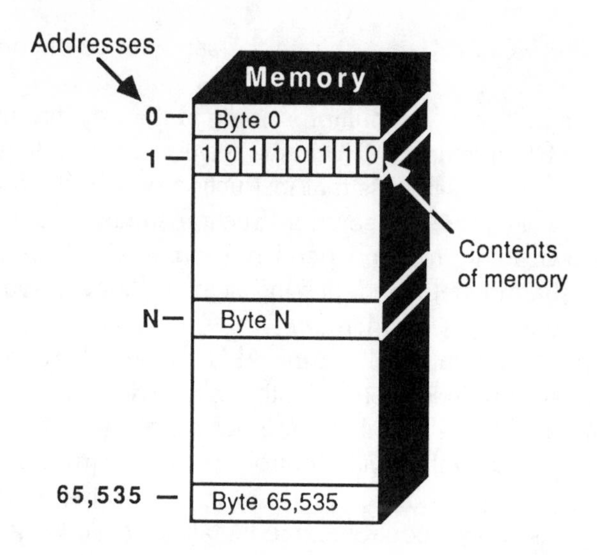

Fig. 1-12 Addressing 64 K-Byte Memory

ADDRESSING MEMORY

As you saw in the read/write cycles, the main characteristic of RAM is that the MPU can read and write data from and to RAM. To determine which of the many byte locations it needs to access, each byte (or group of bytes) is given an address. A 64K-byte memory can be thought of as 65,536 mailboxes, numbered 0 thru 65,535. Inside each mailbox is a byte (8 bits) holding data (256 possible characters, remember).

WHAT ARE WE READING?

If the computer were to read from byte address 1 (see Figure 1-12), it would fetch the byte 10110110. What would this mean? Well, almost anything! Out of context the byte has no specific meaning. If the computer were expecting a number it could be either

10110110 = decimal 182 (unsigned)

or

10110110 = decimal –74 (signed 2's complement)

If the byte were part of a 7-bit ASCII string, the leftmost bit could be a parity bit with the remaining 7 bits giving the numeric character "6". Or it might be a full 8-bit ASCII graphics character or "private" control code.

If the MPU were reading a program, the byte would be interpreted as part of an instruction. The words and bytes that make up instructions have their own peculiar coding schemes built into the MPU. You saw that the instruction decoder has to interpret this code before the MPU can execute it. In Chapter 4, you will see how the M68000 instruction set is encoded into groups of 16-bit words. Recall that each 16-bit word offers up to 65,536 messages, so we have the basis for a very rich and varied set of different operations.

Since the bytes we read from memory can mean so many different things, you may be wondering how the MPU distinguishes all these possible interpretations. The answer lies in the program itself. And the reason that program bugs can produce such bizarre results is because the MPU will blindly interpret each byte as requested. So if you inadvertently ask the system to execute rather than print an ASCII character, it is likely to do strange things.

IMPORTANCE OF MEMORY SIZE AND SPEED

Memory size and speed play a vital role in every aspect of computing. At the simplest user level the amount of memory can dictate both the types of job you can run and the speed with which they are performed. A RAM or ROM that is not matched to the speed of the MPU can, as we've seen, induce wait states in the MPU. Too little memory can often bring the system to a halt with a sneering "insufficient memory" message on your screen. Some programs need to be completely **resident** in RAM before they can run at all. Other programs are arranged to run with just portions of the code in RAM and are smart enough to pull in **overlays** from a disk. Overlays overwrite sections of code in RAM once they have served their purpose. Very large programs can theoretically be made to run in very small memories, but the overhead caused by constant **swapping** can create some ennui for the user.

MEMORY MANAGEMENT

Our simple picture of memory sitting on an address bus deliberately evades many complex problems concerning the interactions between the MPU(s), system and user programs, and memory access. These are particularly severe when the system allows **multitasking**, that is, the "simultaneous" running of several jobs, or different parts of the same job. Clearly, care must be taken to prevent one task from intruding on the memory allocated to another task.

In particular, the **operating system** (OS) which is overseeing all user tasks, is itself running tasks, (including the task of scheduling tasks) and its system memory space must be secure from accidental or deliberate intrusion. Users may bithely kill each other's jobs, but if the OS goes, we *all* go. What makes the system memory sacrosanct is not only the programs resident there (OS, compilers, utilities), but also vital system data, such as tables for handling interrupts and exceptions, and an area known as the **system stack** which holds transient information concerning the status of interrupted jobs.

Even a single-user, single-MPU system nowadays frequently offers many levels of concurrency. The speed of the modern MPU, compared with the speed of most I/O devices, allows it to service many requests in sequence, so quickly that each job is convinced it has the MPU's undivided attention.

There is considerable diversity in the methods used to partition memory safely and economically, and much debate on the merits of various approaches. The initial problem is that of mapping physical to logical memory. By this we mean relating the physical memory addresses as "seen" by the address decoders, with the logical addresses presented to the MPU by the programmer.

Some MPUs, like the Intel 8088/8086, have the solution to this problem designed into the silicon, while others (like the M68000) leave all the options open to the system designer.

SEGMENTED MEMORY

The Intel approach is called **memory segmentation**, as opposed to the Motorola **linear** memory philosophy. In a segmented memory, the programmer looks at several exclusive, fixed memory spaces (or segments), typically 64 K-bytes each. As shown in Figure 1-13, the logical addresses he or she uses are offsets, modified by the MPU to obtain the physical addresses. The modification is achieved by adding values (called segment identifiers) held in segmentation registers, and this can be done in such a way that the user's programs and data are kept apart, safe from other users. The advantages are the security and speed that arise from the use of short 16-bit addresses. The disadvantage is the overhead involved in checking and adding the segment identifiers.

LINEAR MEMORY AND THE MMU (MEMORY MANAGEMENT UNIT)

In the linear approach the programmer looks on memory as one long continuous addressing space from zero to the maximum possible address, addressed by means of a single number. With the 20- to 32-bit address widths available on the M68000, this represents a generous chunk (from 1 M-byte to 4 G-bytes) to play with. Within this maximum, jobs can be allocated the optimum memory size needed. Security must be "supplied" externally, as it were, but the M68000 is designed to facilitate this. Several specialized chips, such as the MC68451

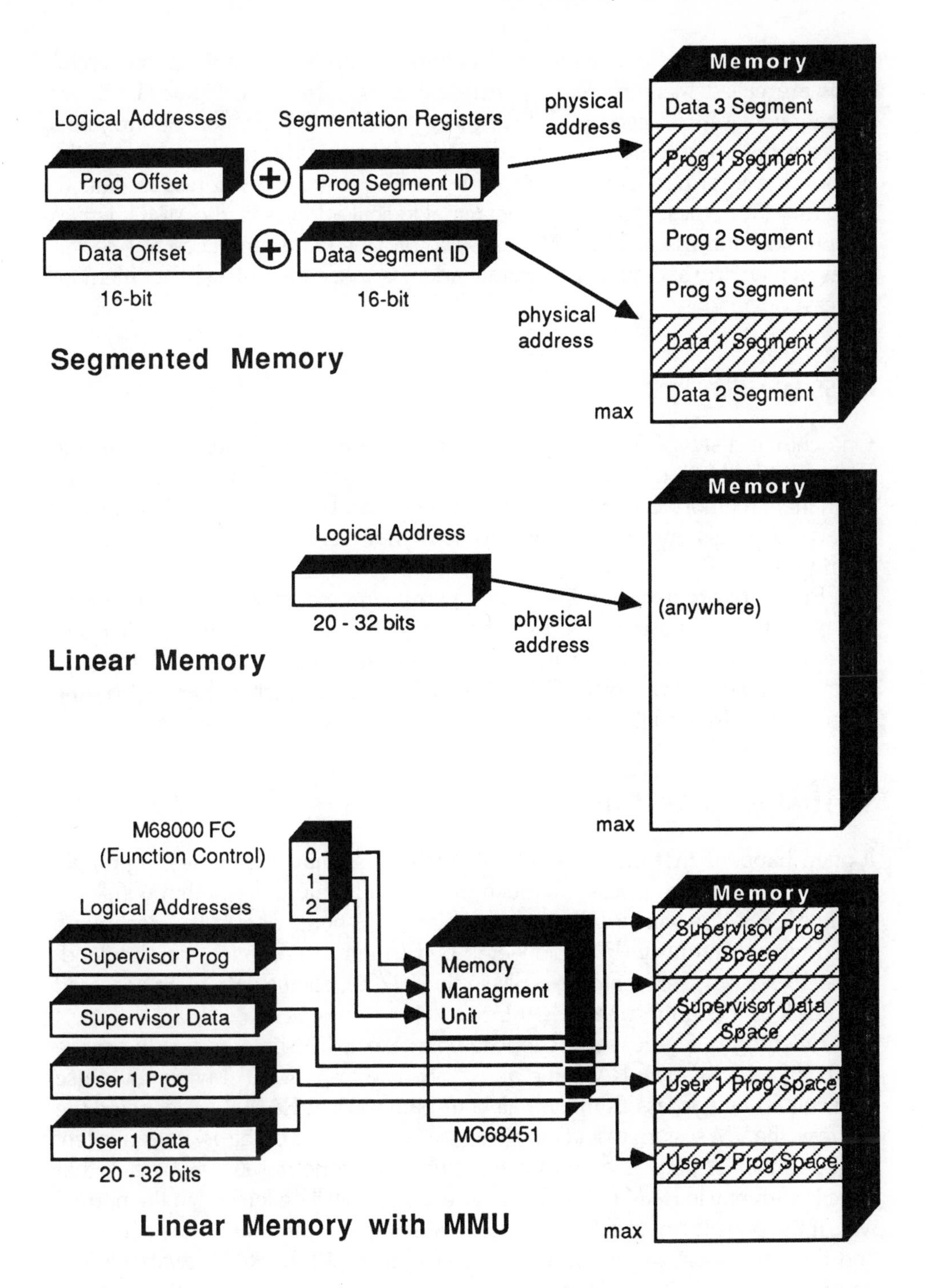

Fig. 1-13 Segmented and Linear Memories

(available from Motorola) perform something resembling segmentation. These chips are called Memory Management Units, or MMUs. In Figure 1-13, we indicate how MMUs accomplish their purpose. The FC (Function Control) pins on the M68000 automatically signal the **processor state**, namely whether the M68000 is in **supervisor** or **user**mode, and whether the address is data or program. From these values and the actual logical addresses, the MMU derives the physical addresses. The MMU can also provide write-protection to selected areas of memory, and allocate separate address space for DMA (Direct Memory Access) operations.

MASS MEMORY

One characteristic of RAM plays a big role in computer design — **volatility**. With most RAM, you lose your data when you switch off the power. So a more permanent memory is needed, and this is provided by various types of backing storage or **mass memory**, in the form of hard and soft disks, tapes, and cartridges.

Programs are usually marketed on permanent media such as floppy disks, but need to be read into RAM before they can be run. During a typical run there will be many I/O transactions — data being output to disk, and data and programs read in from disk. Overall performance is much influenced by the amount of RAM available — the more RAM, the fewer disk accesses.

VIRTUAL MEMORY (VM)

It often happens that the available RAM is far less than the addressing range. In fact, until memory prices fall much lower, it is highly unlikely that you'll see many MC68020s with a full complement of 4 G-bytes of RAM! A technique called **virtual memory** (VM) pioneered by Ferranti Ltd., Manchester, England, in the 1950s (and reinvented by IBM in the 1970s), allows data to be accessed from disk as though it were in RAM.

Referring to Figure 1-14, suppose you have a 1 M-byte addressing space (20 bits), a 128 K-byte RAM and an 872 K-byte disk. With VM you could use your full 20-bit address as though all your data were in RAM. On decoding the address, the VM system would calculate (by table lookup perhaps) its equivalent page number. A page is a convenient chunk of memory, say 1 K-byte. If that page is currently in RAM (case Y, in Figure 1-14), it will be fetched in the normal way. If the page is not in RAM (case X), we say that a **page fault** has occurred, and this causes the system to load the page from disk to RAM, swapping out an unwanted page if necessary.

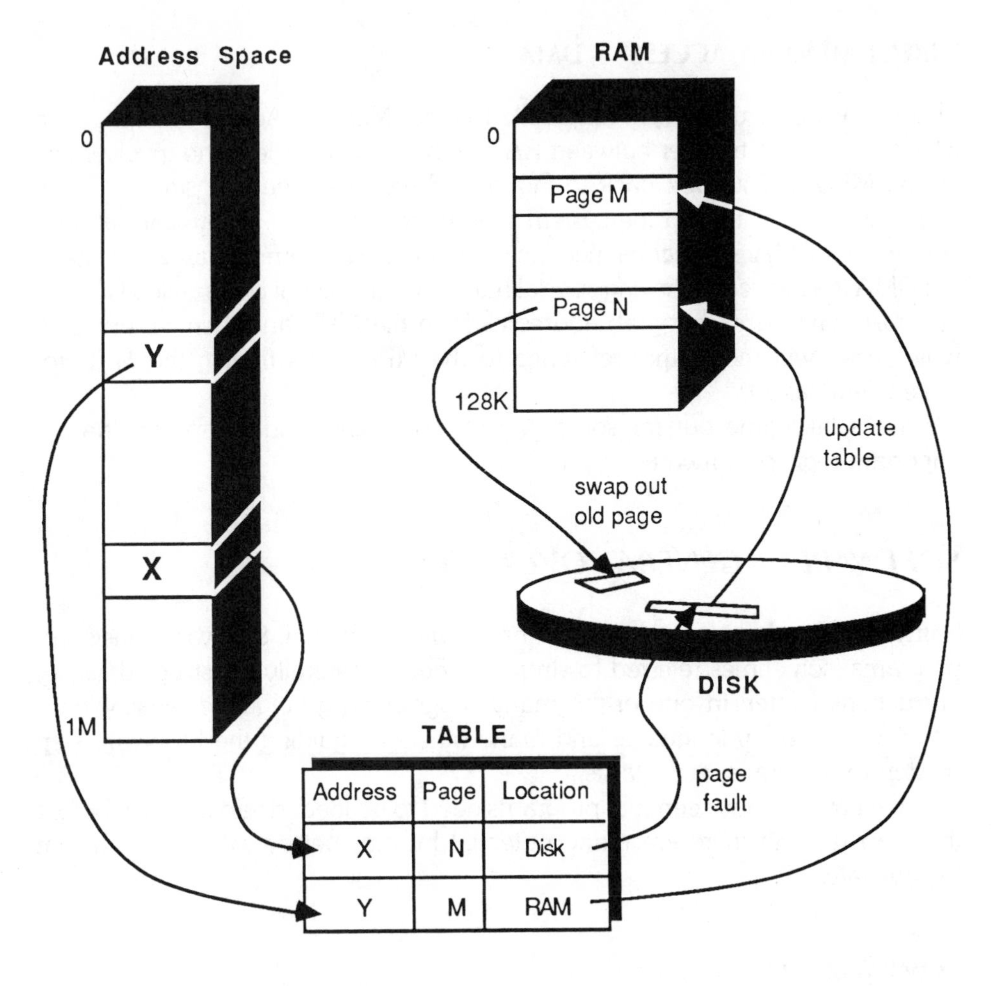

Fig. 1-14 Virtual Memory

Chapters 7 and 8 will discuss virtual memory in more detail, as implemented on the MC68010 and MC68020.

RAM DISK

The opposite to VM is the RAM disk. If your program is written to access files from a disk, and you have plenty of RAM to spare, it is possible to increase performance by loading your files into RAM. The RAM disk software then fools the program into treating RAM like a disk. The starting memory address of each file record can be calculated — provided, naturally, that the disk formatting rules are known.

DIRECT MEMORY ACCESS — DMA

There is a widely used technique called Direct Memory Access (DMA) which allows direct data transfer between RAM and disk with little or no involvement by the MPU. If you look back to Figure 1-8, you can see that since I/O and memory are both tied to the system bus, there is already a physical pathway available for DMA. The actual mechanics are beyond our immediate scope here, but DMA is achieved by having special hardware (intelligent chips called DMACs — DMA controllers) that grab addresses from the MPU and then set up read/write cycles with no further reference to the MPU (thus freeing the MPU for more useful tasks).

Let's take time out for some general comments and recaps on the all-important topic of software.

SOFTWARE — GENERAL OVERVIEW

Software is needed to goad the inert hardware into action. Software consists of programs (sometimes referred to simply as **code**), carefully constructed lists of instructions written in one of the many programming languages available — Basic, C, assembly language, and many others — guiding the hardware step by step to perform specific tasks.

We have already seen that programs need to be loaded into memory before they can run but there are many potential hurdles before we can reach that happy state.

COMPATIBILITY

An essential concept throughout the industry is compatibility — the idea of hardware and software elements throughout the **system** working together in harmony. We will reserve the word *system* for an organized matching set of devices and programs.

Hardware and software exist today in a dazzling profusion of shapes, flavors, and sizes, and creating a system from diverse components, even when you buy from a single manufacturer, is no trivial matter.

Portability in hardware simply means that the thing has a handle and weighs less than 100 pounds; software portability is a less tangible concept. A program written to run on many different systems is clearly more marketable, although sometimes you lose efficiency by aiming at portability.

A group of related programs is often called a **package**. Well-known packages such as WordStar® and Lotus™ 1-2-3™ offer one specialized application (word processing and spreadsheets, respectively). A more recent fashion is the **integrated** software package such as Symphony™ which provides both word processing and spreadsheets. Financial data from the spreadsheet can be transferred automatically to the WP program in order to produce neatly typed reports.

If you want your computer to run your payroll, you'll need to load a payroll package that specifically and in minute detail tells the computer how and when to calculate each element of tax deduction, where to find the various tables, and so on. The hardware has no preconceived notions regarding your wages and is blissfully unaware of the IRS. When we talk about the computer as a general purpose machine, we mean that it can do anything — as long as we have the appropriate compatible software.

APPLICATIONS SOFTWARE

The payroll programs mentioned above belong to what we call **applications software**. Applications software is aimed at solving particular user problems.

SYSTEMS SOFTWARE AND THE OS

The computer also needs **systems software** to handle a variety of basic support functions required by every applications program, such as resource allocation, controlling peripherals, and so on. These support programs, known as **utilities**, are often lumped together under the title OS (Operating System), pronounced "Oh-ess." Without the OS, each applications program would have to know the exact hardware configuration and include all these tiresome details. In the early days of computing, in fact, there were no operating systems, and the programmer just had to code everything. The OS frees the programmer from many **housekeeping** chores. Furthermore, each OS provides its standard way of communicating with the computer and isolates the programmer from many machine-specific features.

The successful operating systems such as CP/M, PC-DOS and UNIX are available on many different computers, so a program written for a UNIX-based computer, say, stands a fair chance of running, with little or no tweaking, on *any* system which supports UNIX. This success is self-reinforcing, in the sense that a widely used OS attracts a plenitude of software, while the computer buyer's choice of OS is greatly influenced by the availability of packages.

As you might guess, rivalry between supporters of different OSs reaches heights of religious fervor. MPUs like the M68000 family are opening up new vistas in computing which will help dampen these passions by offering economic multi-OS systems, capable of running programs from all sources.

SUMMARY — OPERATING SYSTEMS

The operating system is simply a complex set of programs that must reside in the system to provide a uniform set of vital controls and functions for the user's applications software.

Once an OS has been **ported** from system A to system B, programs written for system A become **portable**, and will run on system B (fingers crossed).

So hardware needs software, and applications software needs systems software. Of course, software without the hardware to run it on is also a pitiful sight. Computing is but a mental construct until the two get together.

FIRMWARE

We should mention briefly that programs, including the OS itself, are often supplied *fixed* in ROM (Read Only Memory). Variants exist called PROMs (Programmable ROMs) and EPROMs (Erasable PROMs) that allow factory changes to the ROM program. These programs, falling as it were between hard and soft, constitute the **firmware**. Unlike the software we have been discussing, firmware arrives fully loaded and ready to go.

Firmware, of course, is written and checked most carefully before being permanently attached to the system. A good example of firmware is the BASIC interpreter provided with the IBM PC™.

COUNTING THE COSTS

Spectacular advances in mass production continue to reduce hardware costs. It has been observed that if car makers had achieved the same price reductions as computer makers over the last 30 years, the price of a new Rolls Royce would now be $100! Unfortunately, software has turned out to be an unexpectedly tricky occupation, resisting similar efforts at mass production. Programming is labor-intensive, demands rare creative talents, and commands increasingly higher salaries.

Software costs have become the dominant factor in computer projects large and small. On our car-cost analogy, the $100 Rolls Royce would, alas, require a $100,000 a year chauffeur plus gas at $50 per gallon!

The phrase **software engineering** is often used to describe the efforts being made to apply production methods such as project management and quality control in the mainly cerebral field of programming.

Correcting the imbalance between hardware and software costs is the major challenge facing the computer industry today.

The M68000 family was designed "by programmers, for programmers" and represents a serious attempt to address this challenge.

CONCLUSION

Thus concludes our gallop through some of the basic concepts. Many of them will be amplified and, we trust, clarified in the chapters that follow.

2

The M68000 Family

This chapter offers a little historical background for the Motorola M68000 family of microprocessors, just to place them in the context of today's restless market-place. We also delineate the various members of the family, and show you what they look like (see Figure 2-1). We suggest that you reread this chapter after Chapters 3 and 4. Some of the M68000 design features discussed here will become more meaningful after you have seen the instructions in action.

INTRODUCTION

The first 16/32-bit MC68000 (see Figure 2-2), introduced by Motorola in 1979, represented a quantum leap forward in microprocessor power and flexibility. Since then, Motorola has developed, as promised, a family of compatible MPUs (MicroProcessor Units) and support chips — ranging in price and performance from the "economy" MC68008, via the MC68000, MC68010, and MC68012 up to the latest 32/32-bit MC68020. The MC68000 had already attracted the title of "supermicro", leaving us short of suitable superlatives to describe the MC68020. Adding number-crunching power to the family is the MC68881 FPCP (floating-point coprocessor).

We hope to reveal some of the design features of the Motorola M68000 microprocessor family and to indicate the main areas where radical decisions were made to create this breakthrough in performance, programmability, and future family growth.

The microprocessor chip is mankind's most intricate invention with VLSI (Very Large-Scale Integration) densities now approaching theoretical upper

Courtesy of Motorola, Inc.

Fig. 2-1 The M68000 Family

limits. There are many VLSI technologies offering different densities and power requirements. They are referred to by acronyms including the letters MOS (Metal Oxide Semiconductors). The MC68020, for example, using the 2-micron HCMOS (High-density Complementary Metal Oxide Semiconductor) process, packs 200,000 transistors on 3/8" square of silicon (see Figure 2-3).

A detailed study of the vast field of chip design and microelectronic circuitry is, of course, outside the scope of this primer.

Our aim, therefore, is to give you some feel for the highlights of this remarkable family, stressing those elements which relate to the central theme of our book, the M68000 instruction set.

We will follow Motorola's official designations by referring to the family as M68000, reserving the MC prefix for a particular member of the family. So the MC68000 is a specific MPU chip in the M68000 family.

Figure 2-4 gives a schematic overview of how the family members and support chips might be interconnected. In practice, you would seldom meet

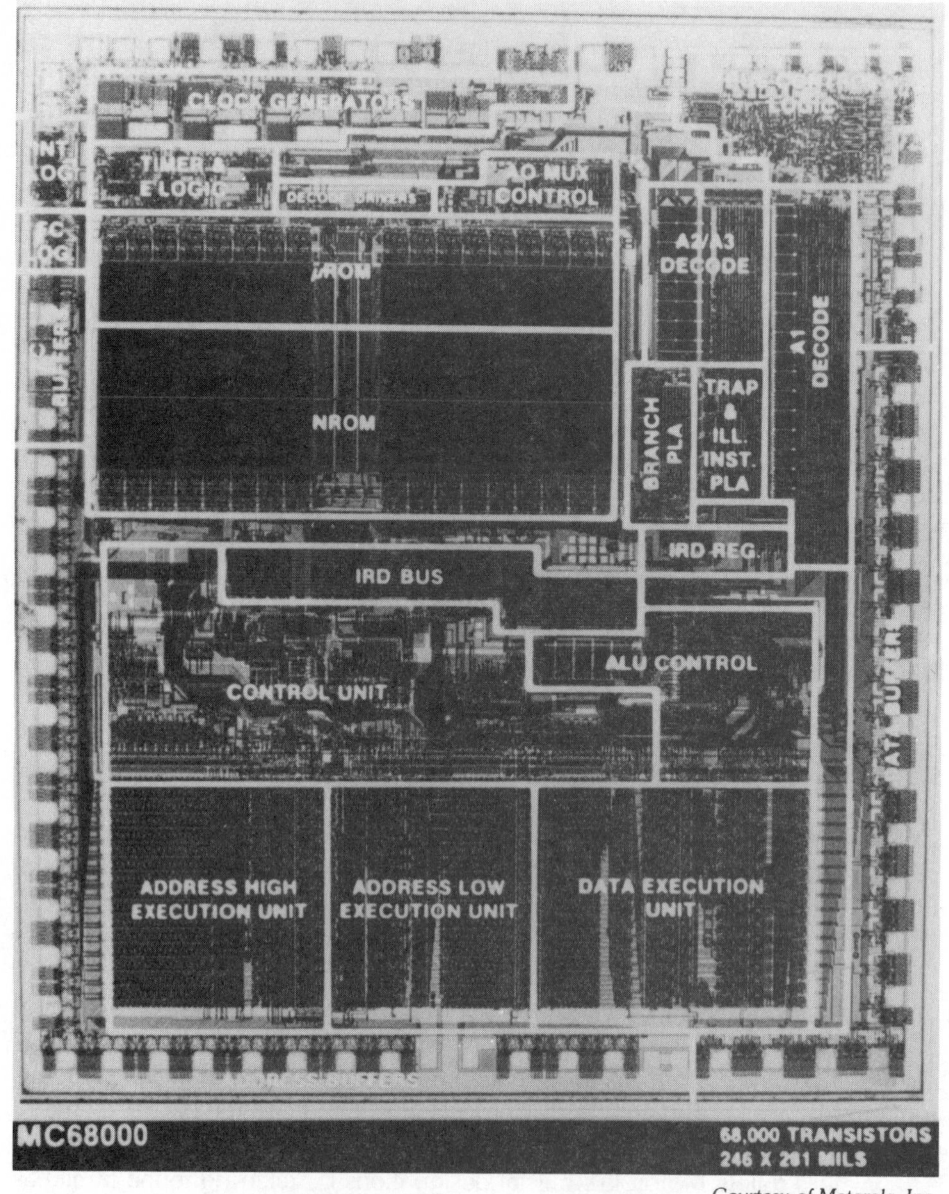

Courtesy of Motorola, Inc.

Fig. 2-2 The MC68000 Microprocessing Unit

Courtesy of Motorola, Inc.

Fig. 2-3 MC68020

such a comprehensive all-Motorola configuration. In fact, mainly through Motorola's own efforts, a standard bus known as the VME bus has received ISO and IEEE approval; its growing acceptance means that devices from many manufacturers can interface with the M68000 — and conversely Motorola's VME-based support chips can be found on many non-Motorola systems. Figure 2-5 shows a typical MC68000 single board computer (from Educational Microcomputer Systems, Irvine, California) complete with 20 K-bytes RAM, 16 K-bytes EPROM and various I/O support chips).

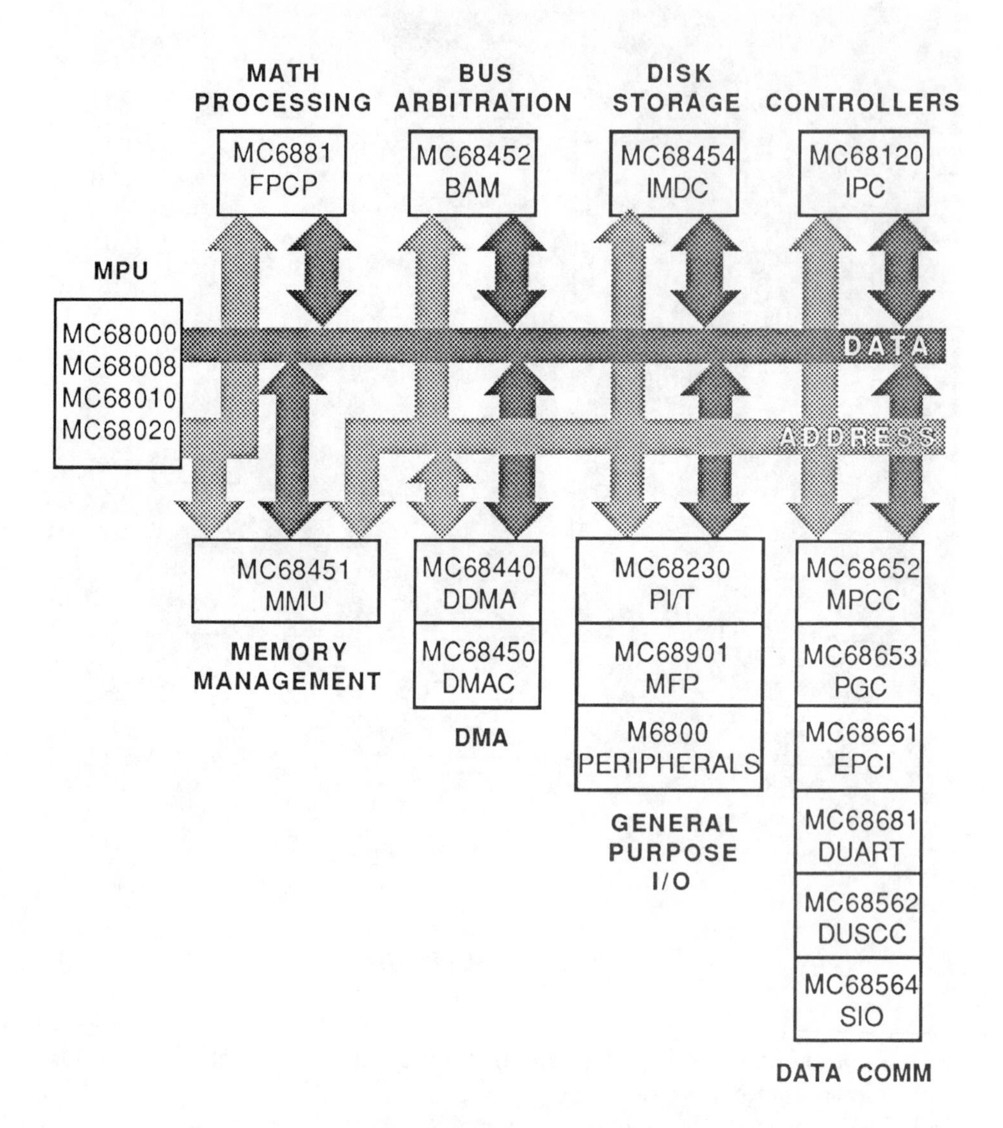

Fig. 2-4 M68000 Family and Supporting Chips

THE M68000 SUCCESS STORY

Nowadays, it takes a lot more than excellent price-performance hardware to gain success in the microcomputer marketplace. Computer manufacturers and independent software suppliers also need basic software support upon which to

Courtesy of EMS (Educational Microcomputer Systems), Irvine, California. See Appendix E for details.

Fig. 2-5 MC68000-Based Single Board Computer

build up complete end-user systems and applications software. To this end Motorola has provided state-of-the-art software development tools, such as the EXORmacs™, EXORset™, and EXORciser™, as well as modular systems components such as the VMEmodules™ and the VERSAmodules™.

These are supported by a host of Motorola-developed operating systems, like the System V/68 UNIX-derived OS, conversion and debugging aids, assemblers, and compilers.

Motorola was also prompt in establishing cross-licensing agreements with major chip manufacturers in the USA, Japan, and Europe (see Appendix E). You can now buy the M68000 from several manufacturers. Without such "second-sourcing" vendors can feel vulnerable, and it can prove difficult, if not impossible, to penetrate the military and industrial markets, both domestic and overseas.

The fruits of these efforts can be seen in the countless M68000 implementations now available. Appendix E lists many of the manufacturers who have adopted these chips. They range from the giants of the industry such as IBM, Apple, Honeywell, NCR, ICL, and Hewlett-Packard, thru the mass-merchandizers like Sinclair and Commodore, to the smaller, specialized firms such as Alpha Micro, Charles Rivers, Alcyon and SBE. It is probably no exaggeration to say that the M68000 is currently the best known if not the most widely used microprocessor family worldwide.

THE DESIGN PROBLEM

VLSI (Very Large Scale Integration) chips like the MC68000 have such a lengthy and expensive design-to-manufacture cycle that, like the proverbial airplane, they can easily become obsolete before they take off. There are two ways around this potential disaster — first, you use the finest possible crystal ball and try to predict how the market will look two or three years from now. Second, you try to reduce the gestation period by automating the design and testing process. As Oscar Wilde once said, predictions are dangerous things, especially when they involve the future.

Nevertheless, a whole subindustry of microelectronic market-watching and trend-plotting does the best it can in a most volatile situation, not only to assess the types of products needed but also the many associated imponderables such as optimum price/performance, market share, demand patterns, and the like. The recurrent fluctuations of over-stocking and shortages, layoffs, and recruitments in the semiconductor industry underline the fact that planning in this area is far from being an exact science.

TIMING

A major ingredient in the success of the MC68000 was undoubtedly timing. Even by the mid-seventies the Motorola crystal ball predicted that the existing 8-bit micros would soon run out of steam — their very success, in fact, was attracting more sophisticated applications. Both commercial and scientific users were demanding faster processing of larger, more complex databases, formerly the preserve of the mainframe and minicomputer systems. The advances in low-cost mass-memory (hard- and soft-disk units) and RAM (Random Access Memory) added to this pressure in many ways. More elaborate operating systems and languages were needed to exploit the larger data banks, and these in turn prompted the call for more powerful instruction sets and addressing modes.

A NEW MARKET

The growing personal computer market was calling for more friendly user interfaces. Although the lively grass-roots hobbyist was happy to hack away with primitive interfaces, the home and office user was asking "What will it do for me?" and "Why are these things so difficult to use?"

An inescapable fact of life is that insulating the user from the harsh realities of bits, bytes, and bugs incurs an enormous software overhead. To offset the inefficiency of user-friendliness you need more sheer processing power and larger memory-addressing space, just as an automobile's automatic gearbox requires a more powerful engine if you want to maintain the comparable performance of a stick shift.

To support the professional systems software engineers in their search for amicable user interfaces, more powerful instruction sets with more flexible addressing modes were called for.

THE MACSS PROJECT

This was the situation facing Motorola when it initiated the MACSS (Motorola's Advanced Computer System on Silicon) project in the mid 1970s. The design challenge was a familiar one in the computer industry — how to reconcile two fundamentally conflicting goals: pushing ahead into a new generation while preserving compatibility with current software and peripherals.

Invocations to the Roman god Janus, reputedly blessed with hindsight *and* foresight, are no longer in favor. In the hurly-burly of the real world the MACSS team settled for gritty compromises between technical and marketing considerations, making literally thousands of trade-off decisions, some backed by hard facts, others based on fallible intuition.

An existing user base represents a substantial hardware and software investment that cannot lightly be ignored, yet at the same time it can inhibit the full exploitation of advances in silicon technology, computer architectures, and the black arts of programming.

Solid state innovations have continued to bedazzle us since the transistor first emerged from Bell Labs in the late 1940s. At any point in time there are hundreds of promising IC (Integrated Circuit) breakthroughs progressing (hopefully) through the following stages: theoretical predictions from the solid-state physicists; mathematical models and simulations; small-scale R & D tests; pilot schemes to establish fabrication and quality control methods; and studies to determine the economic feasibility of large-scale production. Crucial to completing this cycle is predicting market demand and product life. No other industry faces the same delicate equations relating start-up costs, production volumes and yields, and unit cost.

THE LEGACY

The diversity of MPU designs launched between the pioneering Intel 4004 (1969 through 1971) and the MACSS project (1976 through 1979) reveals the variety of responses possible. The evolving story has been one of "leap-frogging" between the major contenders: Intel, Motorola, and Zilog.

By 1979 the Intel 8080/8085, the Zilog Z80, and the Motorola MC6800 were the dominant microprocessors, all 8-bit and not dissimilar in overall architecture and performance. In taking advantage of higher-density IC techniques, such as the HMOS (high density metal oxide) process, all three were moving toward 16-bit designs. Intel and Zilog favored maintaining object code compatibility with their vast existing 8-bit installed base, repeating their earlier design philosophy that had seen, for example, the Intel sequence of 8008 to 8080 to 8080A to 8085, each one a faster sibling of the previous model. When the Intel 8088/8086 16-bit micros emerged, they bore obvious signs of this tradition.

BREAK WITH THE PAST

The MACSS team made the big decision to break away from the past and to create, from scratch as it were, the best possible 16-bit design. The sole concession to the 8-bit MC6800 customer base was the provision of timing circuits to handle the slower synchronous MC6800 peripherals. Although M68000 software would have to be developed from zero, at least there would be a wide range of I/O devices and support chips already in situ.

This break with the past was a gamble in many ways, but it addressed the reality that the 8-bit micro had evolved in a rather ad hoc fashion, during a period when the programmer's needs took second place to the hardware designer's requirements. When the first Intel 4-bit 4004 spawned the 8008 in the early 1970s, the latter inherited many of the features of a calculator or CRT control chip. This is not a criticism, of course, of those noble pioneers. Janus himself could not have predicted the explosion of microprocessor applications that occurred during the following decade.

During this period, once a particular instruction set had been established, and a large body of software had developed around it, subsequent improvements in MPU design had been dominated by program compatibility considerations — the understandable desire to provide a machine that could be put to work immediately.

Table 2-1 The M68000 Family of Microprocessors

Model	*MC68008*	*MC68000*	*MC68010*	*MC68012*	*MC68020*
Technology	HMOS	HMOS	HMOS	HMOS	HCMOS
Pins	64 DIP	64 DIP	64 DIP/68 QP	84 GA	114 SPG
Clock speeds	4-12.5Mhz	4-12.5Mhz	4-12.5Mhz	4-12.5Mhz	16.67Mhz
Number of registers	17	17	20	20	23
Instruction length (16-bit words)	1 to 5	1 to 5	1 to 5	1 to 5	1 to 7
Register width	32	32	32	32	32
ALU width	16	16	16	16	32
Data bus width	8	16	16	16	8/16/32 dynamic
Address bus width	20	24	24	31	32
Addressing range	1Mb	16Mb	16Mb	2Gb	4Gb

The lesson was clear. The new Motorola 16-bit design had to be expandable so that future enhancements preserved software compatibility without restricting the hardware. So far, the MACSS team has been proved correct.

WHY 16-BIT?

As we saw in Chapter 1, the numbers used in describing a micro can be misleading. As shown in Table 2-1, even within a closely knit family the vital statistics vary widely.

All the parameters listed are cunningly interrelated, and they have their particular significance for the overall price/performance of the chip. But, asked to single one out, the programmer would probably opt for the length of the instruction word. This dictates the richness and power of the instruction set —

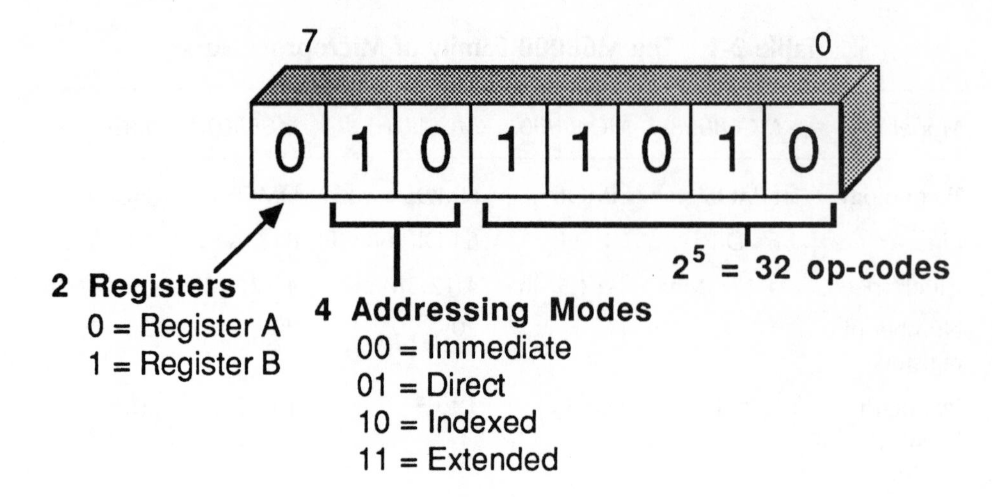

Fig. 2-6 8-Bit Instructions

and these have the most far-reaching consequences from the programmer's viewpoint.

The data bus width, for example, determines the number of read/write cycles needed to access data. But if you cycle fast enough, who cares if the data bus is 1 or 1000 bits wide? Well, Engineering cares, and so does Sales ("How can we market a 1-bit machine?"), but the programmer will be happy provided the registers are reasonably wide and plentiful.

The address bus width, as we've seen, determines the maximum physical addressing space, and we certainly want to end the tyranny of 16-bit addressing and 64K bytes. Various memory management schemes can solve this problem.

The importance of the instruction word size is clear if we look at a typical 8-bit op code, as shown in Figure 2-6. Although, at first glance, it provides 256 distinct codes, once you assign bits for address mode encoding (telling the op code which register or memory location to act on), you are soon down to 32 distinct operation codes. The contention here is among the number and type of registers, the number of addressing modes, and the number of op codes. Eight bits is just far too restrictive.

Motorola's jump to a 16-bit instruction word changes the picture dramatically, but naturally calls for more complex circuitry.

CHIP REAL ESTATE

Designers talk about chip *real estate*, and this is exactly how feature decisions must be made. For a given IC technology (NMOS, HMOS and so on), offering a given component density, and a given chip surface area, you establish an upper limit to the number of logic gates. This, in turn sets a limit to the feature sizes and functions you can build on the plot, and to those functions that will have to be performed by separate support chips.

NUMBER OF PINS

The selected functions obviously have to communicate to the outside world, so careful thought had to be given to the physical design, or packaging of the chip. Just as the 8-bit designs cast a shadow over progress, the number of pins on existing microchips was another hurdle. The standard 40-pin arrangement had the merit of low cost in manufacture and testing — and there were lots of 40-pin sockets out there pining for a chip — but you could only feed in and out a limited number of bus lines for data, addressing, and control. Often designers were forced to multiplex or share signal paths, which is basically self-defeating. The MACSS approach for the MC68000 was a 64-pin DIP (Dual Inline Package) that allowed more freedom in choosing bus widths, and avoided multiplexing data and address paths. The pinouts are shown in Figure 2-7.

Coming back to instruction size, sixteen silicon paths have to be established between buffers and instruction decoders. The 65,536 different instructions that can be encoded in 16 bits have to be allocated — no trivial task compared with the 8-bit situation where the op codes and register encoding almost write themselves.

REGISTER ALLOCATION — TYPE AND NUMBER

You now have enough instruction space to implement a **symmetrical** set of orders, that is, to have op codes that work uniformly with a large number of general-purpose registers. With 8 bits you can only increase the number of registers by having them **dedicated** or special purpose. For example, if ADD works only with register A, there is no need to encode register A in the ADD instruction. We will see that symmetrical registers are programmer-friendly, in keeping with M68000 philosophy.

A key decision was made to implement 32-bit registers throughout, even in devices like the program counter and stack pointer where 24 bits would have served the immediate purpose.

Motorola made a reasonable compromise in the number of registers and register types. By electing to have 16 basic programmable registers, 8 for general

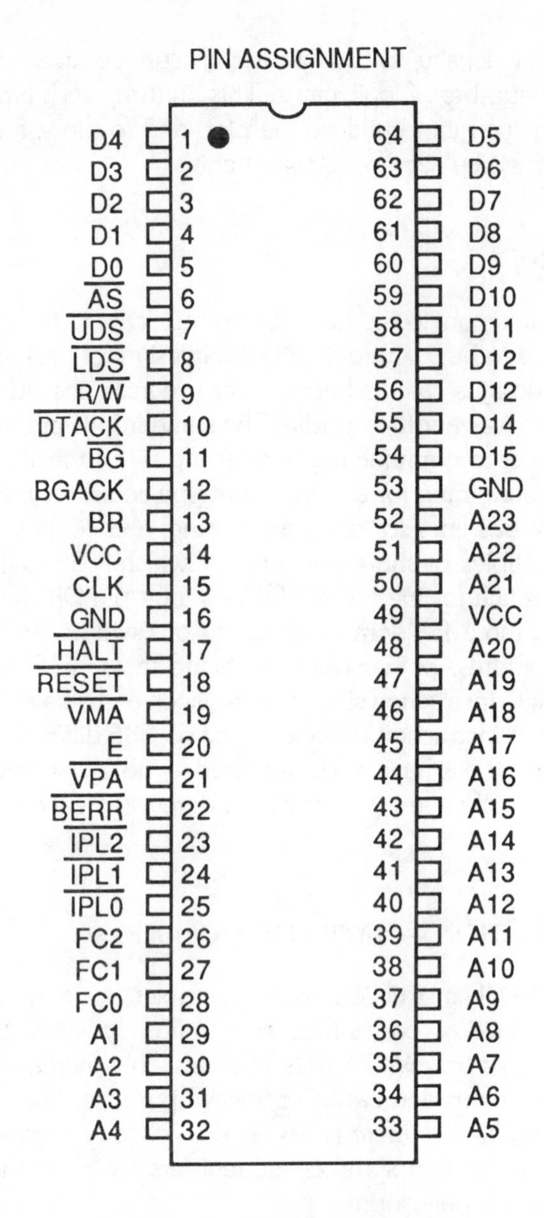

Fig. 2-7 MC68000 Pinouts

data operations and 8 for general addressing operations, 3 bits for register encoding were needed in some instructions (where the type was implied by the op code), and 4 bits for the more general instructions which could work with any register. When you consider that the MC6800 had only 2 general registers plus 1 index register, you can appreciate the good news.

DATA TYPES

The 16-bit instruction word also allows bits to be assigned to selecting the size of the operand. Although the registers are 32-bit and the data bus is 16 bits wide (on the MC68000), Motorola wanted to offer the programmer a simple, uniform way of handling data in units of 8-bit bytes, 16-bit words and 32-bit long words. Two bits were assigned for this in all instructions which allow all three basic data types. At the assembly language level, it needs only a single data-size code (B, W, or L) to select the operand data type.

ADDRESSING MODES

Likewise, the number and power of the addressing modes could be increased from just 4 on the MC6800 to 14 or more on the M68000. The importance of this will emerge in Chapters 4 through 8.

The M68000 also has additional on-chip ALUs and special instructions to speed up the addressing mode calculations.

IMPLEMENTATION

The final design decision, having listed all the goodies—number and size of registers, size of addressing space, instruction op codes, and addressing modes — is how to implement this in silicon. There are two main choices in arranging the complex paths and logical steps needed to put the chip on the road.

RANDOM LOGIC

The traditional method, called **random logic** design required that you mapped everything in perfect detail, then devised particular networks of discrete logical elements to achieve your grand design. This leads to a compact economical chip with no "wasted" real estate. However, as VLSI microchips increased in complexity, it became more and more difficult to implement. Random logic is simply too inflexible. The alternative, which in fact was invented by Maurice Wilkes in the early EDSAC days (Cambridge, 1949-57), is called **microcoding**. In those pre-micro days the name was not as confusing as it is now.

MICROCODING

Motorola adopted microcoding for the bulk of the M68000 implementation. In microcoding, you really have something like an MPU within the MPU. Each instruction is broken down into subinstructions or microinstructions, just as an external (or macro) program can be reduced to procedures and subroutines.

For example, if you write down all the internal MPU steps involved in moving data between registers, then list all the steps involved in adding two registers together, you will find that they have many microroutines in common. These make up the microprogram which is stored in onchip microROM (Read Only Memory).

For each instruction a microsequencer routes the data and control signals according to this microprogram. The advantage is enormous flexibility in design, testing, and fine-tuning, albeit at the expense of silicon real estate. Microcode can be simulated and tested off-line before embarking on costly chip fabrication.

CONCLUSION

Below the microcode level, the M68000 employs nanocode — and so on, ad infinitum. This threatens to take us into levels beyond this chapter's modest aims — so having whetted your programmer's appetite with some of the design decisions behind the M68000, let's proceed to the final product. In Chapter 3 we describe the features accessible by the programmer.

3

M68000 Programmer's Models

Thy gift, thy tables are within my brain,
Full charactered with lasting memory . . .

— Shakespeare, *Sonnet CXII*

In Chapter 1 we covered some of the basic concepts common to all microcomputers, and in Chapter 2 we looked at some of the design decisions and tradeoffs facing Motorola as they moved on from the 8-bit 6800 to create a new range of 16-bit and 32-bit microprocessors, the M68000 family. You saw that Motorola's prime aim was programmer friendliness — so let's look at the M68000 family from the programmer's point of view.

First, though, we must identify more precisely how programming languages are classified, the different roles they play and how they call for different levels of processor know-how from the programmer.

LEVELS OF PROGRAMMING

The term *programming* covers a wide range of activities requiring many different skills and perspectives. As you saw in Chapter 1 all programs sooner or later are reduced to a stream of **instructions** summoned from the processor's memory (RAM or ROM) and translated into specific actions, such as the accessing and manipulation of data from other specified areas of memory.

Programmers, and the programs they write, come in all shapes and sizes. They can be programming to earn their daily bread or to save the Free World or just for the sheer fun of it. The amount of detail they need to know about the inner workings of the processor, such as how it accesses programs and data from memory, varies enormously depending on the **levels** of the programming languages they use. Figure 3-1 illustrates some of the major categories of software, to give you an idea of what we mean by programming *level*.

HIGH LEVEL LANGUAGES

With **high level** languages such as BASIC, FORTRAN, or Pascal, the programmer writes source code which the machine cannot directly run without some intermediate transformations. The programmer is essentially isolated from both the processor and the detailed organization of its supporting memory systems.

The high level programmer can concentrate on solving his or her applications problems in the chosen programming language, leaving a **compiler** or **interpreter** to translate the source code into the **machine language** instructions which the chip itself "understands." These machine language instructions are highly inscrutable sequences of 0's and 1's, whereas a high-level source program uses readable "English-type" sentences that offer a more natural and general way of expressing your problem.

The output from a compiler is a **compiled**, "ready-to-run" machine language version of the source program, known as the **object, executable,** or **run** program or module, to indicate that the processor can directly execute or run the instructions without further translation. As you can see in Figure 3-1, the object code modules created by the compiler are usually stored on disks or other mass storage devices, from which they can be loaded into memory when needed. Interpreters work slightly differently in that the run version is usually executed immediately as each line of the program source code is translated. This technical difference is not relevant to our present discussion, so we will use the word *compiler* to include interpreters as well.

MID-LEVEL LANGUAGES

A mid-level programming language like FORTH or C still needs compiling, but it offers the programmer more control over the processor than, say, BASIC or Pascal.

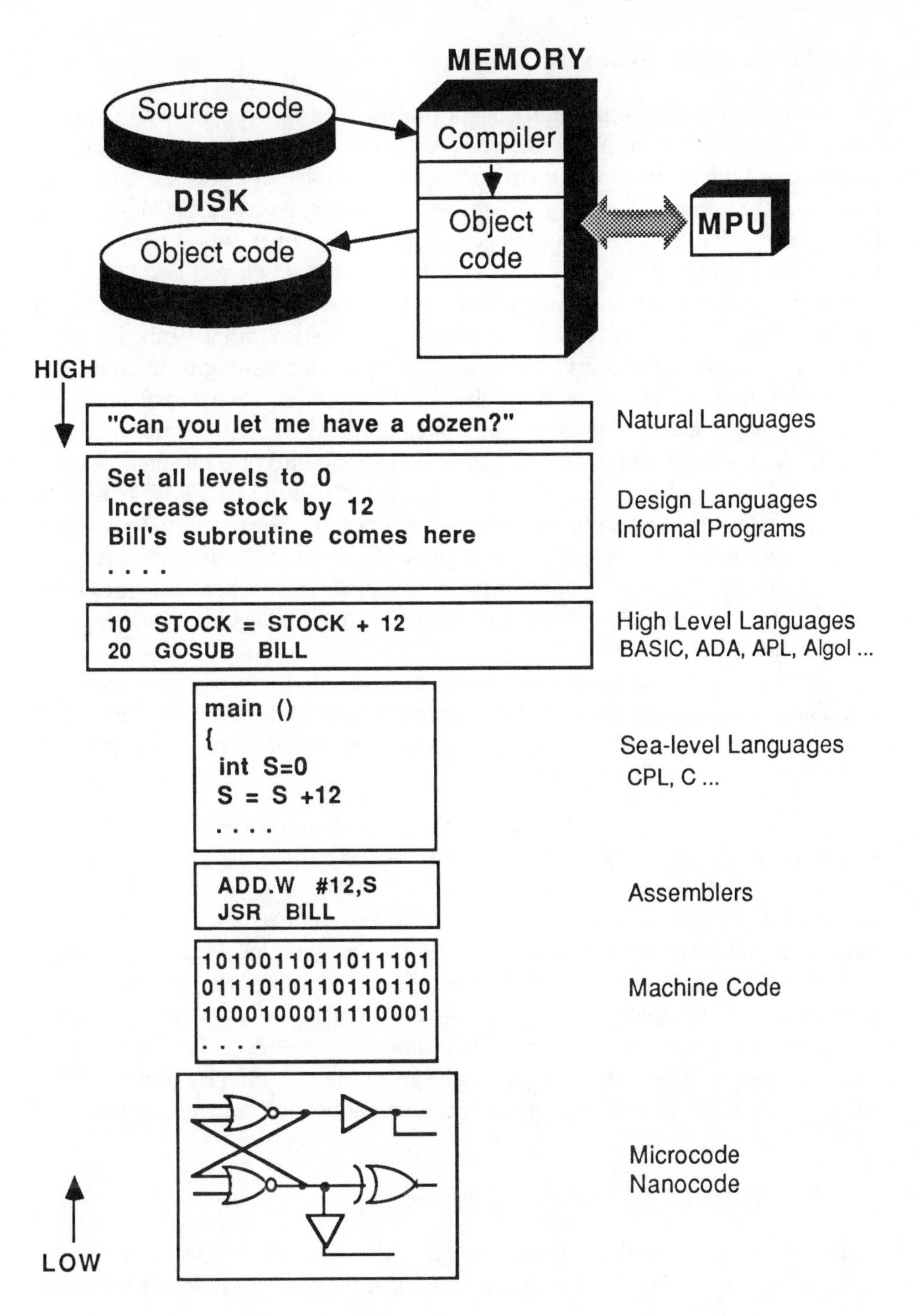

Fig. 3-1 Programming Language Level

LOW-LEVEL LANGUAGES

An **assembly language** program offers precise control over the way the processor will carry out your instructions. At this level we are really writing the processor's built-in machine instructions in a simple, one-for-one symbolic, **mnemonic** version using easily remembered words such as ADD, MOVE, and SUB. (Appendix C has an alphabetical reference list of these — how they all work is the subject of our next three chapters). For now, all you need to know is that they provide a legible version of the processor's machine code. Instead of having to write 0010101100110000 or some such binary mix for each instruction, assemblers allow you to program with more meaningful and readable symbols. But note that, unlike the higher-level languages, each line of assembly corresponds to one machine language instruction. When you write a line in BASIC, for instance, the compiler may well generate fifty or a hundred or even more machine language instructions. With assembly level programs, instead of having a fairly complex compiler between you and the chip, you use a simpler, faster **assembler** to translate the mnemonic symbols into machine code. Assemblers, then, are rather like simple compilers — they convert from one programming level to the one below. They are simpler than compilers because the jump down in level is much smaller.

At the assembly language level you clearly need to know a good deal about how the processor finds and handles each instruction. But the rewards are great. As we'll soon see, assembly language programs are extremely compact, efficient, and superfast — and not that difficult!

MICROCODE AND NANOCODE LEVEL

Even below the machine-language level there are **microcode** instructions permanently built into the chip which translate the machine-level code, and below that, the M68000 has **nanocode** instructions to translate the microcode! We pointed out in Chapter 2 that these esoteric levels are outside the normal programmer's scope, but insofar as they provide tremendous flexibility during the chip design and testing stages, we, the end users, directly benefit. Each language level has its advantages and disadvantages for the programmer.

COMPARISONS OF LANGUAGE LEVELS

One of the reasons for the success of high- and mid-level languages is that the same program can be written and run on different configurations of the same processor, or even on an entirely different processor. All you need in the latter case is a version of the compiler appropriate to the particular target chip. For example, a program written in Microsoft® MBASIC™ can be run on Apple, Radio Shack™, IBM and hundreds of other systems based on many different microprocessor chips with endless variations in memory size and structure. Of course, this happy state of affairs is the result of Microsoft's efforts to provide different versions of the MBASIC compiler and interpreter for a wide range of machines.

Software that can run with little or no change on different systems is said to be **portable**, and in view of constantly escalating programming costs this is a highly desirable property. However, as someone once neatly put it, there are no free lunches; there is a price to pay for portability. Similarly, there is a price to pay for the higher programming productivity that high-level languages provide. That price is paid in reduced speed and efficiency, and in increased size of the programs themselves.

Speed, Size and Efficiency

As you move down the hierarchy of language levels, towards assemblers and machine language, your programs become less portable and more chip-specific. On the other hand, the lower levels allow you more direct control of the chip's resources, and you can take advantage of particular features of the chip in ways not available to the high-level language programmer. In a nutshell, the lower levels are harder to program in, and are less portable, but they are more compact and run much faster. On typical test programs, known as **benchmarks**, an assembly language version of a BASIC program might run 10,000 times faster and take only 1 percent of the system's memory. Many factors, of course, affect overall computer performance, and it is pointless to speed up just one stage in the computing sequence unless the other elements in the system can keep pace.

Compilers themselves are, in fact, programs, and the programmers who write them for specific processors have to know in great detail how the processor functions at the machine-language level. Their constant aim is **optimization**, to reduce the overhead involved in translating from high to low level, and to produce the most efficient-to-run code. For this reason many compilers are written in assembly language. Another common method is to write compilers in C language, translate them down to assembly language format, and then massage them at that level to obtain the best possible executable version. The same techniques are applied in many other software development areas, especially for operating systems, utilities, and the whole field of what we call systems software. Such programs, which are used to support all users and are often permanently stored in ROM, must clearly be as compact and efficient as possible.

A sound general rule is that frequently used programs repay the effort needed to write them at the lowest convenient level, and this usually means the assembly language level. Today most high-level languages offer some way for the programmer to switch or **chain** to commonly needed routines written in assembly language. You might call this the classical "best of both worlds" situation. For this reason, most programmers today are well-advised to seek fluency in several high-level languages and at least one assembly language. Like driving a car, it soon becomes easy to switch from a Ford to a GM — the controls are in different places, but the underlying principles are the same. Continuing with this analogy, assembly language is like slipping behind the wheel of a Ferrari! There are lots of new techniques to master before you gain the maximum performance potential, but gradually they all fall into place and whoosh! — you are driving in style.

PROGRAM LEVEL SECURITY

It is worth mentioning briefly (because it may help to clarify some aspects of language level) that software publishers tend to guard their source code with great intensity against piracy and illegal access. In most cases the public can buy and use only the run version of a program, and even this, of course, is protected against unauthorized use and copying in a variety of ways, ranging from severe written warnings to sophisticated encrypted chips! There are several well-known packages where the run version is available for $500, but the source code would cost $5 million. The key to this is that the source code more readily reveals the strategy of the program and allows the unscrupulous to exploit the efforts of the programmer.

Source code can be printed, read, modified, and recompiled (or reassembled), then resold with some degree of impunity, whereas the run version is useful only for running. Now Homo sapiens, being the cunning species it is, will always seek ways around such situations. Some people patiently and manually trace through all the binary 0's and 1's of a run module to uncover its hidden secrets; others misuse special programs called **decompilers** and **disassemblers** to automate this conversion from run to source code. We stress the word "misuse" because decompilers and disassemblers are quite legitimate tools in the right hands. Even bright programmers occasionally lose their own source code (traditionally, one blames the computer) and decompiling your own stuff is no crime. The big snag is that the full majestic structure of the source code is seldom recoverable by decompiling, and deciphering a disassembled program (remember you are still very close to machine language) is a hard way to make a dishonest living.

LANGUAGE LEVELS SUMMARY

Our language level discussion can be summed up in the following way:

Higher level = Easier to program and update,
more portable, larger, slower

Lower level = Harder to program and update,
less portable, smaller, faster

In order to exploit the speed and power of machine language, you must learn more about the processor's instructions and how the processor finds them in memory. Then you can look at the many essential devices (called **registers**) built into the chip which give the programmer direct control over the processor's operation.

M68000 INSTRUCTION SET — BRIEF INTRODUCTION

You have seen that the microprocessor, when it is running or executing a program, fetches from memory, then obeys, a sequence of machine language instructions represented by strings of binary 0's and 1's. These instructions pack a great deal of information that the processor must **decode** in its **instruction decoder** before it knows where to get its data, what to do with it, and where to put the results. After all that, it needs to know where to get the *next* instruction.

As in sending and receiving Morse Code, for example, certain conventions must be observed at both ends for sensible communication to occur. An obvious convention is needed for the processor to know how many 0's and 1's must be looked at before it starts decoding. In the M68000 these rules are simple:

Instructions are groups of 16-bit words.

A simple instruction may need just one word.

More complex instructions may require additional extension words, up to a maximum of seven in total.

The first word in the instruction tells the processor whether to look for extension words or not.

So the processor fetches and decodes an instruction from memory 16 bits at a time, until it "knows" what to do. Depending on the particular instruction,

Table 3-1 M68000 Family: Bus Sizes

Model	*Register Width*	*Data Bus Width*	*Address Bus Width*	*ALU Width*
MC68000	32	16	24	16
MC68008	32	8	20	16
MC68010	32	16	24	16
MC68012	32	16	30	16
MC68020	32	8/16/32	32	32

the processor will carry out certain tasks. If the instruction says "MOVE data from one place in memory to another," for example, it will also contain information on what is to be moved and to where.

To understand how these instructions and the data they refer to are located in memory, you must take a closer look at the way the M68000 memory is organized. You are not concerned here with the nuts and bolts of memory boards or memory chips or whether it is RAM or ROM. What you need is a conceptual model of memory as seen by the programmer. The M68000 memory is a model in simplicity — just a huge set of numbered boxes, each holding 8-bit bytes. The number on the box is called the **byte address**.

MEMORY MODEL

M68000 memory, from the programmer's standpoint, is a simple succession of byte addresses ranging from 0, 1, 2, 3 up to the maximum address allowed. At each byte address you will find 8 bits of data sitting in memory waiting for action. This straight sequence of consecutive addresses forms what we call a **linear address space**, to contrast it with other, more complex addressing schemes in which memory is segmented, such as the Intel 8086/8088 approach (see Chapter 1.)

The maximum legal address is set by the width of the address bus which in turn depends on which chip in the M68000 family you are using. Members of the M68000 family differ in the number of physical address lines wired out to the address bus (see Table 3-1).

Determining your maximum legal address is a simple exercise in binary arithmetic. Each bit you add to an address bus line *doubles* the number of

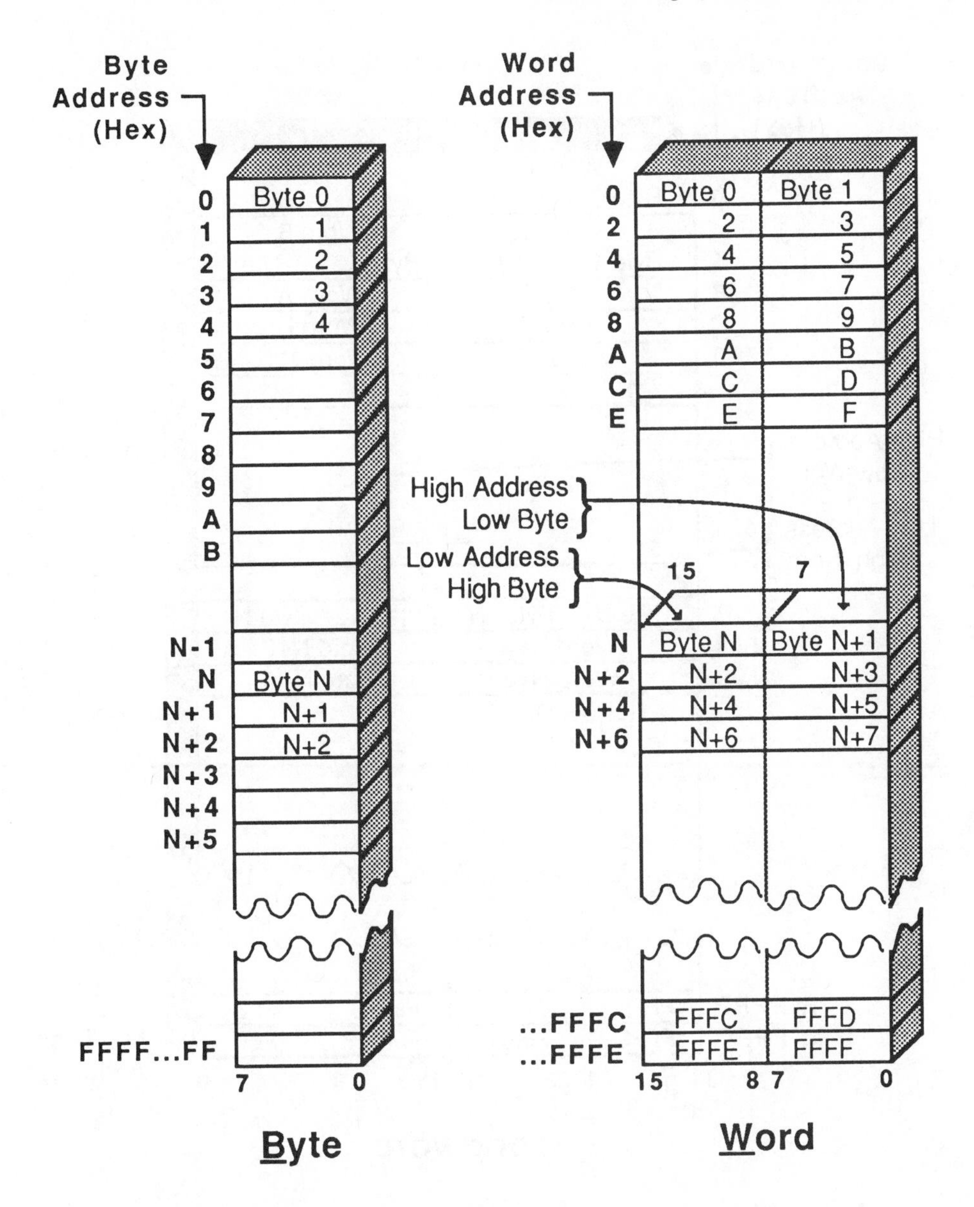

Fig. 3-2a M68000 Memory Model (Part One)

memory bytes you can legally address. A one-line address bus could access only two addresses, namely address 0 and address 1. A two-line address bus would double this to four possible byte addresses, namely 0, 1, 2, and 3.

The full 32-bit address bus of the MC68020 allows a **linear memory space** of 2^{32} = 4 gigabytes = 4,294,967,296 bytes. So, byte addresses on the

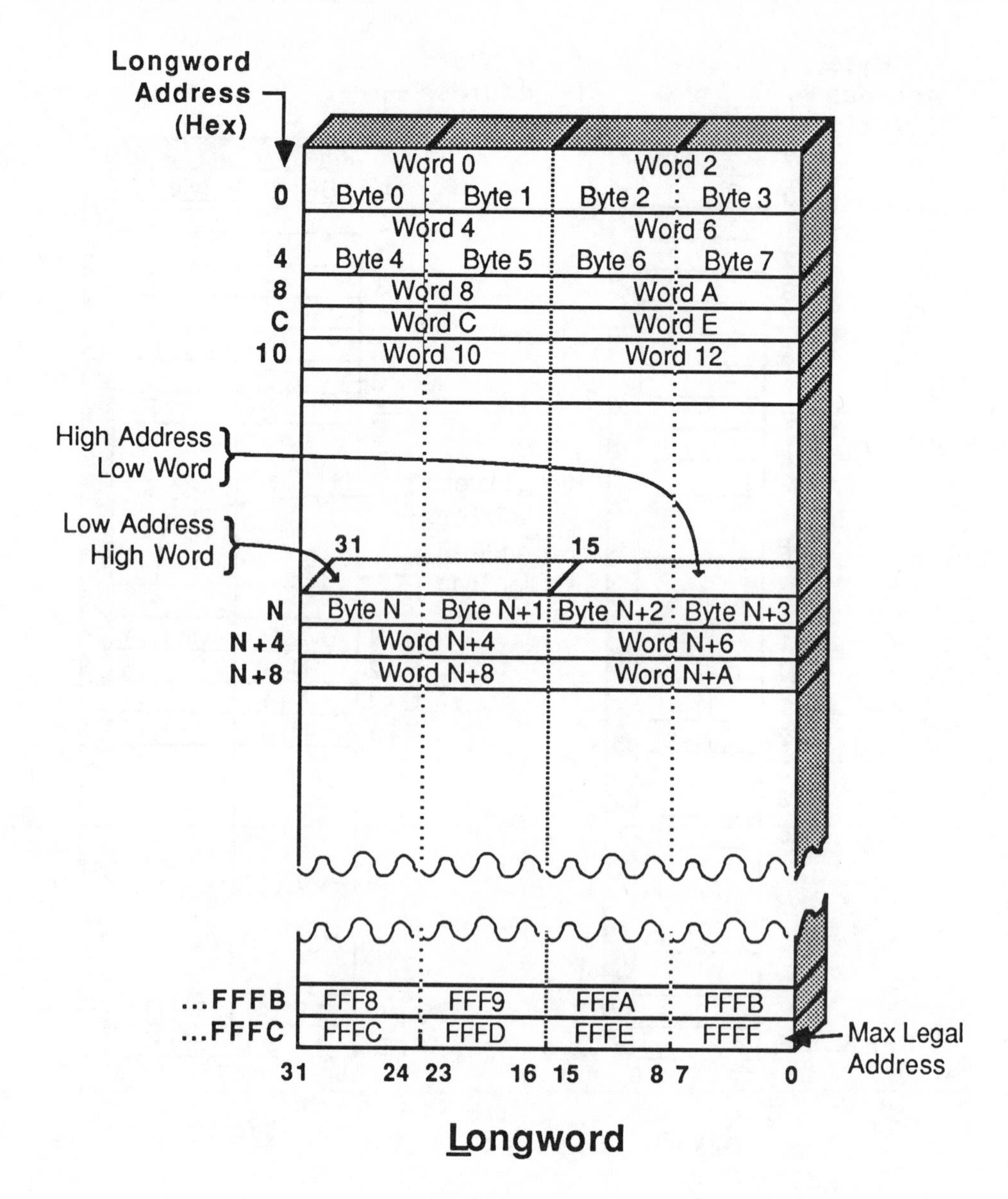

Fig. 3-2b M68000 Memory Model (Part Two)

MC68020 can run from 0 to 4,294,967,295. This upper limit is worth remembering. It will crop up many times as the maximum unsigned number you can store in a 32-bit device. You may find it easier to remember in binary:

11111111111111111111111111111111 (count them)

or in hexadecimal:

$FFFFFFFF (note that the "$" means hex, not money)

THE IMPORTANCE OF EXTRA-LARGE ADDRESSING SPACES

Memory prices have been falling dramatically over the years, but it may be some time before 4 gigabytes of physical RAM become an affordable feature for the average user! However, VM (Virtual Memory) techniques, originally developed on the Ferranti ATLAS in the late 1950s, are now available on the latest supermicros. VM allows you to access mass storage data using memory addresses beyond the range of the actual RAM installed, so you don't need lots of RAM to justify a large addressing space. Systems programmers are constantly thinking up new ways of making one thing look like another, an art known as **emulation**. The RAM-disk, for example, allows you to access RAM as though it were a disk, while VM lets you access disks as though they were RAM! The ultimate in emulation is the **virtual machine**, a technique that allows one microprocessor to look and behave like another (even like one that you haven't yet built). As we'll see in Chapters 7 and 8, the MC68010 and the MC68020 have many special features that encourage the use of virtual machine techniques.

The MC68000 has 24 of the 32 address bits **wired out**, giving it an address space of 2^{24} = 16 megabytes = 16,777,216 = $1000000 bytes.

The "budget-scaled" MC68008 has only 20 of the 32 internal address bits connected for external use, providing an address space of "only" 2^{20} = 1 megabyte = 1,046,576 = $100000 bytes. How quickly times change! It seems like only yesterday we were swooning over microprocessors that supported 64K bytes!

THIS SPACE RESERVED — FOR SYSTEM USE ONLY

Having established our wide open linear address space, let us immediately grab addresses 0 through 1024 for essential M68000 business known as **system memory** and **system data**. These hold important tables for interrupts, reboots, etc. and should not be altered by the average user. Some of these sacrosanct areas have to be in ROM so that they are preserved when you power down the system, but they still take up addressing space just like any other memory allocation.

There will almost certainly be other areas of memory assigned permanently to other vital systems functions, and therefore not available for user-only programs or data. As most systems and user programs grow more "friendly", they increase in complexity and size. Hence the large M68000 address space is a real blessing. There are, for example, many microprocessors boasting 128K bytes of memory, but by the time the essential systems programs are loaded, the user may be left with 50K or so.

ACCESSING MEMORY

You still have lots of logical address space remaining and we assume you have some boards of RAM to physically relate to some or all of your available addresses. How do you get data and instructions from physical memory? You need to look at the M68000 **data bus**, the electrical two-way path between memory and processor.

DATA BUS

Table 3-1 reminds us of another important and relevant fact about each M68000 family member — the **data bus width**. This dictates how much data can be transferred during each memory read or write cycle. A narrow data bus will require more read or write cycles to transfer a given amount of data.

Note first that the data bus lines are completely independent of the other bus lines. Many MPUs economize on silicon and pinouts by multiplexing or time-sharing data and address lines, and maybe other lines too. A **dedicated** data bus means that on each memory read or write cycle, all the bits on the data bus can be transferred in parallel without waiting for other line activity to finish.

Now since different members of our happy M68000 family have different data bus widths (ranging from 8 to 32), you may wonder how the same memory accessing instructions can apply to all of them. Here is how. Each instruction, regardless of data bus width, includes a **data size** letter code, L, W, or B. The MPU interprets this, and will transfer a 32-bit **longword** (L), a 16-bit **word** (W), or an 8-bit **byte** (B) to or from memory. Each 68000 takes the appropriate action for you. The actual number of read/write cycles is **transparent** to the programmer — a longword operation will take 4 cycles (4 x 8-bit fetches) on the MC68008, 2 cycles on the MC68000, and just 1 cycle on the MC68020. Clearly the MC68020 is faster, but the point we are making (yet again) is the high degree of instruction-level compatibility between the members of the M68000 family.

The basic MC68000 reads 16 bits at a time which is quite neat since we already know that instructions are encoded into 16-bit words or multiples thereof. But if you just want a byte from memory this will still take 1 cycle, the same as reading 2 bytes.

Because of the M68000's data size instructions we can look at its memory as though it were divided into either bytes at byte addresses, or words at word addresses, or longwords at longword addresses. Figures 3-2a and 3-2b show how we do this.

Here are the rules:

1. Byte addresses can be even or odd. Byte addresses increase by 1 as you go up.
2. Word addresses are even. Word addresses increase by 2 as you go up.
3. Longword addresses are also even. Longword addresses increase by 4 as you go up.
4. When you access a word at address N (where N is any even number), it will contain the byte of address N in its **upper byte** and the byte of address (N + 1) in its **lower byte**. Read this rule again. It says that when you look at a word in memory, its most significant byte is at the lower byte address and its least significant byte is at the higher byte address. Now embroider the following on a sampler and hang it over your bed:

   Low address/high byte, high address/low byte

5. When you access a longword at address N (where N is any even number), it will contain the word of address N in its upper word and the word of address N + 2 in its lower word. As in rule 4, we have an inversion to watch out for. Of the two words found in any longword the most significant word is at the lower word address and the least significant word is at the higher word address. So recite the following mantra:

   Low address/high word, high address/low word

6. If you try to access memory by longword or word using an odd-numbered address, you will get a bus error message. (The MC68020 is more forgiving, but this is still a wise rule to follow.)

If the M68000 is the first microprocessor you have ever studied this closely, you may not be puzzled by Motorola's byte/word/longword addressing conventions. Others will immediately notice that Rules 4 and 5 are exactly opposite to most other chips. It's like driving on the wrong side of the road in Europe — it's not a deep ethical question of right or wrong, but you do have to know the rules. When we come to registers in the next sections, you will see that the M68000 addressing rules are consistent and sensible.

Let's sum up what we have learned so far on M68000 memory addressing and organization.

MEMORY MODEL SUMMARY

- A large linear addressing space. No restrictions on program size (up to maximum space).
- MC68008 can address 1 Mbyte. MC68000/68010/68012 address 16 Mbytes. MC68020 can address 4 Gbytes.
- Byte (8-bit), word (16-bit), or longword (32-bit) addressing is controlled by data size code in instruction.
- Word and longword addresses are even.
- Program instructions are stored as words. Data can be stored as bytes, words, or longwords.
- Word at address N has its most significant byte at address N and its least significant byte at address N + 1.
- Longword at address N has its most significant word at address N and its least significant word at address N + 2.
- Longword at address N contains the 4 bytes at addresses N, N + 1, N + 2, and N + 3.

REGISTER MODEL

Now that you have a general picture of how the M68000 addresses external RAM and ROM, you can venture into the chip itself and look at the internal devices, called **registers**, which allow the programmer to directly or indirectly control every facet of the M68000's operation.

The programming "beef" of the M68000 is its powerful yet simple instruction set. Each of the 60 or so basic instructions in the set, such as ADD or MOVE, performs a specific program step by manipulating or interacting with the contents of on-chip registers and off-chip memory, so our programmer's model must include the registers and the memory addressing **modes** available to the programmer before you can make sense of the instruction set.

To some extent you face a "double-egg-and-chicken" situation since the registers, the addressing modes, and the instructions are all closely intertwined and mutually dependent. Some of the M68000 register features can appear rather arbitrary until you reach a related instruction in Chapters 4 through 6 that suddenly reveals the full beauty and symmetry of the M68000. We urge you to hang in there while we build up a picture of what registers are, and the many roles they play.

WHAT IS A REGISTER?

As a first approximation, you can look at a register as a small piece of very fast RAM built into the chip — fast because the data held in a register can be accessed and updated directly by the processor without any time-consuming memory-fetch cycles. Registers even have numerical addresses like RAM, but these are for internal reference within the machine language instruction; the assembly language programmer always uses symbolic addresses such as D1, PC, or A6. The big difference between RAM and registers is that registers have various built-in functions and are connected directly to control units on the chip in order to provide these functions. From the programmer's stance, registers are bits of "smart" ultrafast RAM.

REGISTER TYPES AND FUNCTIONS

As you saw in Chapter 2, a major chip-design question is how many on-chip registers to supply, and how many different functions they should each provide. The following essential register functions are always needed in some form or other:

Passive work areas for holding intermediate results The simplest, but nonetheless important function of registers is to hold intermediate results during a program. The key fact here is that the data held in on-chip registers can be accessed and processed very quickly using short economical instructions. And the more registers you have, and the wider they are, the more data (both numbers and addresses) you can hold at the ready, without wasting time switching data to and from external memory.

However fast your RAM is, machine cycles are used in calculating addresses, then accessing, retrieving, and storing the data in memory. To attain the highest possible throughput we always try to keep the engine stoked with fuel-data from the registers. A simple analogy exists with desk adding machines — if you have only one register, you often have to write down and reenter intermediate subtotals, whereas judicious rolling of subtotals with a multiple register machine avoids this chore.

Arithmetic and logical operations Registers, traditionally known as **accumulators**, are linked to the ALU (Arithmetic/Logic Unit) to receive the results of an ALU operation. The early microprocessors usually offered only one such accumulating register, forcing the programmer to shuffle data about before and after performing an arithmetical operation.

With general purpose **data registers**, as provided on the M68000, arithmetic can be performed directly without this coding overhead.

Addressing operations Address registers supply the processor with memory addresses for fetching and saving data. Before an instruction can access or save data in memory it must obviously determine the target memory address; in the most common case this address is obtained from an address register, but there are other more complex modes where the address is calculated from two or more registers.

Different microchips use widely different memory addressing schemes, and this is reflected in the diversity of special purpose registers used for the fundamental task of providing the **effective** address for the data needed by an instruction. With the Intel 8086/8088, for example, as we explained in Chapter 1, special registers exist for the sole purpose of providing base, segment, and index values from which the effective address is formed. We'll see that the M68000's nonsegmented addressing structure simplifies the situation considerably; there is just one type of general-purpose address register (although you get seven of them) and any register (including the data registers) can be used as an index register.

Program sequencing The PC (Program Counter) is a special addressing register dedicated to keeping track of the memory address of the current instruction, so that the processor knows where to go next during a program run.

Stack pointers Theoretically, a stack pointer is simply an address register used to access a dedicated area of memory known as a stack. Stacks, as you'll see in Chapter 5, play an important role as places for saving data while the MPU breaks off to do something else. Most MPUs have one or more registers dedicated to the job of keeping track of stack addresses.

Processor status Registers known variously as the SR (Status Register), the PSW (Processor State Word), or the CCR (Condition Code Register) are needed to report on various important states or conditions that can arise after each program step.

Typically the processor will **flag** events, such as whether the result of a sum is zero or negative, by setting 1's or 0's in certain bit positions of the SR. Instructions allow the programmer to test these bits in the SR, and alter the course of the program accordingly.

Other bits in the SR indicate **interrupt priority** levels. These are used to control the types of jobs which will be allowed to temporarily suspend the currently active program. Such suspensions are naturally called interrupts. When an interrupt is requested by, say, an I/O unit, the MPU must decide the relative urgency of what it is doing, compared with what the I/O unit wants to do. Such decisions are made on the basis of numeric priority levels stored in the SR.

After this quick review of register types and functions, we are ready to examine the M68000 basic register model.

M68000 BASIC REGISTER MODEL

Figure 3-3 shows the basic register model that applies to all members of the M68000 range. As you move up-market from the MC68008 through the MC68000 to the MC68010 and MC68020, you'll find enhancements to this model, but there is nothing to unlearn. For the programmer, the M68000 models are **upward compatible** — which is probably the most friendly thing you can ever find in a range of microprocessors.

Although the IC technology, pinouts, shapes and sizes, speeds, and memory addressing ranges of the chips in the family may be different, the M68000 family is object code upward compatible. Programs written for a vintage 1979 MC68000 will run without change on the latest 1985 MC68020.

We'll quickly run through the five types of register in our basic model, and then explain each type in detail.

1. 32-bit *data* registers: There are eight of these, named D0-D7.
2. 32-bit *address* registers: There are seven of these, named A0-A6.
3. 32-bit *stack pointers*: There are two of these, the USP (User Stack Pointer) and the SSP (Supervisor Stack Pointer). Since only one of these registers can be active at any point in time, they are both referred to as A7 — but remember that there are two distinct stack pointers maintaining two distinct stacks (naturally called the user stack and the supervisor stack), and they retain their own pointer values in spite of sharing the same register designation.
4. 32-bit *program counter*: There is just one program counter, called the PC. It is rather like an address register, but it specializes in keeping track of the address of the instruction being obeyed. The number of active bits in the PC will depend on the model, that is, 24 for the MC68000, 32 for the MC68020.

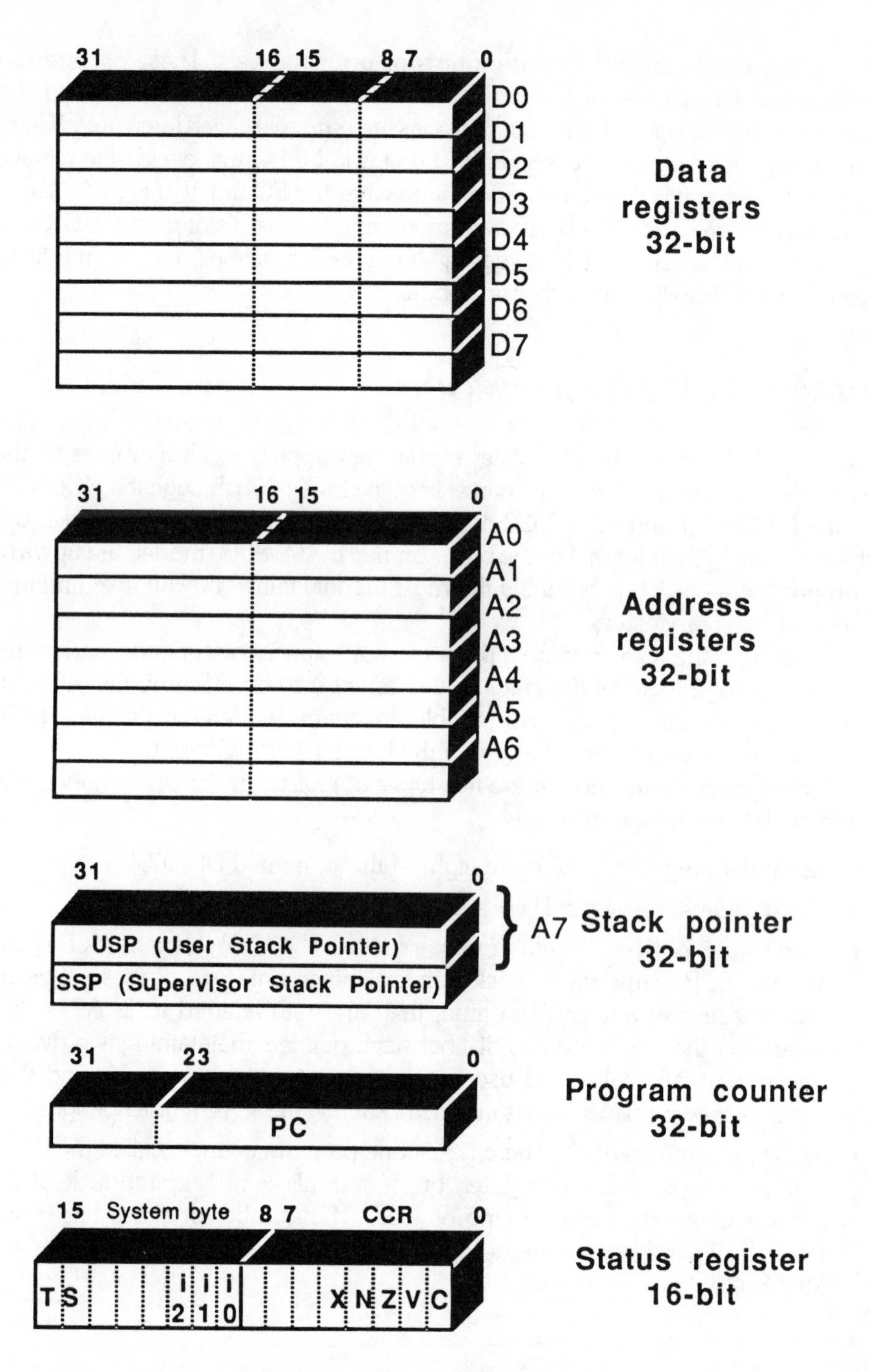

Fig. 3-3 Basic Register Model

5. 16-bit *status register*: There is just one, called the SR. The lower byte (bits 0-7) is called the *CCR* (condition code register); the upper byte (bits 8-15) is called the **system byte**. The CCR has 5 flags which are set to 1 or cleared to 0 to signal various conditions arising from each operation:

   C = Carry flag
   V = Overflow flag
   Z = Zero flag
   N = Negative flag
   X = Extend flag

   The system byte has a flag or flags to indicate which of two states the processor is in (either the **privileged** supervisor state or the **unprivileged** user state); it is this flag that determines which of the two stack pointers, SSP or USP, is active. The system byte also contains a 3-bit interrupt mask (i0-i2) to signal the interrupt priority level (0-7), and a flag (T) to indicate that the processor is in **trace mode** (a mode allowing the MPU to single-step through the program).

DATA AND ADDRESS REGISTERS

The data and address registers are the work horses of the M68000, and most instructions involve them in one way or another. As the names imply, the data registers, D0-D7, are used for general *data* manipulation, while the address registers, A0-A7, hold the addresses needed to access or update items in memory.

Typically, an instruction would use an address register to fetch a number from memory and place it in a data register; you then do your sums by referencing the data register, and finally, use the address register to direct the answer back to memory.

The different functions of data and address registers are reflected in the way they are wired, and in the rules governing which instructions you can use.

The only arithmetic you ever want to do on addresses is adding and subtracting in order to **index** or point to a given location — it is very seldom necessary to multiply or divide addresses. Also, addresses are always 16- or 32-bit numbers, so it makes no sense to design address registers to handle bit or byte operations.

The instruction set reflects this by having instructions that work only with data registers or only with address registers, or that perhaps work slightly differently with each. These apparent exceptions soon become quite natural and sensible throughout the M68000.

The data registers are designed to handle all the usual arithmetic and logical operations, and since they are 32 bits wide, they can hold addresses and act as index registers too.

REGISTER SYMMETRY

All the data registers behave the same, and all the address registers behave the same, so compared with many other microprocessors, there are fewer personality quirks to remember.

If you compare the M68000 with its closest rivals, you'll see that Motorola offers a very clean, symmetrical set of registers and a uniform 32-bits for data and addresses. An instruction set that has this kind of uniformity is said to be **orthogonal**, and although it may increase the complexity of the MPU, it makes programming much easier.

Let's look at the data registers in greater detail. We will look at the basic subdivisions of the 32 bits and how they are handled by the MPU.

DATA REGISTERS

The eight 32-bit data registers, D0-D7, all look like the sample shown in Figure 3-4. The bits are numbered from 0 on the right, the LSB (least significant bit) position, up to 31, the MSB (most significant bit). You need to remember that we start numbering with bit number 0 on the right up to bit number 31 at the extreme left. You'll get most peculiar results if you ever get this wrong. Bit number 1 is the *second* bit from the right.

The 32 bits can be used in almost any combination (you could access just bits 5, 19, and 28, say, if you felt so inclined); however, the instruction set is specially geared for fast manipulation of the three most common subdivisions, namely:

The 32-bit longword — one per data register

The 16-bit word — two per data register

The 8-bit byte — four per data register

Less frequently, we may be involved in the further subdivision of eight 4-bit nibbles but we'll defer this aspect until we meet BCD (Binary Coded Decimal) operations in Chapter 6.

Figure 3-4 shows the names applied to these subdivisions. We talk about the upper and lower words in a longword, and the upper and lower bytes in a word.

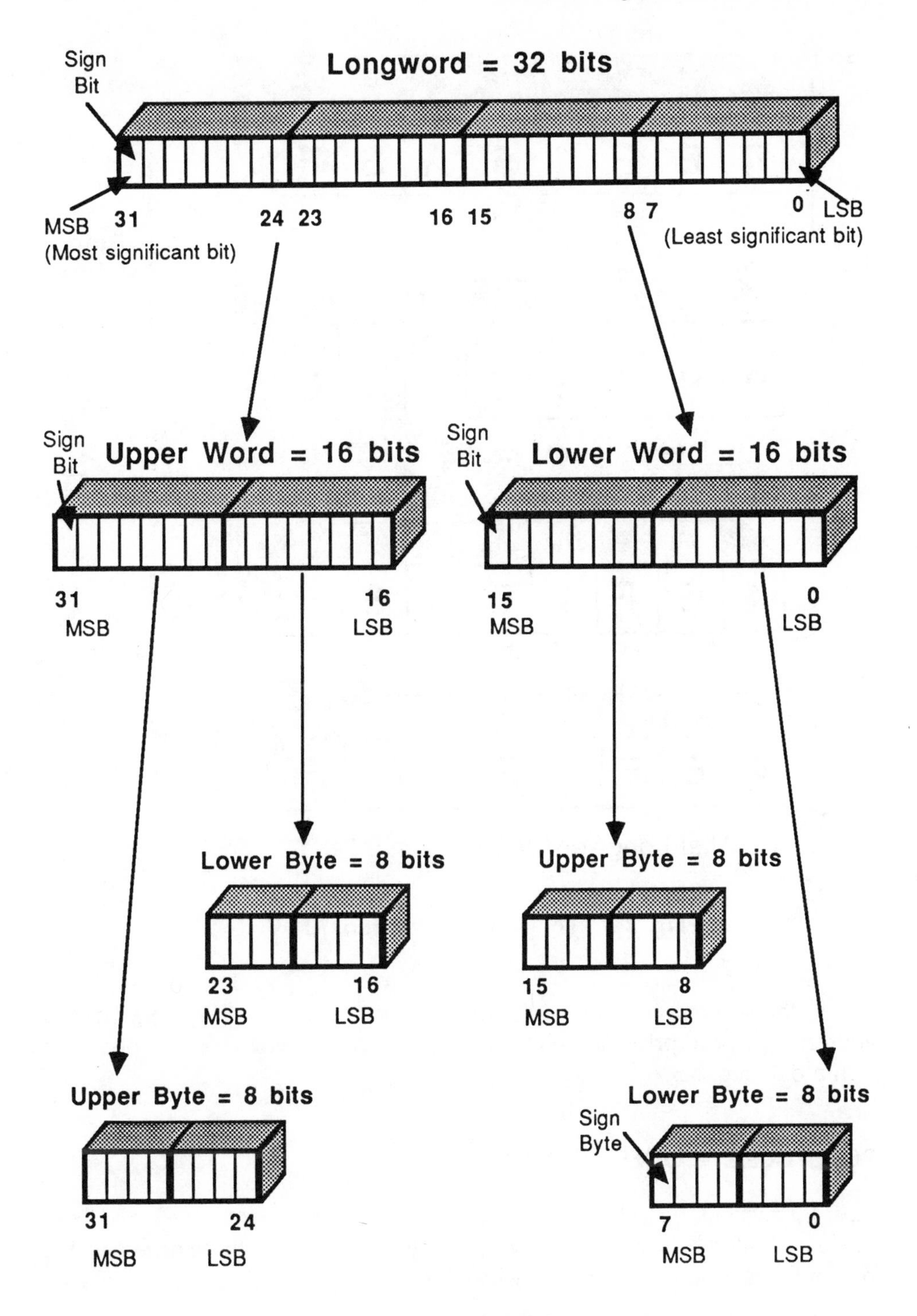

Fig. 3-4 Data Register

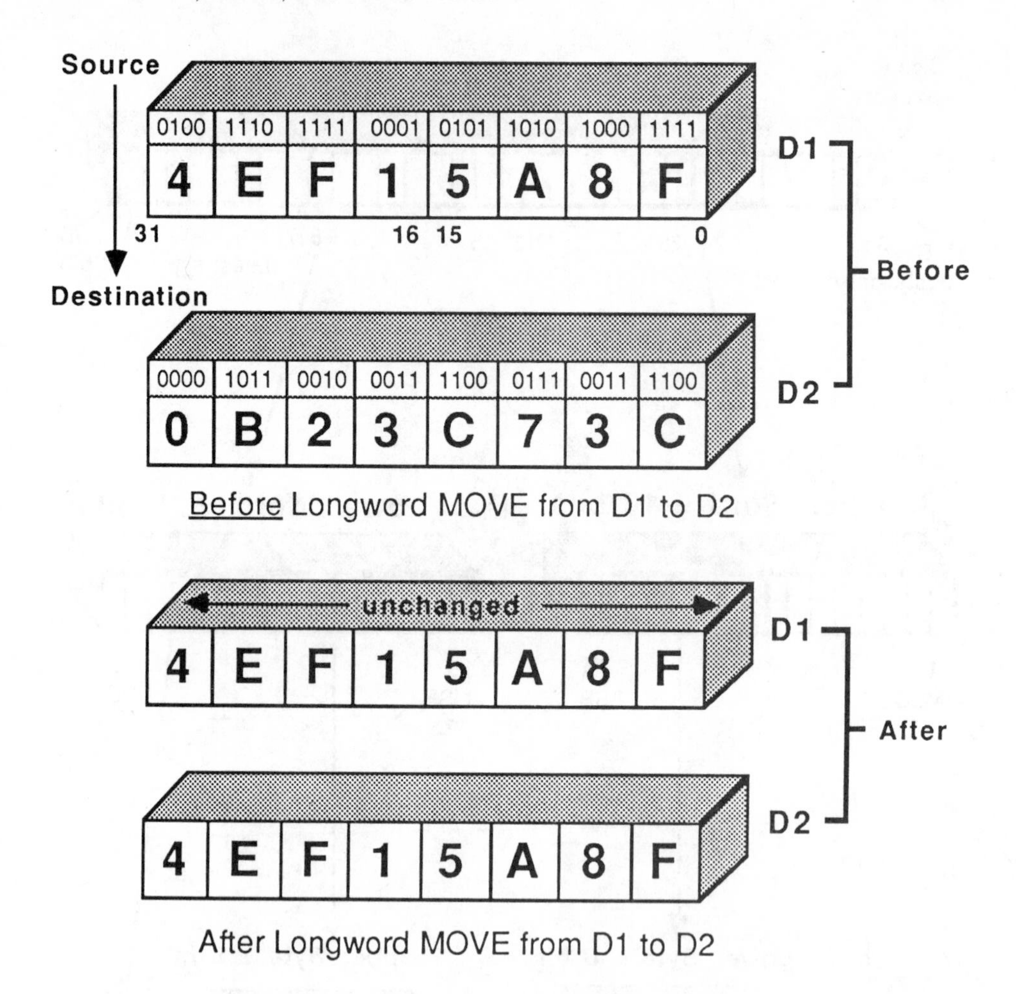

Fig. 3-5 Longword Operation: MOVE.L

In the section on memory you met the idea of byte, word, and longword addressing. Not surprisingly, you have the same choices when you do operations with a data register.

REGISTER SIZE-CODES

Most instructions operate in three modes, namely longword, word, and byte mode, indicated by the letters L, W, or B in the instruction. These dictate which part of the register is affected: the whole longword, the lower word, or the lower byte.

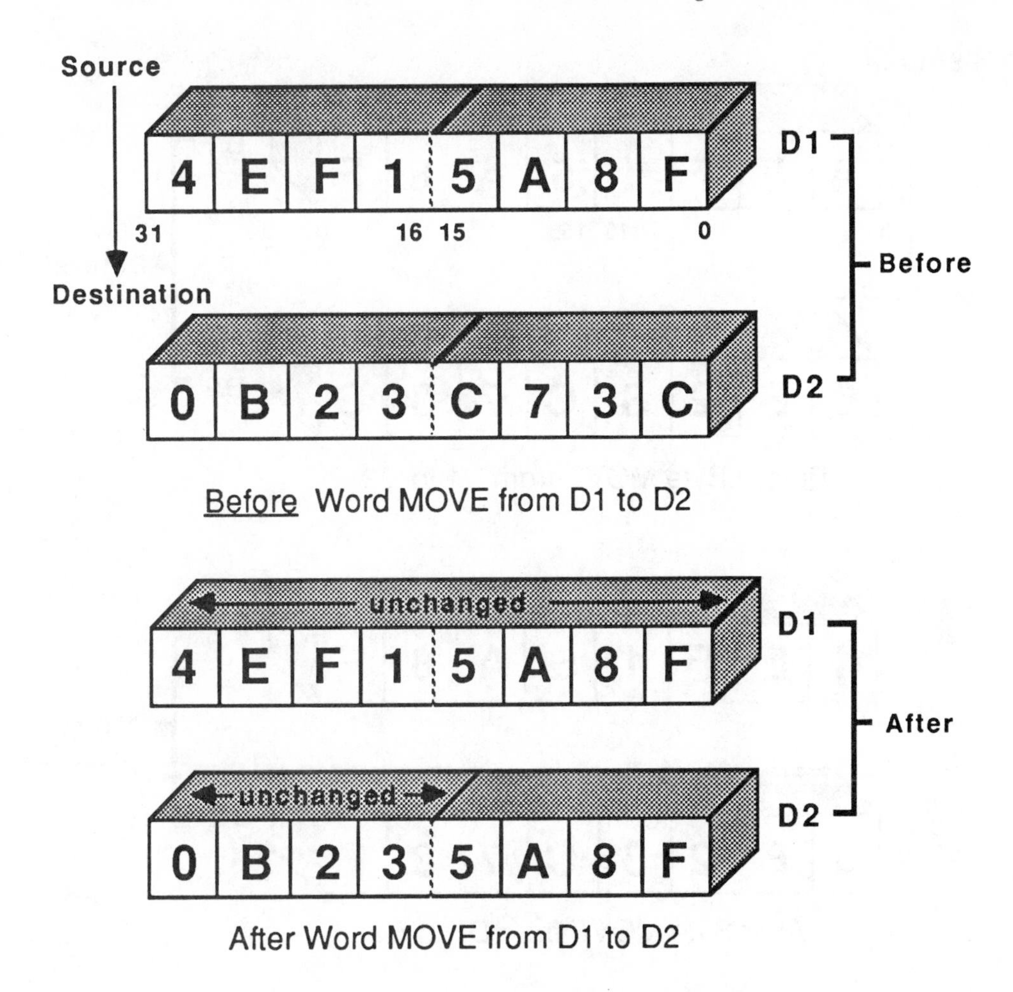

Fig. 3-6 Word Operation: MOVE.W

Let's see how this works, using the MOVE instruction to move data from one data register to another. We always describe moves as follows: *from* the source data register *to* the destination data register.

The format of the MOVE instruction is:

```
MOVE.<size-code> <source>,<destination>
```

Our examples will use:

```
MOVE.L D1,D2
MOVE.W D1,D2
MOVE.B D1,D2
```

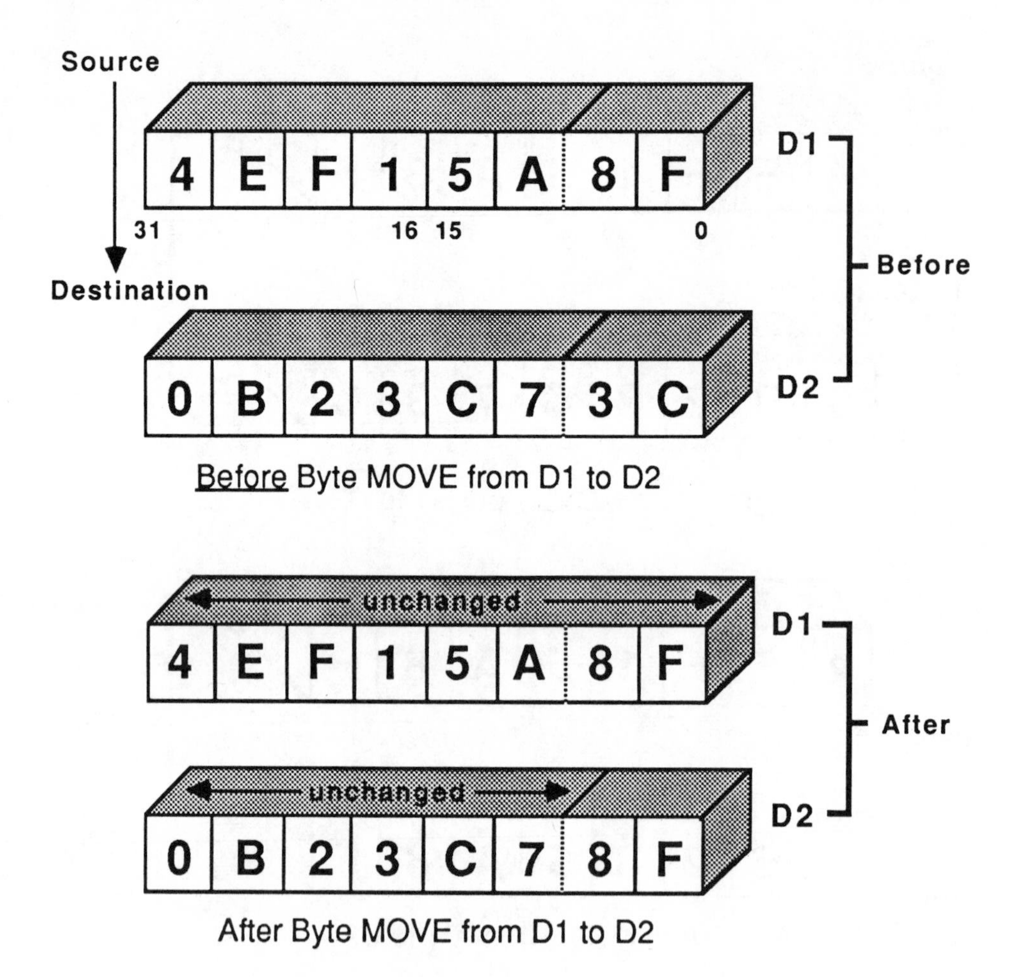

Fig. 3-7 Byte Operation: MOVE.B

Let's assume that before the moves, D1 contains the decimal number 1,324,440,20 = $4EF15A8F ($ = hex) and D2 contains 186,894,140 = $0B23C73C.

In Figure 3-5 the instruction MOVE.L D1,D2 moves the longword in D1 to D2. Not unexpectedly, D2 ends up with $4EF15A8F. All 32 bits have been transferred. The source register is unchanged.

In Figure 3-6 we have changed the size-code to MOVE.W. This time only the lower word of D2 is affected; it picks up the lower word of D1. The upper word of D2 is unchanged.

Finally, in Figure 3-7, we look at a move from D1 to D2 in **byte mode**. Only the lower byte (bits 0 – 7) of D1 is transferred to the lower byte of D2. The three upper bytes of D2 are unchanged.

Being able to operate on parts of a register without altering its other parts proves to be useful in many programming situations. On some computers, the byte move shown in Figure 3-7 might require three or more steps, possibly using a third register as you shuffle the data around.

REGISTER ARITHMETIC

Since data registers are mainly used for doing sums, you need to look at the arithmetic of 32-bit registers. You will see that, as with MOVEs, you can perform 8, 16, or 32-bit calculations. Also, just like MOVEs, byte and word sums do not disturb the upper parts of the register. The choice of data size will determine the numeric range of the numbers you can handle.

DATA SIZE-CODE AND NUMERIC RANGE

As we explained in Chapter 1, each bit the designer can add to a register doubles its range and, therefore, its numerical accuracy. So, wider registers mean more accuracy — hence the excitement when 8-bit registers replaced 4-bitters, and when 16-bit registers replaced the 8-bitters. The endless search for accuracy is reflected in the 80-bit registers available on the Motorola MC68881 and similar number-crunching coprocessors. As you will see, there are many programming tricks available for combining registers to get what we call multi-precision results, but the ideal is to have the hardware do this for you.

As we saw in Chapter 1, the unsigned range of a 32-bit register is 0 through +4,294,967,295 while the 2's complement mode allows signed numbers in the range of –2,147,483,648 through +2,147,483,647.

SEEKING A SIGN

In the 2's complement notation (see Table 1-1 in Chapter 1), we find that the above negative numbers have a 1 in bit position 31 (the leftmost bit), while the positive numbers, including zero itself, have a 0 in bit position 31. This bit is therefore called the **sign-bit**.

Similarly, with 16- and 8-bit operations on 2's complement numbers, the sign-bit in positions 15 and 7, respectively, indicates the sign of the number in a word or a byte.

The important rule for signed numbers is:

Sign-bit = 0 for positive numbers (including zero)

Sign-bit = 1 for negative numbers

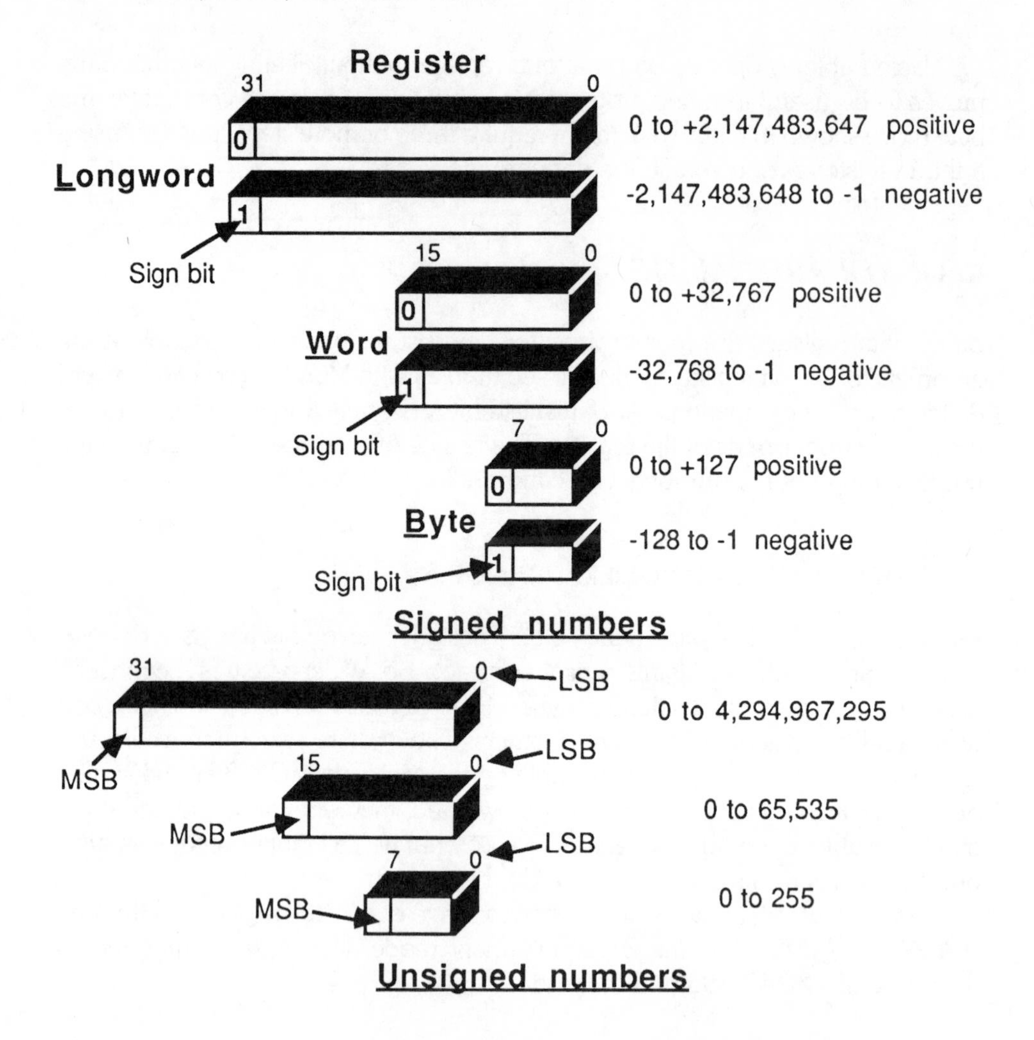

Fig. 3-8 Range of Signed and Unsigned Numbers

For unsigned numbers, of course, this bit represents a normal binary value (2^{31}, 2^{15}, or 2^{7}). Unsigned numbers have no sign-bit; they use all the available bits to give us the maximum positive range. In Figure 3-8 we show the ranges available for each data-size, L, W, and B.

Now, if you peep into any data register you will see a row of 32 bits — 0's and 1's in profusion. The M68000 attaches no intrinsic meaning to these bits; they could be signed or unsigned numbers or nonnumerical characters. Whatever legal operation you program on this register will be obeyed without question. If you use an instruction such as ADD, to add 1, say, to the register, then the MPU will treat the bits in the register as numbers. But does the MPU know whether the register represents a signed or unsigned number? The answer is no! ADD happens to be an operation that works equally well on signed and unsigned numbers, provided that the answer stays within the ranges we have listed in Figure 3-8.

Since the ranges are different for signed and unsigned numbers, the M68000 gives us two distinct warning signals via the CCR (condition code register) flags. The V (overflow) flag = 1 warns if the signed range is exceeded. The C (carry) flag = 1 warns if the unsigned range is exceeded. You'll see shortly how this is done. The important thing to note here is that the MPU does not know or care whether you, the programmer, are using signed or unsigned numbers. The V and C flags simply report a condition arising from your instructions. It is entirely up to the programmer to heed or ignore these warnings.

If you are using signed numbers, the C flag warning is irrelevant, but the V flag warning is crucial. If you are using unsigned numbers, the V flag warning is irrelevant, but the C flag warning is crucial. (An exception to this can arise during unsigned division. We will cover this in Chapter 5.)

Both the V and C flag warnings are based on the ranges appropriate to the data-size of your instruction. Adding in the byte mode, for example, would flag unsigned numbers exceeding 255, or signed numbers outside the range −128 to +127.

Let's probe this situation. First, a closer look at the carry flag.

CARRY

Unsigned registers are rather like automobile odometers; after a certain mileage they flip back to 0, you lose the vital 1 (meaning 100,000 miles) and you are suddenly the proud owner of a low-mileage car (or register). With a 32-bit register you can get this result by adding 1 to 4,294,967,295. The correct answer to this sum is:

$$4{,}294{,}967{,}296 = 2^{32} = 100000000000000000000000000000000$$

Alas, this needs 33 bits, so our register, doing the best it can, reports only the lower 32 0's. The register gives a 0 result, which is on the low side, by 4,294,967,296!

Unlike the automobile's odometer, happily, the most significant 1 at the left is not lost. Rather, it is carried to a bit position in the CCR — yes, the C for carry flag.

You can test this bit. If it is 0, you know there was no carry; if it is 1, you can take action to correct your result. In our example we would need to make sure that 2^{32} rather than 0 is returned as the answer. (We shall see in Chapter 6 that there are special extended arithmetic instructions for achieving this).

In many ways the carry bit acts as an extension to your data register when doing unsigned sums, giving you, effectively, 33-bit arithmetic.

However, there is only one CCR, and therefore the one carry bit serves all eight data registers. If you fail to check for carry immediately after the crucial addition there is a danger that the next operation could change the carry bit, resulting in another 4,294,967,296 mistake. The mysterious X (extend) flag is provided to help you handle this situation. The X flag is normally *set* the same as the C flag, but many instructions that clear the C flag leave the X flag undisturbed. For the moment, you can consider the X flag as a sort of C flag memory. Upon detecting a carry, you may have to move stuff around prior to correcting the situation. If the C flag gets lost, you still have the X flag available.

If you are working with word instructions, you'll get a *carry* when the lower word flips past its maximum unsigned limit of 65,535; likewise byte instructions set the carry flag when the lower byte exceeds 255. This, again, is all very uniform and programmer-friendly. The data-size code does a lot for you.

The carry flag also indicates another kind of danger in unsigned arithmetic. If you subtract two unsigned numbers and the answer is negative (for example $1 - 2 = -1$), the result cannot be held correctly in an unsigned register. In this case the carry bit indicates that a **borrow** has occurred at the top end of the difference operation. So the programmer can test the carry flag after subtractions and take evasive action.

The standard unsigned multiplication on the M68000 does not require tests on the carry flag. In this case, multiplying two 16-bit unsigned values gives you a perfect 32-bit result and always clears the carry flag. You cannot exceed the limit.

CARRY AND EXTEND — SUMMARY

Summing up, there is a C (carry) flag or bit in the CCR byte of the status register which warns us that our unsigned sums have gone over the 32-, 16-, or 8-bit unsigned limit. Both the C and X (extend) flags are set to 1 whenever a carry or borrow occurs. The X flag is preserved for later use, even if the C flag is cleared. The programmer can test the carry flag and take corrective measures.

OVERFLOW

The V (overflow) flag or bit warns you of errors in signed arithmetic. Let's look at a simple example of signed arithmetic to help us understand overflow. We'll use just 4 bits, but the principle extends readily to 8, 16, and 32. If we add 1 and –1, like this:

	Decimal		*Binary*
	−1	=	1111 (2's complement)
	+1	=	0001
SUM	0	=	10000

We have a good-looking answer in bits 0-3, so we ignore the carry in bit 4. This explains our rule that the C flag is irrelevant in signed arithmetic. In 2's complement addition you simply discard the carry.

Now try adding 6 + 7:

	+6	=	0110
	+7	=	0111
SUM	+13	=	1110 ??? = −2 (2's complement)

Here we get the wrong answer, and yet there was no carry. Why is the 2's complement sum wrong? The reason is that +13 is outside the signed range of 4 bits (-8 through +7).

Similarly, when we add two 32-bit signed integers the carry flag does not warn us if the limits have been exceeded. To guard against results violating the signed range of –2,147,483,648 through +2,147,483,647, the M68000 has to be a lot more devious. It has to watch the sign-bits of the two integers as well as the *carries* from bit 30 to bit 31. The details of this are not important, provided you understand the end result: if the V flag is set to 1 by your signed arithmetic, then the answer is wrong — you have exceeded the legal limits for 2's complement mode.

Our diversion into register ranges, sign-bits, carry, and overflow has set the scene not only for the CCR, but also for our next type of register — the address register.

ADDRESS REGISTERS

The seven 32-bit address registers, referred to as A0-A6, can each physically store the same range of data as a data register. So what's the difference? The difference lies in the permissible subdivisions of the 32 bits.

Byte mode is never allowed in address register operations.

Address registers are designed to handle either 32-bit long addresses or 16-bit short addresses, so you are restricted to longword and word modes when you operate on A0 through A6 (and A7 too).

Although M68000 addressing is based on 32 bits, the short 16-bit format, which allows you to address the top and bottom 64K bytes of physical memory, is used whenever feasible to save bus cycles. The M68000 has a neat feature for handling short addresses, called **sign-bit extension**. Let's see how it works.

The longword mode on address registers works exactly the same as for data registers; all 32 bits are involved just as we saw in Figure 3-4. Look at the first move in Figure 3-9. We have D1 set up as before, but this time we are moving in Longword mode to A0 rather than D2. The end result is the same — A0 picks up all 32 bits from D1.

Word-moves to address registers work differently, and the difference is important. In the second part of Figure 3.9 we show the effect of a word move from D1 to A0. This time the whole of the destination register (A0) is affected, not just the lower word. The lower word of A0 picks up the lower word of D1 in the usual way, but the upper word of A0 undergoes sign-bit extension.

The sign bit involved is the sign bit (bit 15) of the lower word of D1, which happens to be 0. This 0 is replicated in bits 16 through 31 of A0. The net result is that A0, taken as a whole, reflects the value and sign of the source word, namely the lower word of D1. The lower word of D1 happened to be positive (sign bit 0), so A0 was forced to be positive by setting bit 31 to 0.

Figure 3-10 shows what happens if D1's lower word is negative, with the sign bit (bit 15) equal to 1. A longword move from D1 to A0 works as usual, but the word move sets 1's into the upper word of A0. The sign-bit extension has preserved the sign of the register A0.

ADDRESS REGISTERS SUMMARY

The address registers are for full 32-bit addresses, but the short 16-bit form saves space and time in many situations. The sign-bit extensions preserve arithmetical integrity without bothering the programmer.

You now come to the all important SR (status register) which you saw has two bytes of important data, one for the system and one for the user.

SYSTEM BYTE

The upper byte of the SR is the **system byte**. The name of this byte derives from the fact that it is a protected area holding global data about the entire

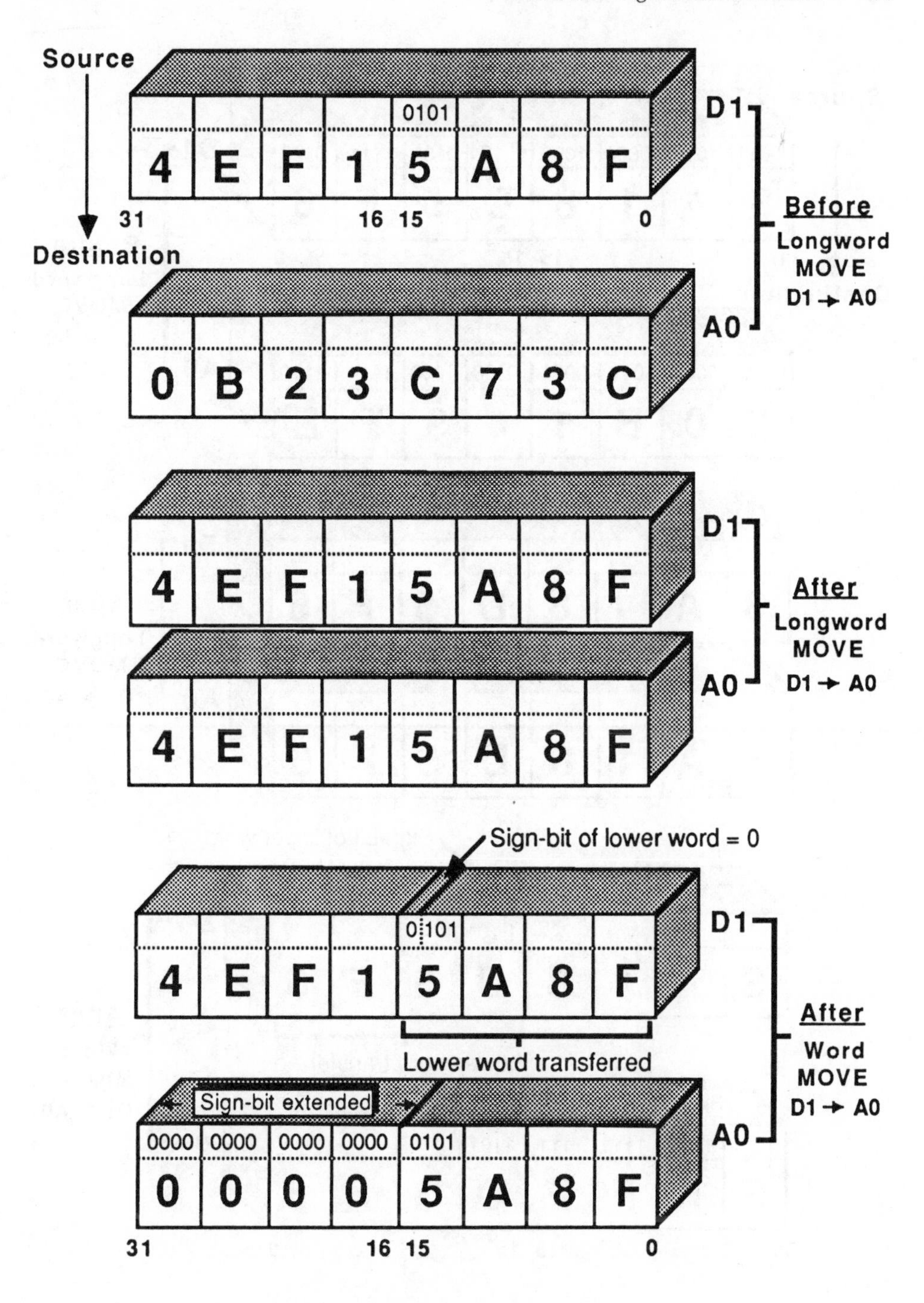

Fig. 3-9 Sign Bit Extension in Word Address: Sign Bit = 0

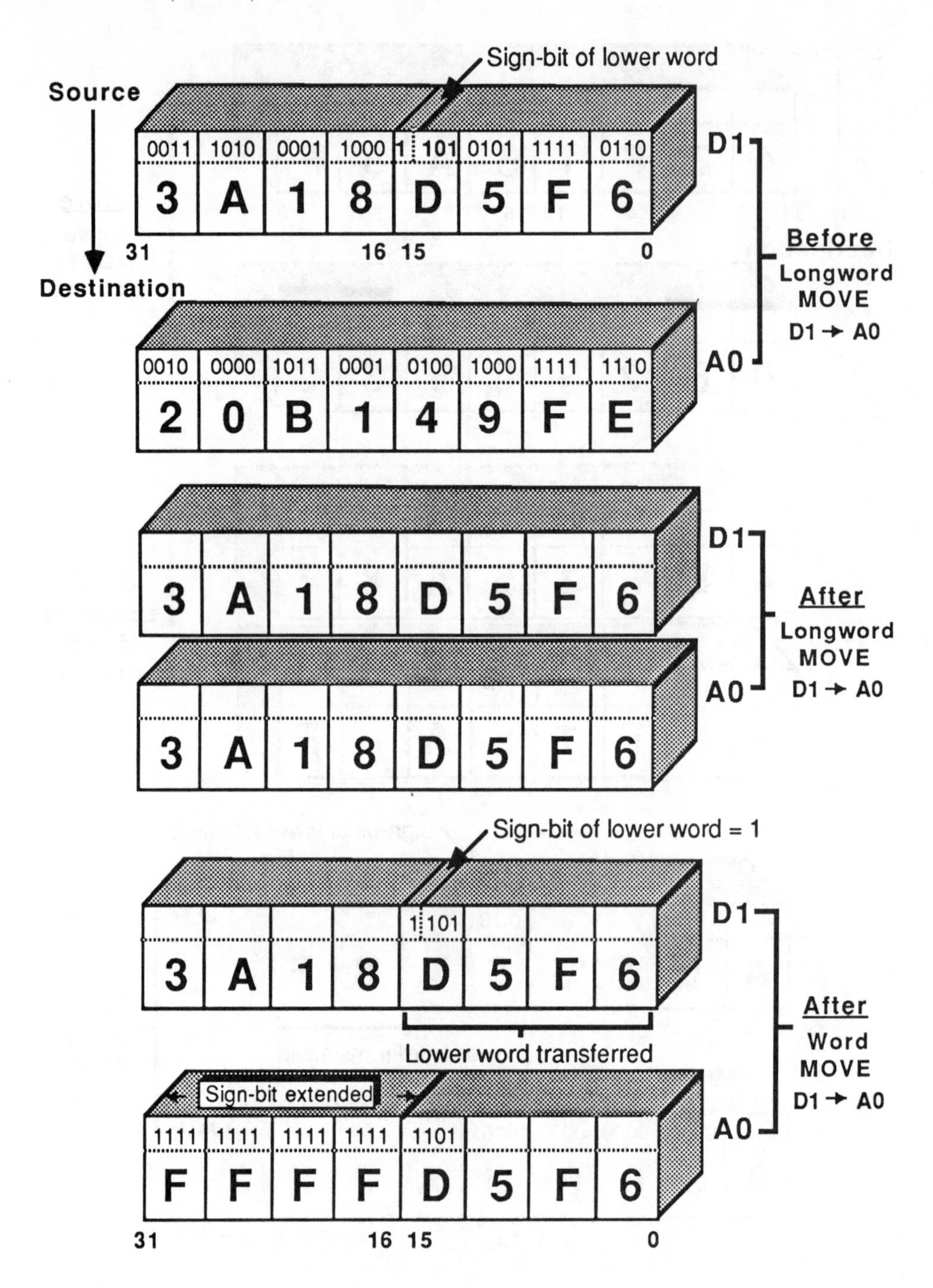

Fig. 3-10 Sign Bit Extension in Word Address: Sign Bit = 1

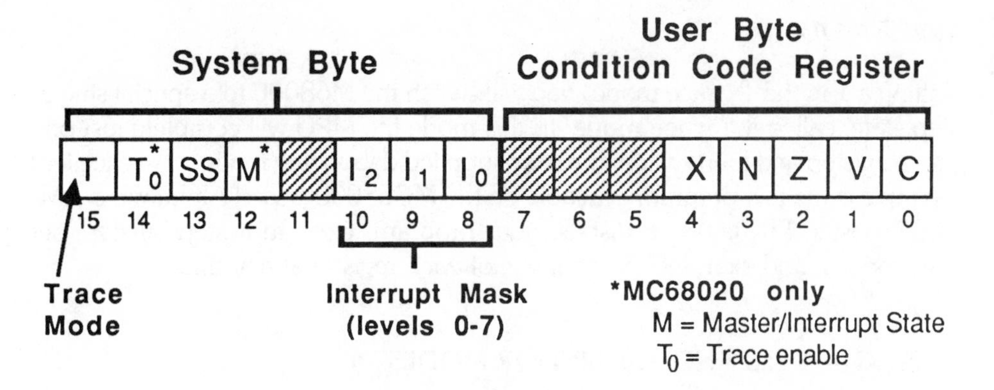

Fig. 3-11 Status Register: System/User Byte

system. It can be read by all users, but can only be written (changed) when the machine is in a privileged supervisor state.

As shown in Figure 3-11, five bits of the system byte are allocated as follows (bits 12 and 14 are used only on the MC68020; they are explained in Chapter 8):

Bits 8-10 = Interrupt mask (I0, I1, I2)

Bit 15 = T (trace mode flag)

Bit 13 = SS (supervisor state flag)

INTERRUPT MASK

These three bits allow the system to set up 8 priority levels (0 through 7) that determine which interrupts will be accepted or serviced by the M68000. The name mask gives a useful insight into this concept, since certain level interrupts are masked or disallowed by these 3 bits.

External devices can request an interrupt of priority level 1 through 7 (7 being the highest priority) by sending a 3-bit signal to the MPU. When the MPU has completed its current operation, it will compare the requested level against the current mask level. Only if the incoming request level is higher than the mask setting will the interrupt request be serviced. Otherwise the request is ignored. If the mask is set to level 0, then obviously all interrupt requests are serviced. A mask set at 7 means, "Don't interrupt!"

TRACE MODE

Setting a 1 in the T (trace mode) flag will switch the M68000 to a special single-step state, called the **trace mode**. In this mode the MPU will complete just one program step and then switch to a user-supplied debugging routine. An excellent example is the FIX program available on the MC68000-based AlphaMicro AM-100™. Using FIX you can display your program, execute it step-by-step, set breakpoints, and examine the contents of each register at any time.

SS FLAG — USER AND SUPERVISOR MODES

The M68000 operates in one of two exclusive modes (or states): **user** mode or **supervisor** mode. It is easy to tell which mode is in force — you just test the SS (supervisor state) flag in the status register. If SS = 1 you are operating in supervisor mode. If SS = 0 you are operating in user mode.

A program running in supervisor mode has access to all resources in the system, including special areas of memory, the supervisor stack and the system byte, by means of **privileged** instructions. A program in user mode will generate error conditions if it encroaches on these systems resources.

In a typical working system, the mode will be regularly switched between supervisor and user states. Roughly speaking, normal applications software is run in user mode, while the OS and other systems software will run in the privileged supervisor mode.

You will see in Chapter 6 that many different events trigger these state changes. These events can be deliberately programmed or they may arise from unexpected exceptions known as **traps**.

This two-state approach is Motorola's solution to the problem of system integrity which we discussed in Chapter 1. Or, rather, it offers the systems designer methods of increasing systems security. In particular, it helps protect the OS memory areas from accidental or deliberate incursion by user programs.

The state is not only indicated in the SS flag of the system byte, it is also **broadcast** to all external devices via the 3 FC (Function Control) pins to the control bus. Referring back to Figure 1-13, you saw how a memory management unit could use these signals to segment memory into system and user areas.

SUPERVISOR MODE SUMMARY

The supervisor mode has access to all the user mode resources but additionally enjoys some extra privileges and resources needed by the operating system for added efficiency and security. Normal user programs run in user mode, but interrupts, traps, and exceptions are processed in supervisor mode.

STACK POINTERS

A stack is simply a portion of memory with a pointer address, allowing you to **push** data in, and **pull** data out, on a LIFO (Last In First Out) basis. In Chapter 5 we will show in detail how stacks are easily handled on the M68000 using MOVE instructions with built-in stack pointer increments and decrements.

Stacks are commonly used to save all kinds of parameters and status words while you jump off to do other things, such as subroutines, which in turn jump off, and so on, in what is called **nesting**. Even if you have plenty of registers for saving and recalling data during the nesting, the stack is more convenient for the programmer, since the sequence of pulling (recalling) automatically reverses the sequence of pushing (saving).

Some care is needed to avoid confusion in the 68000 terminology for stack pointers. You are free to set up your own private stacks using any convenient address register as a stack pointer. However, such private stacks are entirely your responsibility.

The M68000, on the other hand, maintains two **systems stacks**, the user systems stack (active only in user mode) and the supervisor system stack (active only in supervisor mode). Some M68000 instructions make implicit use of the systems stacks, others allow the programmer to reference them with the mnemonic SP, or **systems pointer**. SP is, in fact, another name for A7. Because the two systems stacks are never active simultaneously, they can both be referenced with SP (= A7). Remember, though, that the meaning of SP is determined by the M68000 mode at execution time.

CONDITION CODE REGISTER

The single 8-bit CCR (condition code register) forms the lower user byte (bits 0-7) of the SR (status register).

The lower 5 bits of the CCR, as we've seen, are used to signal various conditions following arithmetical or logical operations. The top 3 bits of the CCR are not currently used.

The five condition flags (sometimes called *status flags*) are designated as:

Bit	7	6	5	4	3	2	1	0
CCR flag				X	N	Z	V	C

Where:
X = eXtend
N = Negative
Z = Zero
V = oVerflow
C = Carry

We discussed the X, V, and C flags in depth in the data register section above. The remaining flags are extremely simple. The Z flag is set to 1 if the result of the last instruction was zero, otherwise the Z flag is cleared to 0. A nonzero answer gives Z=0. A zero answer gives Z=1. The N flag is set with the value of the MSB (most significant bit), also known as the sign bit. So, for signed arithmetic we have: N=1 for negative answers; N=0 for positive/zero answers.

CONCLUSION

In this chapter we have set the scene for a more detailed look at the M68000 instructions. In Chapter 4, you will look at the most commonly used op codes and see, with program examples, just how they work and when to use them.

4

M68000 Instruction Set — First Steps

Bloody instructions, which being taught, return to plague the inventor.

— Shakespeare, *Macbeth* I, vii

Chapter 4 will explain what an instruction is, and introduce you to some of the simpler, more commonly used M68000 instructions. The program examples we offer as illustrations are not meant to be complete, practical programs, all ready to be entered and run, although we have tried to make them interesting and rooted in the real world.

INSTRUCTIONS

As far as the M68000 is concerned an **instruction** is a set of 16-bit words sitting in memory and a **program** is a sequence of such instructions which will hopefully guide the system through some useful work.

To the untrained human eye machine-level instructions form a bewildering sequence of 0's and 1's, but as they are read in and decoded by the chip, these instructions are obeyed according to very precise rules — and this is what is called **running** a program.

In this chapter we will be dissecting each M68000 instruction to see how it works and why it is used. The functional side of the instructions will be illustrated with before-and-after diagrams. Where and when to use them is the creative art we call machine-language programming, and we can only hint at the infinite number of possibilities by showing you isolated program examples.

There is no substitute for practical hands-on experience — Appendix E (M68000 Resources) is designed to help you acquire the hardware, software, and further documentation needed for this.

If we were purely binary creatures we could refer to machine instructions as "0111001000000001" (which actually tells the M68000 to move the number 1 to data register 1) or "0101111010010010" (which would add 7 to a number in memory) and so on. Alas, life is too short and humans are just not built to communicate like this. Dropping a 1 or misplacing a 0 can have a disastrous impact on the meaning of the instruction. Worse still, some instructions have one or more **extension** words and may take up to 80 bits to spell out. Imagine learning Morse with over 150 million different codes!

The obvious way out is to have recognizable English symbols for each instruction — and, in fact, this is exactly how an assembly language programmer thinks, writes, and talks about each instruction. The symbols you use are called **mnemonics** since they help you to remember the function of each instruction.

In the two examples just mentioned, 0111001000000001 is written

```
MOVEQ  #1,D1
```

and 0101111010010010 is written

```
ADDQ.L #7, (A2)
```

The English versions may still look bizarre to you but you have to admit that they are better than all those 0's and 1's! As you proceed, the full beauty and precision of the instructions will become clear — what they can achieve and how they are combined to produce working programs is, after all, the reason for learning their secrets.

Keep in mind, though, that the M68000 itself never "sees" these mnemonic symbols. They are simply an aid to human learning and programming. As we saw in Chapter 3, our symbolic instructions have to be translated or assembled into binary machine code before they can run. The actual binary patterns of each instruction are shown in Appendix D. Feel free to memorize them if you wish, but we still think that a good assembler is the answer.

INSTRUCTION FORMATS

Each symbolic instruction is rather like a sentence in English. As well as getting to know the meaning of each word, you also have to know the correct grammar or syntax so that you avoid illegal or nonsensical combinations. For example, "bites dog man" contains three perfectly understandable words, but the overall meaning is somewhat obscure to say the least. And just as English usage varies as you travel around, you will find different M68000 implementations using slightly different names and formats for the same instruction. Luckily there is a natural standard, and not surprisingly, it was invented and promoted by Motorola — so we will use it throughout. If you spot any deviations on your own machine you know who to blame.

Since our object is to teach the basic workings of the M68000 instruction set, we will avoid most of the technicalities of assembly by adopting the following plain "vanilla" version of the Motorola syntax.

INSTRUCTION SYNTAX

There are three different instruction layouts in the M68000:

1. No operand: op code stands alone
2. One operand: op code followed by operand
3. Two operands: op code followed by source operand and destination operand

The **op code** is a mnemonic such as JMP, MOVE, ADD, SUB which tells you what the instruction will do. The M68000 has about 60 basic op codes, and many of these can have up to 500 variations! Even experienced 68000 programmers do not carry all these combinations around in their heads. Rather, they understand the governing principles and consult the reference sheets when in doubt on a particular instruction. For this reason we have constructed some useful appendices cross-referencing the op codes in various ways to help you.

The **operands** are registers or memory locations which tell you what the op code acts on. Continuing our analogy with English, you can consider the op code as the verb, and the operands as the direct or indirect objects in a sentence.

To get a feel for these three instruction formats let's look at some examples, without delving too deeply into how they work.

No Operand

RTS	The op code is ReTurn from Subroutine. No operand is needed for the RTS instruction.

One Operand

ASL.W (A0)	The op code is Arithmetic Shift Left.Word. The single operand (A0) tells the M68000 where to find the data to be shifted, namely the word at the memory address stored in address register A0.

Two Operands

MOVE.B D3,D4 — The op code is MOVE.Byte, which needs two operands, namely the **source** operand, data register 3, and the **destination** operand, data register 4. Our example says move the lower byte of D3 to the lower byte of D4, that is, *from* source, *to* destination.

Since most of the instructions are of the two-operand type, let's examine this layout in more detail (see Figure 4-1). However simple or complex our two operands may be, you will always find a comma separating them. The source operand always comes first; this is where the instruction gets its initial data from. The destination comes after the comma, and indicates where the result of the operation is to be found.

Source operands are not changed by an instruction.
Destination operands are changed.

So, MOVE.B D3,D4 leaves the contents of D3 undisturbed and replaces the D4 byte with the D3 byte. Later on we'll show you particular examples of MOVE and its many variations.

Here is another example of a very popular two-operand instruction called ADD.

ADD.L D6, D7 — ADD.Longword says: add the 32 bits of source, D6, to the 32 bits of destination, D7, and place the sum in the destination, D7. Here again we see the destination operand receiving the result of the instruction's op code.

DATA SIZE CODES — L, W, AND B

In the above examples you will see that some op codes have a letter attached to them. We call this the **data size code** because it dictates how many bits of the source and destination operand are involved in the instruction. The rules are very simple and apply whether the operands are values in registers or in memory:

L means Longword — operate on all 32 bits.

W means Word — operate on lower 16 bits.

B means Byte — operate on lower 8 bits.

Most instructions work with any of the three data sizes, so we will often use a shorthand notation, for example, ADD.z, where the z can represent L, W, or B.

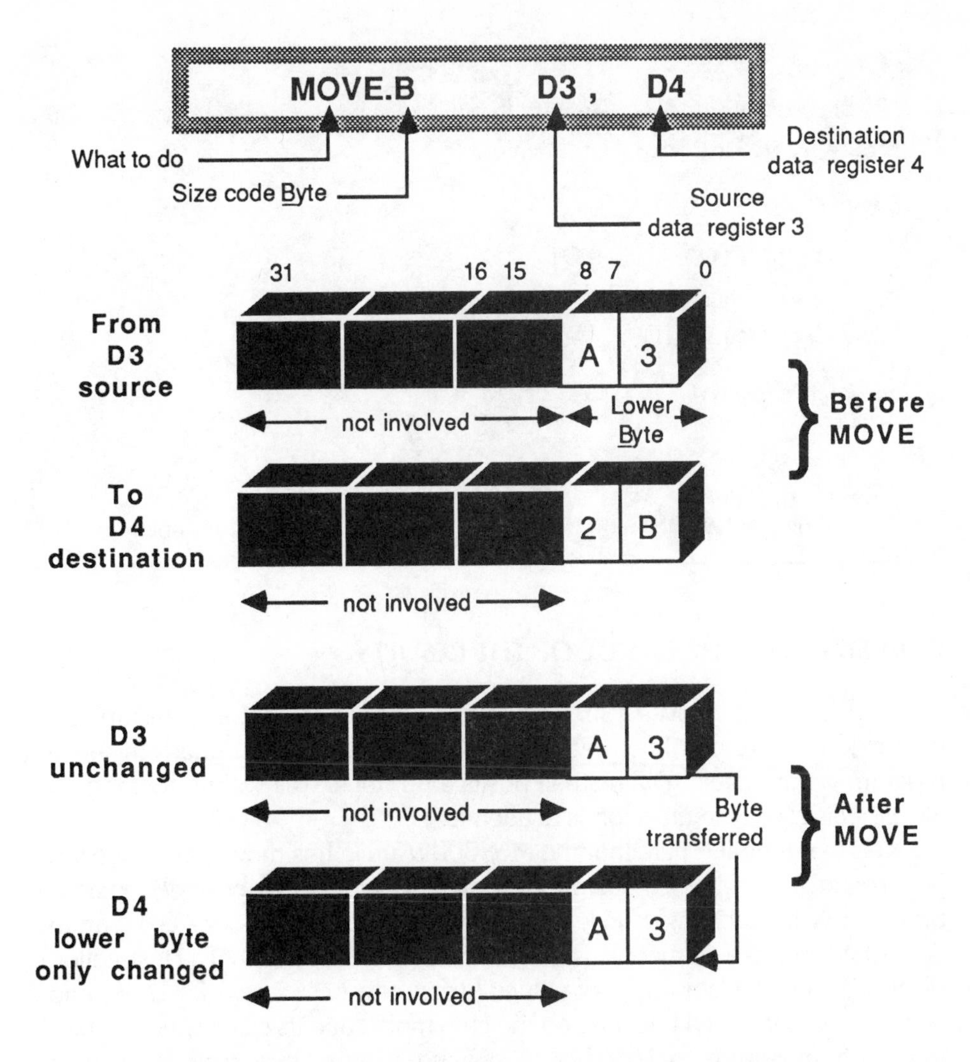

Fig. 4-1 Two Operand Instruction: MOVE.B D3,D4

You already know enough to write a real program, so we've created a hypothetical situation to test your mettle.

PRACTICAL APPLICATION

Problem: You are running a payroll program at the end of March, and need to update the total hours worked year-to-date (YTD) to include the hours for March. Use ADD and MOVE, and put the updated total in data register D3.

Given:

1. Total hours worked YTD, January through February, stored in register D1.
2. Hours worked in March stored in register D2.

Sample Case:

Hours YTD = 320 in D1
Hours March = 138 in D2
New Hours YTD = 458 place in D3

Solution: Program 4-1

```
MOVE.L    D1,D3
ADD.L     D2,D3
```

D3 now contains the sum (D2 + D1) = 458. D1 and D2 are unchanged.

DATA SIZE AND THE RANGE OF THE RESULTS

The ADD instruction gives a straightforward binary addition, and it is up to you to decide whether you interpret the results as signed or unsigned. In this tiny program we are dealing with small positive numbers well within the range of a 32-bit register, so the question is academic.

It is worth noting here that the M68000 *usually* has more work to do when performing a 32-bit (.L) operation compared with a 16-bit (.W) operation. Similarly, W instructions *usually* require more internal processor steps than their 8-bit (.B) variants. If someone asks, "How fast is the M68000 ADD instruction?" — all we can give is a range of values (worst and best cases) for L, W, and B variants. Even these will depend on the chip model and its clock speed (typically ranging from 8 MHz to 16.7 MHz — giving a basic clock cycle ranging from 125 nsec to 60 nsec). No, we are not evading the question! ADD effectively takes from 0 (yes, zero) to 30 clock cycles depending on "where, when, and what" is being added. The effective zero miracle is, briefly, due to the way the MC68020 overlaps instructions.

In any case, there is no simple formula to relate the timing of L, W, and B operations. For example, W instructions seldom take twice as long as their B versions — however, common sense dictates that when there is a choice of data size, you pick the smallest which will handle the data range for the job at hand.

Indeed, in the above example you could have saved a few clock cycles by using MOVE.W and ADD.W since you know your numbers are all within the range of a 16-bit operation (signed or unsigned). MOVE.B and ADD.B, however, would not work since our data values exceed 255 (11111111), the unsigned limit for a byte. The most common situation in practice is to work in signed (2's complement) numbers — so the above program, for example, would allow a negative value in D2 to adjust the hours YTD (ADD a negative to SUBtract).

As you develop your payroll program you will be watching out for the range and sign of various data values, so you can use the appropriate data size letter. You will also see how to use the CCR (condition code register) to check the accuracy of your arithmetic.

COMMENTS

A useful convention offered in all levels of programming is the ability to add titles, dates, revision numbers, comments, remarks, notes, and reminders in a program text intended for human consumption only. Such comments are ignored by assemblers and compilers but can prove remarkably useful when you (or your colleagues) come to read your program listing months later and wonder "What's going on here?" or "Why did I do *that*?"

Adding succinct comments is a good habit, especially in low-level languages where the actual intent behind each line may not be immediately obvious. Motorola commenting conventions are simple. They allow both separate comment lines and "in-line" comments as follows:

```
* anywhere signals a whole line of comment
```

so that the assembler ignores all characters following the * (asterisk) until the next line of source code is read. Alternatively, you can comment anywhere to the right of a program line:

```
        <OP CODE>  <operand(s)>          In-line comments here
```

provided you have at least one space (or tab) between operands and comment.

Let's develop good habits by adding a few comments to our first program example.

```
* Program 4-1 with comments

* Update YTD 4 rev 1 SKB

        MOVE.L    D1,D3     Old YTD now in D3 (32 bits)
        ADD.L     D2,D3     Add March hours to old YTD

* D3 now has updated hours YTD
```

CCR — CONDITION CODE REGISTER

In Chapter 3 you saw how the flags in the CCR monitored various processor conditions, warning you of possible errors. It is important to know how each op code affects the five CCR flags, so we'll use the following notation:

CCR flag	X	N	Z	V	C
MOVE	–	*	*	0	0
ADD	=C	*	*	*	*

Where:

–	means unchanged
0	means always cleared to 0
1	means always set to 1
*	means either cleared or set depending on the result of the instruction
U	means undefined, that is, the flag will not tell you anything useful
=C	means set or cleared the same as the C flag

Figure 4-2 shows how the registers and CCR change during Program 4-1. Let's embellish our program by testing the CCR. This will require several new instructions for **branching** and a construct known as **label** to mark the place in the program where you want to branch to.

```
* Program 4-2: Testing the CCR

* Update YTD 4 rev 2 SKB

          MOVE.L    D1,D3        Old YTD now in D3 (32 bits)
          ADD.L     D2,D3        Add March hours to old YTD

* D3 now has updated hours YTD

          BVS       ERROR.1  Branch if oVerflow Set to label ERROR.1
          BEQ       IDLE     Branch if EQual zero to label IDLE
          <rest of program>
          *    *    *
          BRA       OVER       BRanch Always to OVER
ERROR.1   <take action: D3 overflow>     We have detected overflow
          *    *    *
```

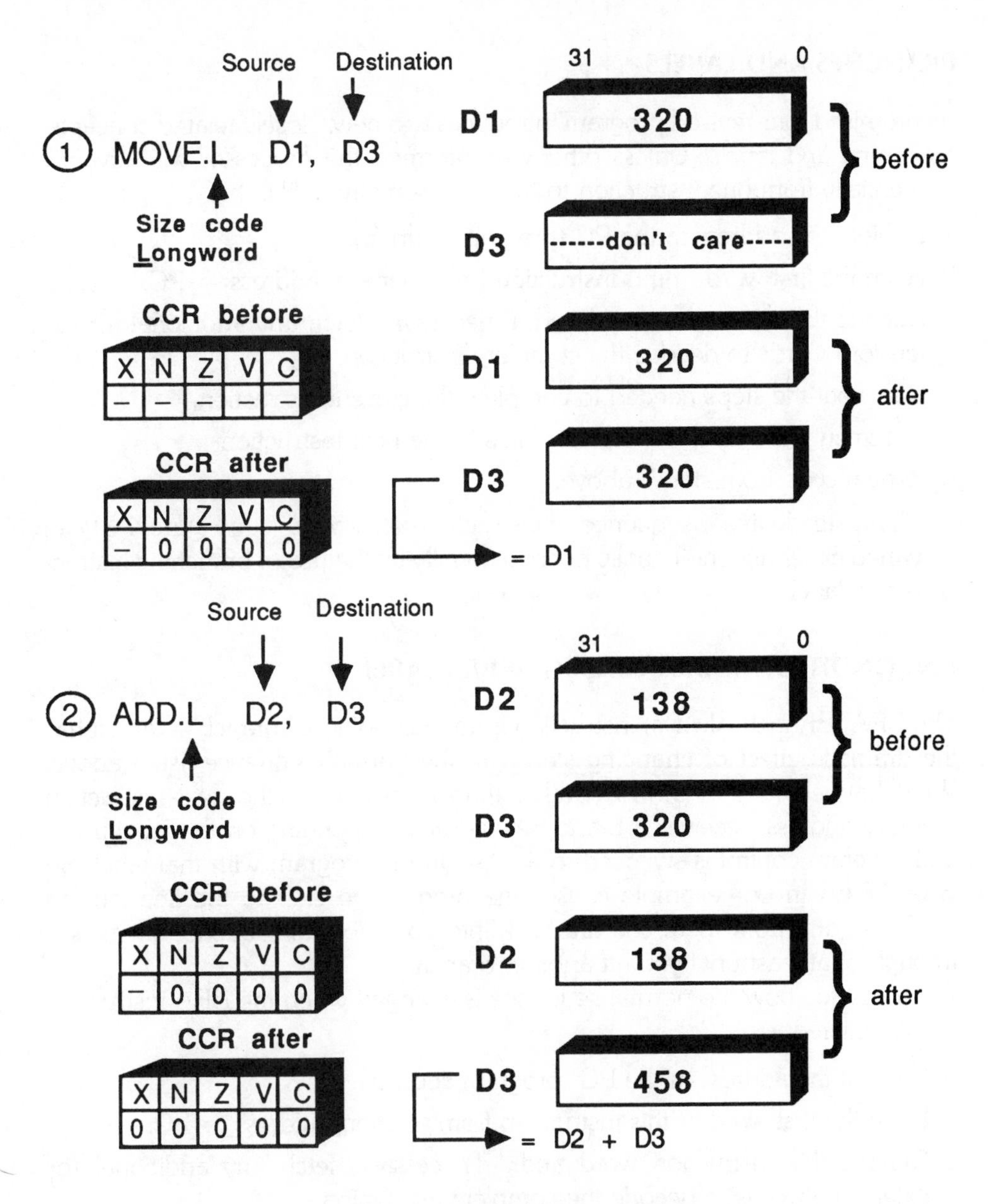

Fig. 4-2 Update Hrs YTD

```
        BRA   OVER            BRanch Always to OVER
IDLE    <take action: hours YTD = 0>       D3=0 Possible error?
        *    *    *
OVER    <wind up program>
```

BRANCHES AND LABELS

As promised, our revised program introduces two new, closely related concepts, branching and labels. Unless otherwise informed the processor will advance sequentially from one instruction to the next, something like this:

1. Look at the address in the PC (program counter).
2. Fetch the first word of this instruction from memory address = PC.
3. Decode this instruction-word and, if necessary, fetch any additional (or extension) words to decode the complete instruction.
4. Carry out the steps needed to complete the current instruction.
5. Increment the value of PC so it points to the next instruction.
6. Repeat cycle from step 1 above.

This steady linear sequence of instruction-fetch-obey (see Figure 4-3) can be varied either unconditionally or conditionally by the use of branching instructions and labels.

UNCONDITIONAL BRANCHING — BRA LABEL

The BRA (BRanch Always) instruction is an unconditional branch — and it has the dramatic effect of changing step 5 in the normal sequence listed above. What happens is that the PC, rather than increment to the next instruction memory address, receives a brand new address depending on the label used, and program control is switched to the line in the program with that label. So BRA OVER in our example causes the program to skip to the line labeled OVER — and from there you are back into your normal sequence of steps 1 through 5, at least until you hit another branch.

Let's see how the normal sequence is changed when the BRA instruction is encountered:

1. Look at the address in the PC (program counter).
2. Fetch the first word of this instruction from memory address = PC.
3. Decode this instruction word and, if necessary, fetch any additional (or extension) words to decode the complete instruction.
4. If instruction is BRA OVER, step 3 will have obtained a signed number, called the **branch displacement**, which depends on the location of the label OVER in the program.
5. ADD this branch displacement to the value of PC and place the SUM back in PC. PC now points to the instruction labeled OVER.
6. Processor is now ready to proceed with step 1 above, where it will fetch, decode, and obey the instruction labeled OVER.

```
          BVS      ERROR.1  Branch to ERROR.1 if Overflow???
     <rest of program as in 4-2>
          *     *     *
ERROR.1  <take action: D3 overflow>     We have detected overflow???
          *     *     *
```

We have inserted a MOVE.L between the ADD and the BVS, as indicated by the + + comment. Can you spot the mistake? Yes, the V flag is cleared by the MOVE and the BVS test is now meaningless. We will never branch to ERROR.1 even if ADD sets the V flag.

Bcc — THE FULL STORY

You have now seen two of the 14 Bcc branches. The other 12 Bcc instructions test a variety of CCR flag conditions, both single flags and combinations of flags. We postpone discussion of the multiple flag tests until we cover CMP (CoMPare) in Chapter 6. Here are the single flag Bcc's which all work like BVS and BEQ.

BVC — Branch if oVerflow flag Clear (V = 0).

BVC and BVS are therefore **complementary** tests; if one is true, the other must be false.

BNE — Branch if Not Equal to zero, that is, if Z = 0.

BNE and BEQ are also complementary tests — again, if one is true, the other must be false.

BCC — Branch if Carry flag Clear (C = 0)

BCS — Branch if Carry flag Set (C = 1)

Here once more, BCC and BCS are complementary tests. By the way, be careful not to confuse CC (Carry Clear) with cc (any condition code).

BPL — Branch if PLus (positive), that is, if N = 0

BMI — Branch if MInus (negative), that is, if N = 1

You guessed it. BPL and BMI are complementary tests.

This choice of cc's (and remember, there are more complex ones to follow) allows considerable flexibility in testing results and taking the appropriate action by branching to a labeled program line. They come, as you can see, in pairs of opposites, which may seem wasteful at first sight. For example:

```
BPL  ANS_PLUS        Do program P if answer +ve
<program M>              Do program M if answer -ve
*    *    *
```

```
ANS_PLUS  <program P>
*    *    *
```

can also be written as:

```
BMI  ANS_MIN          Do program M if answer -ve
<program P>           Do program P if answer +ve
*    *    *

ANS_MIN   <program M>
*    *    *
```

Both programs achieve the same result, so you could survive with just BPL or with just BMI. In practice, however, it turns out that the choice is useful — you can often produce more legible programs by picking the natural Bcc for each situation, for example, by branching if the abnormal condition prevails.

BRANCHING SUMMARY

- BRA LABEL causes unconditional branch to label.
- Bcc LABEL branches to label only if cc condition is true. If cc is false, obeys next instruction.

Now that you have seen a few simple instructions working with data register operands, you can look at other types of operands that are specified by various combinations of registers and/or memory addresses, known as addressing modes.

ADDRESSING MODES

You can imagine an instruction saying "OK, I know I'm supposed to ADD or MOVE or whatever, but you have to tell me where to get the source and destination operands." This is done by expressing each operand in a certain format, laced, as it were, with sufficient information to direct the instruction to the correct operand data. These operand formats are called **addressing modes** — and they fall into two main groups, **register direct modes** and **memory modes**. As you'll see, each of these groups can be broken down further into smaller groups of addressing modes. Also, you'll find that most instructions allow a choice of modes for both source and destination operand, in many combinations.

Having stated earlier that understanding Bcc is 150% of M68000 fluency, we can now add that the remaining 150% of M68000 fluency comes with mastering the addressing modes!

REGISTER DIRECT MODES

In our programs, so far, the initial data was available from data registers, D1 and D2, and the result of the program, D1 + D2, was then stored back in a data register, D3. All our operands, therefore, both source and destination, were expressed directly in a simple format called register direct addressing mode. This mode has two variants:

Address Mode	*Symbol*	*What Is the Operand?*
Data Register Direct	Dn	The value in Dn
Address Register Direct	An	The value in An

where Dn is any data register (D0 through D7) and An is any address register (A0 through A7). To reduce verbiage we will often refer to these direct modes as the Dn mode or the An mode.

You saw in Chapter 3 how the address registers are used to hold 16- or 32-bit addresses, and for this reason the An mode has some special rules prohibiting Byte operations and certain purely "data" operations. Apart from these differences, which will be detailed later, the Dn and An modes are broadly similar.

So, the two direct modes are used when the source operands are values (data or addresses) actually available in registers. When the direct mode is the destination, you are telling the processor which register is to receive the result of the instruction.

The next section deals with operands in memory.

MEMORY ADDRESSING MODES

In most practical situations the initial data input for a program is loaded into user memory (RAM) via some external device such as a disk or keyboard. The results of the programs' various calculations are then stored in user RAM, and thence back to some output device such as a disk, printer, or CRT. To achieve this you need **memory addressing modes,** which "tell" the op code where to locate its source and destination operands in memory. The MC68000 has 10 and the MC68020 has 16 distinct memory addressing modes as listed in Appendix B.

MEMORY ADDRESSING AND THE EFFECTIVE ADDRESS

The memory addressing mode formats range from extremely simple ("Here is the memory address of the operand") to very complex ("To get the memory address of the operand you will need to add two numbers to form an address, go to that address in memory where you will find another address, add a number to it, and that's the address of your operand!") Luckily, the beginner can gently build up from the simple modes. The complex example was intended to stress the fundamental fact about memory addressing modes:

A memory addressing mode allows the instruction to calculate the <ea> or effective address of an operand.

Any operand sitting in memory is uniquely identified and located by its <ea>, effective address. For each addressing mode, the processor has a specific <ea> calculation to perform before it can fetch the source operand from memory address <ea>, and similarly, before a destination operand can be written to memory, its <ea> must be calculated. These calculations (and associated fetches, if any) can take from 0 to 24 clock cycles. The importance attached to these <ea> calculations is typified by Motorola's inclusion of two additional ALUs that can perform the <ea> arithmetic while the main ALU is handling the normal data arithmetic.

How does the M68000 know which <ea> calculation to perform? Without digressing too far, we can simply say that each instruction word, at the machine-code level, has bits assigned that uniquely encode each possible addressing mode for the source and destination operands. When the instruction word is decoded, the M68000 knows both the operation required and how to derive the operand <ea>s.

We saw in Chapter 2 that one advantage in moving from 8-bit to 16-bit processors was that a 16-bit instruction word allows a richer instruction set, and with this comes the possibility of more complex addressing modes.

WHY SO MANY ADDRESSING MODES?

This abundance in addressing modes, formerly available only on mainframes and minis, is a major key to the success of the M68000. The novice may consider it paradoxical, but the apparent complexity of the addressing modes actually simplifies the programming of the M68000's huge addressable memory for today's wide and growing range of sophisticated multiuser operating systems, language compilers, relational databases, and bit-mapped graphics applications. All of these require the rapid manipulation of complex data structures in memory, such as linked lists, "trees" that grow in all directions, multidimensional arrays and tables, stacks, and queues. Much of this manipulation, especially in commercial as opposed to scientific applications, involves address rather than data calculations.

To locate complex memory operands on the earlier 8-bit micros with few addressing modes, the programmer had to write specific, often tedious, code to compute the <ea>. The more advanced addressing modes available on the M68000 dramatically reduce this effort. In effect the programmer can pass the onus of <ea> arithmetic to the chip's fast internal ALUs.

In essence the M68000 addressing modes (and the modern assemblers that exploit them) provide a sort of high-level language for accessing complex data structures in large amounts of RAM.

As you'll see, each addressing mode is designed to solve a particular memory-access and data-manipulation problem. Our first example is probably the simplest addressing mode, called **immediate**, which is used only for source operands.

IMMEDIATE ADDRESSING MODE

In many situations we want to use fixed numeric constants — that is to say, numbers that are predetermined and not the result of some calculation. Suppose, for example, that in Program 4-2 we want to keep a count of the number of idle employees — all those with zero hours YTD. Let us assign data register D4 to keep this count. Each time you branch to the label IDLE you will increment (add 1 to) D4. At the end of the payroll you can print out the number in D4. Program 4-3 shows the new program (with the additions highlighted).

```
* Program 4-3: Count Idle Employees

* Update YTD 4 rev 3 SKB

        MOVE.L    D1,D3        Old YTD now in D3 (32 bits)
        ADD.L     D2,D3        Add March hours to old YTD
        CLR.W     D4           Set lower 16 bits D4 to 0

* D3 now has updated hours YTD
```

```
        BVS     ERROR.1     Branch if oVerflow Set
        BEQ     IDLE        Branch if EQual Zero
        <rest of program>
        *    *    *
        BRA     OVER        BRanch Always to OVER
ERROR.1 <take action: D3 overflow>    We have detected overflow
        *    *    *
        BRA     OVER        BRanch Always to OVER
IDLE    ADDQ.W    #1,D4     Increment D4 = idle count
        *    *    *

OVER<wind up program>
       <print value in D4>
```

NOTES ON PROGRAM 4-3

There are two new op codes in the revised program, CLR (CLeaR) and ADDQ (ADD Quick). CLR is a simple but useful one-operand instruction with the following syntax:

```
CLR.z <operand>
```

which clears some or all of the operand to 0, depending on the data size letter z. CLR.L will clear all 32 bits. CLR.W will clear just the lower 16 bits. The upper 16 bits are unchanged. CLR.B will clear just the lower 8 bits. The upper 24 bits are unchanged.

In this example, we have chosen to use just the lower 16 bits of D4 as the ''counter of the idle'', leaving you free, if you wish, to use the upper 16 bits for something else. For a small payroll (less than 255 employees) you might consider using only a byte of D4 (unsigned) — the data size code z gives great flexibility in register utilization. You CLR.W D4 to make sure that your 16-bit counter is ''zeroed'' before you start counting. Remember that CLR.W does not affect the upper 16-bit word of D4. It is a surprisingly common oversight to forget to CLR counters.

CLR changes the CCR in a reasonably predictable way:

CCR flag	X	N	Z	V	C
CLR	–	0	1	0	0

since the operand is now 0 (Z = 1), non-negative (N = 0), and there is no overflow or carry (V = 0, C = 0). The X flag is unchanged, as we saw in the MOVE instruction earlier.

Like ADD, ADDQ is a two-operand instruction. The general format is:

```
ADDQ.z    #<data>,<destination operand>
```

where <data> is a number between 1 and 8. This means ADD the number in <data> to the destination (L, W, or B, depending on the size code) and place the sum in the destination. The Q in ADDQ stands for the Quick form of the ADD op code. The immediate source data, written always with the # (pound sign) symbol, is simply added to the destination. In our case,

```
ADDQ.W    #1,D4
```

increases the lower word of D4 by 1.

The reason it is quick is that the processor does not have far to look for the source data. In fact, the source data is stored as 3 unsigned bits in the ADDQ instruction word itself — and this explains why ADDQ can only add small unsigned constants in the range #1 to #8.

Here is a quick check to see if you are paying attention. How can you store the numbers 1 to 8 in 3 bits? Surely 3 bits can only store the numbers 0 to 7? Well, the M68000 performs a trick! It will be instructive to explore this trick because it gives us a chance to peep "inside" a simple instruction word and see its bit pattern. The ADDQ instruction word looks like this:

Bit	15	14	13	12	11	10	9	8	7	6	5	4	3	2	1	0
	0	1	0	1	d	d	d	0	z	z	m	m	m	r	r	r

Where:			
ddd	—	Bits 9-11	specify the #<data>
zz	—	Bits 6-7	specify the data size code
mmm	—	Bits 3-5	specify the destination mode
rrr	—	Bits 0-2	specify the destination register

Bits 8 and 12-15 identify the instruction as ADDQ

The mode and register codes (mmm and rrr) are the bits we mentioned earlier that tell the M68000 which <ea> calculations are needed — in this case mmm and rrr are encoded for the destination operand <ea>. Their format is not of immediate concern, apart from noting that 6 of the 16 bits in an instruction word are commonly assigned for this purpose. Complete instruction bit patterns are listed in Appendix D.

The data size code is simple: 00 = Byte, 01 = Word, 10 = Longword (leaving data size 11 unused, a useful spare for the future). Now for the trick — how to code #1 to #8 in 3 bits:

#1	Sets ddd = 001
#2	= 010
#3	= 011
#4	= 100
#5	= 101
#6	= 110
#7	= 111
#8	= 000

So, the instruction decoder translates ddd = 000 not as #0 (which would be a waste of time and effort) but as #8. This small digression will prove helpful in giving you an early feel for what we mean by decoding an instruction. In the more complex multiword instructions you shall meet, it will become necessary to know how different forms of data (including addresses) are stored in instruction words and their extensions.

We hope, also, that this inside view of an instruction gains your respect for the people who wrote your assembler! Remember that the assembler program has to convert

```
ADDQ #<data>,<destination>
```

from your source code into the bit patterns shown above (as well as performing many other chores).

ADDQ AND THE CCR

ADDQ changes the CCR just like a normal ADD:

CCR flag	X	N	Z	V	C
ADDQ	=C	*	*	*	*

so you get all the usual warnings about the result of your arithmetic. But what if you need to add larger constants than 0 through 8? Read on.

2. Hours worked in March stored in the longword at address $6004.

Sample Case:

Hours YTD = 320 at address $6000

Hours March = 138 at address $6004

New hours YTD = 458 at address $6008

Solution: Program 4-5

```
        MOVE.L    $6000,D3        D3 = hrs YTD
        ADD.L     $6004,D3        D3 = hrs YTD + Hrs March
        MOVE.L    D3,$6008        Save D3 in memory at address
                                      $6008
  *Address $6008 now holds the sum ($6000) + ($6004) = 458.
```

Note the use of brackets to indicate the value stored at a given address. Thus at address $6000 we have the value ($6000) = 320. In the next section we will elaborate on this notation and explain in detail how addresses can access longwords, words, or bytes in memory.

Absolute addressing mode simply means using the actual address as source or destination — it must not be confused with immediate mode. Compare the following:

```
MOVE.L    #$6000,D3
```

and

```
MOVE.L     $6000,D3
```

The little symbol # for immediate data makes a dramatic difference. The first line says: replace the contents of D3 with the number $6000. The second line says: replace the contents of D3 with the number found in memory at address $6000.

ABSOLUTE ADDRESS — SHORT AND LONG VERSIONS

The absolute address you supply in your source or destination operand can be stored in one or two extension words following the instruction word, known as the **short** and **long versions** of the absolute addressing mode. In the long version your absolute address is a full 32-bit number stored in two 16-bit extension words, and therefore allows access to the entire address space of the M68000. The price paid for this is that the processor needs to fetch two extension words from memory and then combine them into one 32-bit address before it can access your operand. To save time when you do not want to access the full address space, the short 16-bit mode can be used. In this mode the processor sign bit extends the single extension word to form a 32-bit address — and this is much faster than fetching a second word from memory. The short mode gives you access to addresses in the ranges $000000 through $007FFF (the lower 32K of memory) and $FF8000 through $FFFFFF (the top 32K of memory), depending on whether the sign bit is 0 or 1. (When we talk about the sign bit of an address, of course, we are not implying that we can have negative addresses — all absolute addresses are positive numbers. The sign bit here means bit number 15 in the word address, which happens to be 1 for addresses greater than $7FFF.)

Assemblers differ widely in the way they handle the short and long versions. Some will automatically create the optimum mode for you (our $6000, for example, would be assembled as short), while others require a letter code L (long) or W (short — that is, one extension word) after the address.

LABELS AS ABSOLUTE ADDRESSES

So far we have used labels with branching instructions, and we explained briefly that when your program has been assembled and loaded each label symbol is effectively translated into the unique address of the instruction you want to branch to. From a novice programmer's point of view it is sufficient to think of labels simply as addresses, and as such they can be used as mnemonics not only for branching but as absolute address operands. The obvious advantage is legibility and ease of programming. To see this, let's dress up Program 4-5 as follows:

```
* Program 4-5A: Use of Labels as Absolute Addresses
* Data as in program 4-5 with following labels
* HRSYTD = address $6000 holding 320 hours
* HRSMAR = address $6004 holding 138 hours
* NEWHRS = address $6008 = destination for sum

          MOVE.L   HRSYTD,D3        D3 = (HRSYTD)
          ADD.L    HRSMAR,D3        D3 = (HRSYTD) + (HRSMAR)
          MOVE.L   D3,NEWHRS        Save D3 in memory at address
                                    NEWHRS
```

```
* Address NEWHRS = $6008, now holds the sum ($6000) + ($6004) = 458.
* Note, again, the use of brackets to indicate the contents of an
* address.  HRSYTD=$6000 but (HRSYTD)=320.
```

There is no doubt that version 4-5A is more immediately understandable than version 4-5 (dare we say, a little nearer to BASIC), and this helps the writing, modifying, and debugging of code. It is no exaggeration to say that you will hardly ever see lines like:

```
MOVE.L    $6000,D3
```

other than in classroom exercises. Of course you have to tell the system what the labels HRSYTD, HRSMAR, and NEWHRS mean, and for this you need some help from the assembler. Once you have "assigned" addresses to these labels, you can program in terms of HRSYTD and so on, rather than taxing your human memory with meaningless hexadecimal numbers. The allocation of addresses to data fields is almost as simple as labeling instruction lines for a branch.

ASSEMBLER DIRECTIVES

To tell the assembler what you have in mind, you need a few **assembler directives**, sometimes known as **pseudo-op codes** because, at first sight, they look like M68000 instructions. Directives, however, merely direct and control the assembly process, and unlike "real" instructions they do not generate machine-language code. Modern assemblers have hundreds of different directives with many nonstandard variations, most of which are outside the scope of this primer.

Fortunately, you need only three or four directives to make sense of the addressing modes, and we'll present them briefly using standard Motorola "vanilla" syntax. Once we have covered these, we will be able to fill out Program 4-5A so that HRSYTD actually represents the address we have in mind.

ORG — THE ABSOLUTE ORIGIN DIRECTIVE

The following line

```
ORG       <address>           Load program at <address>
```

simply tells the assembler/loader that you want the next program lines to be assembled and eventually loaded starting at the specified absolute address. For your immediate purposes you will need just one ORG directive at the very start of a program:

```
ORG  $6000      Program starts at address $6000
```

Thereafter, each line of source will be translated into machine instructions, some taking one word, some five, with each being allocated appropriate word addresses as the assembler increments its **location counter** — a simple counter that "starts" at $6000 and increments one or five or whatever the instruction takes. When it meets a label, presto, we know (or rather the assembler knows) the label address. You saw earlier how branch labels work, now you can look at data labels, and the two directives used to define them.

DATA AREAS IN MEMORY USING DS AND DC

There are two basic directives, DS and DC, that allow you to allocate labels to data areas in memory:

```
LABEL     DS.z      <number> Define Storage

LABEL     DC.z      <data>   Define Constant
```

DS just reserves the <number> of memory locations (z = L, W, or B) at address = label, whereas DC will allocate whatever memory is needed (starting from address = label) and store the <data> you list in the right-hand column.

DATA STORAGE — EXAMPLES

```
NEWHRS    DS.L     1          Define storage= 1 longword at NEWHRS
```

simply reserves 1 "empty" longword for data storage at memory location NEWHRS, which is exactly what we need for program 4.5A. The following lines would achieve exactly the same result:

```
NEWHRS    DS.W     2          Define storage= 2 words at NEWHRS

NEWHRS    DS.B     4          Define storage= 4 bytes at NEWHRS
```

The words **buffer** or **data buffer** are often used to describe areas of memory assigned with a DS for future holding of information. You will often find, for example, the line:

```
DSKBUF    DS.B      512       Allocate disk buffer 512 bytes
```

or a similar line, to define a general area into which a whole disk block can be loaded and then scrutinized.

You can, in fact, use DS to reserve any number of longwords, words, or bytes, provided you are careful to avoid odd-numbered addresses for longwords or words. For example:

```
LABEL1   DS.B   5   Allocate 5 bytes starting at label1
LABEL2   DS.L   2   Whoops! If label1 is even then label2 is Odd
                    address! Cannot reserve 2 longwords starting at
                    odd address.
```

The lesson here is that as the assembler reserves the memory space requested, its location counter is incremented past the assigned area, so the address it assigns to a subsequent label is incremented accordingly. Hence it would try to give label2 the value {label1 + 5 bytes} which may or may not be legal. A DS.B at label2 would be fine (byte addresses can be odd or even), but a DS.L or DS.W could invoke an address error.

Assuming you have not broken the odd/even rules, the absolute address assigned to a DS label will naturally depend on two factors: ORG — the starting address of the program, and the location of the label within the program.

Before we illustrate this with a program, let's look at the other data labeling directive, DC, in more detail.

DATA CONSTANT — EXAMPLES

Data Constant (DC) syntax is slightly different, but the difference is of galactic importance:

```
HRSYTD    DC.L      320       Define constant = 320 at HRSYTD
```

does not allocate 320 longwords of memory.

The 320 represents a single field of <data> and you will end up with one longword (because of the DC.L) containing the binary equivalent of decimal 320 at whatever address the assembler assigns to HRSYTD. You can use DC to store any amount of data. Lists of related data items stored consecutively are often called **tables**, just like the log and trig tables at the end of old-fashioned textbooks.

```
TABLE     DC.B       $10,$2A,$F4,$09  Set up 4 byte constants at TABLE

* Byte address TABLE   now contains $10
* Byte address TABLE+1 now contains $2A
* Byte address TABLE+2 now contains $F4
* Byte address TABLE+3 now contains $09
```

The general format is:

```
LABEL     DC.z       <data>,<data>,....
```

DC.z allocates sufficient area to hold the <data>,<data>,... you have listed, thereby overwriting any previous data at label. The <data> can be expressed in many useful ways — binary, decimal, hex, or ASCII.

It is worth stressing again, at this point, that ORG, DS, and DC are pseodo-ops, not M68000 instructions. They are not translated into machine-level instruction words like MOVE or ADD. They do, however, affect the location of the program, the way you write your program, and the values you would find if you looked inside the instruction extension words after assembly and loading.

Moreover, pseudo-ops and directives have been an essential ingredient of assemblers for many years, and this exerts considerable influence on all microprocessor designers when they come to decide the type and format of the chip's instruction set.

DATA LABELS IN ACTION

We now update Program 4-5 once more to show our directives at work:

```
* Program 4-5B:  Data Labels with DS, DC
* Program 4-5A revised
*    HRSYTD = address $6000 holding 320 hours
*    HRSMAR = address $6004 holding 138 hours
*    NEWHRS = address $6008 = destination for sum

          ORG       $6000               Start at absolute $6000

* Set up data areas
* First label HRSYTD will be = address $6000
* After storing 32 bits there, next label, HRSMAR, will be =
* $6004, and so on.
```

```
HRSYTD   DC.L     320               Store 320 at HRSYTD
HRSMAR   DC.L     138               Store 138 at HRSMAR
NEWHRS   DS.L     1                 Reserve 1 longword at
                                    NEWHRS

* Rest of program as in 4-5A

         MOVE.L   HRSYTD,D3         D3 = (HRSYTD) = ($6000)
         ADD.L    HRSMAR,D3         D3 = (HRSYTD) + (HRSMAR)
         MOVE.L   D3,NEWHRS         Save D3 in memory at address
                                           NEWHRS = $6008

* Address NEWHRS = $6008, now holds the sum ($6000) + ($6004) = 458.
```

In the above example we have used ORG to grab an area of memory, starting at absolute address $6000, which holds not only our data but our program too. The first MOVE.L instruction would be located at address {$6008 + 4 bytes} = $600B just after NEWHRS.

It is perfectly possible, and often preferable, to separate your data and program in memory. The simplest way to achieve this is to use a second ORG <address> directive to define the start of the program. Here is Program 4-5C with one line added to show this.

```
* Program 4-5C: Separate Data and Program Areas
* Program 4-5B revised. Data as in 4-5B
*   HRSYTD = address $6000 holding 320 hours
*   HRSMAR = address $6004 holding 138 hours
*   NEWHRS = address $6008 = destination for sum

         ORG      $6000             DATA starts at absolute $6000

* Set up data areas
* First label HRSYTD will be = address $6000
* After storing 32 bits there, next label, HRSMAR, will be =
* $6004, and so on.

HRSYTD   DC.L     320               Store 320 at HRSYTD
HRSMAR   DC.L     138               Store 138 at HRSMAR
NEWHRS   DS.L     1                 Reserve 1 longword at
                                    NEWHRS

         ORG      $8000             PROGRAM starts at
                                    absolute $8000
```

```
* First instruction will be at $8000
* Program and results same as 4-5B

        MOVE.L    HRSYTD,D3        D3 = (HRSYTD) = ($6000)
        ADD.L     HRSMAR,D3        D3 = (HRSYTD) + (HRSMAR)
        MOVE.L    D3,NEWHRS        Save D3 in memory at address
                                         NEWHRS = $6008

* Address NEWHRS = $6008, now holds the sum ($6000) + ($6004) = 458.
```

The program still works in its new location because when it references HRSYTD and the other labels, it still picks up the data from the memory addresses defined by ORG $6000 and our DC and DS data labels. HRSYTD is defined as $6000 wherever we locate our program.

One immediate advantage of separate data and program areas is the possibility of several users with different programs sharing a common data table in a mutually agreed-upon portion of memory. In real installations you will find endless variations on this theme of data and program location. The point here is that you have considerable flexibility regarding where you put things.

ABSOLUTE ADDRESS — SUMMARY

Data in memory can be accessed (read) or stored (written) using absolute addresses as source or destination operands. The absolute address can be written explicitly as $6000 or $FFFFFF, or by means of a suitably defined symbolic label.

Absolute addressing, even with labels, is not flexible enough for most applications. A more versatile way to access operands in memory is via the address registers, as shown in the next section.

ADDRESS REGISTER INDIRECT MEMORY ADDRESSING MODE

The main function of address registers, as you might guess from their name, is to provide addresses for operands in memory. A useful concept in this connection is the idea of a **pointer**. If address register A3, for example, contains the value $3000, we say that A3 points to memory location $3000.

To distinguish the pointer A3 from the operand in memory being pointed to, we use the following standard Motorola syntax: A3 is the pointer and (A3) is the operand at address A3. The brackets in (A3) represent what we call **indirection**. A3 is address register direct but (A3) is address register indirect.

In the "Memory Model" section of Chapter 3 you saw that the M68000 uses byte, word, and longword addresses — so what does A3 really point at? If A3 contains an odd-numbered address such as $3001, there is no ambiguity — A3 must point at the byte at $3001, but if A3 is even, like $3000, it is pointing at three possible memory values. If we go and look at this location we might conceivably find the following values:

The byte at byte address A3 = $3000 is (A3) = $E2

The word at word address A3 = $3000 is (A3) = $E278

The longword at longword address A3 = $3000 is (A3) = $E278B01C

The actual values shown are less important than how they are related. So before we can answer the question, "What is (A3)?" we have to know the data size involved — is it L, W, or B. For example:

```
MOVE.L  (A3),D7 moves $E278B01C to D7
MOVE.W  (A3),D7 moves $E278 to lower word of D7
MOVE.B  (A3),D7 moves $E2 to lower byte of D7
```

You can see that the source operand (A3) behaves very much like a data register — the L, W, or B size code selects which parts of the operand are involved. The important differences are: L and W operations on memory need even addresses. B operations on memory can use odd or even addresses. Remember the Low Address-High Byte, High Address-Low Byte rule (see Chapter 3).

Let us revamp Program 4-5 using address register indirect mode in place of absolute address mode.

PRACTICAL APPLICATION

Problem: Calculate the new total hours worked YTD (January through March) using indirect memory operands. Put the updated total in the longword at address $6008.

Given:

1. Total hours YTD (January through February) stored in the longword at address $6000
2. Hours worked in March stored in the longword at address $6004

Solution: Program 4-6

```
* Set addresses in address registers

        MOVEA.L   #$6000,A1       A1 has address of YTD
        MOVEA.L   #$6004,A2       A2 has address of hrs March
        MOVEA.L   #$6008,A3       A3 has address for new YTD

* Do calculation

        MOVE.L    (A1),D3         D3 = hrs YTD
        ADD.L     (A2),D3         D3 = hrs YTD + hrs March
        MOVE.L    D3,(A3)         Put D3 in memory at address
                                       A3 = $6008

*     (A3) now contains the sum (A2) + (A1) = 458.
*     (A1) and (A2) are unchanged.
```

MOVEA — MOVE ADDRESS

Program 4-6 introduces a new op code, MOVEA (MOVE Address), which is a version of MOVE used when the destination is an address register. The general format is:

```
MOVEA.L   <source>,An
```

or

```
MOVEA.W   <source>,An
```

M68000 addresses are essentially 32-bit values (even if your MC6800X uses only 20 bits or 24 bits for addressing), so MOVEA.B is not allowed. Even MOVEA.W turns out to be a 32-bit move, because 16-bit addresses are always sign-bit extended to 32 bits, as explained in Chapter 3. Also MOVEA, like all operations on address registers does not affect the CCR, because you are not concerned with overflow, carry, negatives, zeroes, or positives when you manipulate addresses.

You use MOVEA here with immediate source data to set up your three address registers. Once you have the proper addresses in A1, A2, and A3, the program uses (A1) and (A2) as source operands and (A3) as a destination operand.

RESTRICTIONS ON ADD

You may wonder why we used D3 in the above program. Why not save a line (and a register) by having

```
MOVE.L  (A1),(A3)        OK
ADD.L   (A2),(A3)        ILLEGAL
```

The first line is legal: it would move the contents of address $6000 to memory address $6008. The second line, however, is illegal because: ADD must have at least one data register and SUB must have at least one data register. The M68000 does not allow ADD or SUB on two memory operands. So you can

```
ADD.z  Dn,Dm             OK
SUB.z  Dn,Dm             OK

ADD.Z  An,Dm             OK for Z = L, W only
SUB.Z  An,Dm             OK for Z = L, W only

ADD.z  Dn,(Am)           OK
SUB.z  Dn,(Am)           OK

ADD.z  (Am),Dn           OK
SUB.z  (Am),Dn           OK
```

But you cannot

```
ADD.z  (Am),(An)         WRONG
SUB.z  (Am),(An)         WRONG

ADD.z Dn,Am    is        WRONG
SUB.z Dn,Am    is        WRONG
```

The above rules forbid ADD and SUB with An as a destination — so how can you increase or decrease an address in an address register? There is a way; it's called ADDA (ADD Address). Let's tackle Program 4-6 in a different way, to show how ADDA works:

```
* Program 4-6A:  Alternative Solution to 4-6 Using ADDA

* Set addresses in address registers

        MOVEA.W   #$6000,A0        A0 has address of YTD
        MOVEA.W   A0,A1            A1 also has address of YTD
```

```
            ADDA.W     #4,A0          A0 = $6000 + 4 = $6004
            MOVEA.W    A0,A2          A2 has address of hrs Mar
            ADDA.W     #4,A0          A0 = $6004 + 4 = $6008
            MOVEA.W    A0,A3          A3 has address for new YTD

* Do calculation--same as 4-6

            MOVE.L     (A1),D3        D3 = Hrs YTD
            ADD.L      (A2),D3 .      D3 = Hrs YTD + Hrs Mar
            MOVE.L     D3, (A3)       Put D3 in memory at address
                                             $6008 = A3
```

So, to ADD something to an address register, we use ADDA (ADD Address), just as we use MOVEA to move something to an address register. The general format is:

```
            ADDA.L     <source>,An
            ADDA.W     <source>,An
```

To subtract something from An we have:

```
            SUBA.L     <source>,An
            SUBA.W     <source>,An
```

Note again the fundamental fact of M68000 life — no byte operations allowed on An. Also, as with MOVEA, there are no CCR changes when we manipulate addresses in An.

The key to Program 4-6A is the way ADDA is used on the pointer A0. By adding 4 to an even-valued address register you make it point to the next longword in memory. Similarly, adding 2 or 1 to a pointer "moves" it to point to the next word or byte. Frequently you find that the data you are manipulating are stored in memory in sequences or tables — so ADDA and SUBA are useful in "setting" address register pointers to scan tables of data in either direction. This type of operation is so common that the M68000 provides two special variants of the (An) addressing mode to simplify the scanning of consecutive addresses. The new modes automatically increase or decrease the pointer An. We look first at the address register indirect with post-increment mode.

ADDRESS REGISTER INDIRECT WITH POST-INCREMENT: (An)+

The address register indirect with post-increment mode, written (An)+, is best explained with an example.

```
* Program 4-6B: Alternative Solution to 4-6 Using (An)+
* Set address of first value in table

        MOVEA.W   #$6000,A1      A1 has address of hrs YTD
                                 i.e. A1 points to hrs YTD
* Do calculation

        MOVE.L    (A1)+,D3        Set D3 = ($6000) = hrs YTD
                                      then add 4 to A1
        ADD.L     (A1)+,D3        Add ($6004) to D3
                                      then add 4 to A1
        MOVE.L    D3,(A1)         Put D3 in memory at address
                                      A1 = $6008
```

Rather than using three address registers for the operands, this solution uses just A1 — and the post-increment advances A1 to the next longword after each operation. The automatic increment of A1 saves using ADDA #4,A1, but better still, it saves worry about the size of the increment.

(A1)+ will increment A1 by either 4, 2, or 1, depending on the data size code used in the op code. For example:

```
        MOVE.W    (A2)+,D5        Set word D5 = word (A2)
                                      then ADD 2 to A2
```

will conclude with A2 pointing to the next word (A2+2), and

```
        MOVE.B    (A2)+,D5        Set byte D5 = byte (A2)
                                      then ADD 1 to A2
```

ends up with A2 pointing to the next byte (A2+1).

TEMPUS FUGIT — A TIME-OUT TO LOOK AT TIMINGS

Since we've now shown you so many different ways to perform the same simple hours YTD addition, it might prove useful to compare them briefly from a timing standpoint. In our simple context we are not going to quibble over a few microseconds here and there, but from the broader, practical perspective it is important to gain an insight as to what we are asking the MC68000 to do. (Note that in the following table, the 8-bit data bus of the MC68008 would need more cycles while the 32-bit data bus of the MC68020 would need fewer.)

Program 4.1 Register Direct:
Get data from registers—very fast—no memory access needed. Store answer in register—very fast. But how did

the data get into the registers? And how will we print the answer? Sooner or later we will need memory accesses.

Program 4.5 (+ variants)	Absolute Addressing: Get address of data from extension word(s)—takes 1 or 2 memory reads. Then get data—takes 1 or 2 memory reads. Get address to store answer—takes 1 or 2 memory reads. Store longword answer—takes 2 memory writes.
Program 4.6	Indirect Addressing: Set up 3 address registers with immediate data—takes 3 to 6 memory reads. Get addresses from An—very fast. Then get data—takes 1 or 2 memory reads. Store answer—takes 2 memory writes.
Program 4.6A	Indirect Addressing Using ADDA: Set up 1 address register with immediate data—takes 1 to 2 memory reads. ADDA immediate data twice—takes 2 memory reads. Get addresses from An—very fast. Then get data—takes 1 or 2 memory reads. Store answer—takes 2 memory writes.
Program 4.6B	Indirect Addressing with Post-Increment: Set up 1 address register with immediate data—takes 1 to 2 memory reads. Get addresses from (An)+—fast. Then get data—takes 1 or 2 memory reads. Store answer—takes 2 memory writes.

So far, then, indirect with post-increment seems to offer the best overall method — providing you can arrange your data in suitable sequential memory locations. A typical situation where data naturally occupies successive addresses is in word processing where you have to handle long **strings** or sequences of ASCII characters, each needing a byte of memory. The M68000 is often criticized for lacking explicit string handling instructions. Our next program refutes this criticism.

STRING MANIPULATION USING (An)+

Here is a powerful example of (An)+ in action. The problem will be familiar to all readers who have ever moved or copied a block of text while word processing.

```
* Program 4-7: Copy a String of Characters from One Memory
* Location to Another
* A1 points to first ASCII character of a block of text in
* memory.
* Assume that the last character in a string is ASCII NULL (0).
* We want to copy the block of text excluding the final NULL to
* another part of memory starting at address A2.  Any old data at
* A2 can be overwritten.
* A2 is larger than <A1 + length of string>!
* If the string at A1 is empty (that is, starts with NULL) don't
* bother to move it!

LOOP      TST.B     (A1)              Have we reached a NULL?
                                      Test byte at address A1 = 0?
          BEQ       FINI              If yes exit to FINI
          MOVE.B    (A1)+, (A2)+      Move byte at A1 to byte at A2
                                      Then increase A1 and A2 by 1 to
                                      point to next byte in memory
          BRA       LOOP              Back to LOOP to test next
                                      byte.
FINI            <rest of program>


* WARNING—remember that A1 and A2 have changed unless first (A1)
* was NULL.
```

You can see how (A1)+ as byte source and (A2)+ as byte destination neatly advance each pointer (the "sending" pointer A1 and the "receiving" pointer A2) through each character of the string. Without a test for the end of the string, MOVE.B (A1)+,(A2)+ would continue right through all available memory, with strange results! So the simple little TST.B introduced above has saved wiping out all the data in RAM.

```
          TST.z     operand
```

tests the z = L, W, or B of the operand and sets the N and Z flags in the CCR depending on whether the operand is negative or zero. The N flag happens to be irrelevant in this particular example. So,

```
          TST.B     (A1)
```

"asks" the question: Is the Byte in memory at address A1 = 0? If yes the Z flag is set=1; if no the Z flag is cleared to 0. The M68000 has no knowledge or interest in ASCII codes as such — it is entirely our problem how we interpret the 8 bits in each byte of our string.

Our TST.B works on the assumption that the string ends with an ASCII NULL character which equals binary 00000000 (sometimes called **blank** and not to be confused with ASCII "space" which equals 00100000 or with ASCII "zero" which equals 00110000). All of which is to remind the beginner that NULL is an ASCII character like the rest and takes up a byte of your precious memory. It just happens to look like a 0 to the TST.B instruction.

The BEQ after TST.B checks the CCR and branches to FINI only if the Z flag is 1, that is, only if the byte (A1) is NULL.

Notice that we TST.B right at the beginning of the loop. If the first (A1) byte of our string were NULL we would branch to FINI right away without moving anything. Zen programmers enjoy pondering the question whether an empty string, that is, one which starts (and therefore also ends) with a NULL is worth copying. You should certainly distinguish between an empty string and no string at all. Program 4-7 will just ignore an empty string — since we branch out *before* copying NULL. It is not difficult to rewrite 4-7 so that the NULL in (A1) would copy to (A2). In many walks of life such nitpicking would be condemned as outlandishly metaphysical, but in computer programming, alas, such details can be vital. A good reason for not copying NULL to (A2) might be that you want to append more text at the end of the copy string or, for the sake of a longer, more impressive word, to **concatenate** it with something. If you insist on an exact copy of a non-empty string including the final NULL, here is Program 4-8:

```
* Program 4-8: Copy a String of Characters from One Memory
* Location to Another

* A1 points to first ASCII character of a block of text in
* memory.
* Assume that the last character in a string is ASCII NULL (0).
* We want to copy the block of text including the final NULL to
* another part of memory starting at address A2.  Any old data at
* A2 can be overwritten.
* A2 is greater than <A1 + length of string>.
* If the string at A1 is empty (that is starts with NULL) don't
* bother to move it!

         TST.B     (A1)           Is first byte NULL?
         BEQ       FINI           If yes exit to FINI
                                  because string is empty.
LOOP     MOVE.B    (A1)+, (A2)+   Move byte at A1 to byte at A2
                                  then increase A1 and A2 by 1 to
                                  point to next byte in memory
```

```
            BNE       LOOP          If byte moved is not NULL(=0)
                                    there's more to copy.
FINI            <rest of program>

* Remember that A1 and A2 may change.
```

(An)+ MODE SUMMARY

The (An)+ mode as either source or destination or both, is the most efficient way of manipulating successive low-to-high memory locations. You set An to point at the starting location, and having chosen the data size of the operation (L, W, or B) you can trust the M68000 to increment the pointer correctly.

We promised you two ways of scanning consecutive addresses, so having seen (An)+ going *forward* through memory, we present the converse mode, –(An), for accessing memory *backwards*.

ADDRESS REGISTER INDIRECT WITH PRE-DECREMENT: –(An)

Closely related to the (An)+ mode is the Address Register Indirect Pre-Decrement Mode, written –(An). The pointer An is reduced or **decremented** by 4, 2, or 1 before the operation takes place. As with (An)+ the change in pointer value is determined by the data size code used in the instruction. A simple example:

```
* A5 contains $8008 when we start
CLR.L     -(A5)  would reduce A5 by 4, then clear longword ($8004)
```

but

```
CLR.W     -(A5)  would reduce A5 by 2, then clear word ($8006)
```

and

```
CLR.B     -(A5)  would reduce A5 by 1, then clear byte ($8007)
```

Using –(An) you can scan data tables from end to beginning (which is sometimes quicker), providing you remember to set the address register pointer pointing *just beyond* the end of the table to allow for the *pre*-decrement. (An)+ and –(An) work nicely together, when you think about it! (An)+ leaves your pointer in the correct position, after a forward scan, one place beyond the end

— ready for a reverse scan using –(An). This idea is used in word processors, such as WordStar, that allow a forward or backward search of your document for a matching string.

–(An) MODE — SUMMARY

The –(An) mode as either source or destination or both, is the most efficient way of manipulating successive high-to-low memory locations. You set An to point just beyond the higher location, and after you have chosen the data size of the operation (L, W, or B), the M68000 will decrement the pointer correctly before each operation.

CONCLUSION

We conclude this chapter with a brief overview of the addressing modes we have covered. In Chapter 5, we will discuss more advanced uses of these modes, and introduce fresh modes and instructions.

Mode Description:

Dn	Data register direct } Jointly called register direct
An	Address register direct } Jointly called register direct
(An)	Address register indirect
(An)+	Address register indirect with post-increment
–(An)	Address register indirect with pre-decrement
Immed	Immediate data operand—also written as #(data)
Abs.W	Absolute short address (16-bit, sign-extended)—also written xxx{.W} or label
Abs.L	Absolute long address (32-bit)—also written xxx{.L} or label

5

M68000 Instruction Set — Advanced Topics

In this chapter we build upon the basic instructions and modes covered in Chapter 4. Our first topic deals with what is generally described as **housekeeping** — a word used to describe a wide variety of situations faced by the programmer: keeping track of where things are in memory, saving and restoring register values, and so on. This subject provides a real and practical reason for many of the M68000 instructions and features.

PRESERVING REGISTER VALUES — WHY AND HOW

With the (An), (An)+ and –(An) modes you face a problem that crops up in many disguises, especially as your programs get longer and you start "using up" your registers. Although the M68000 is more generous than most in providing 16 versatile registers, you can easily reach a position in a program when they are all "assigned". In other words, you may be holding 8 important intermediate results in D0 through D7, and each of the normal address registers A0 through A6 may hold pointers you don't want to lose.

Suppose you now embark on a string copy using

```
MOVE.B (A3)+, (A0)+
```

for example. Obviously, as you saw in Chapter 4, you "lose" the initial values of A3 and A0, since they end up pointing at an address that depends on the length of the string — which is often unpredictable. Obviously you can "save" A3 and A0 by writing their values to memory before the string copy, then "restoring" them afterwards, as in:

```
* Program 5-1

* We want to copy string (A3) -> (A0) without losing pointer
* values in A3 and A0.

        MOVE.L    A3,$4004        Save A3
        MOVE.L    A0,$4000        Save A0
                                  <Copy string (A3) -> (A0)>
        MOVEA.L   $4000,A0        Restore A0
        MOVEA.L   $4004,A3        Restore A3
```

The same "trick" can be used to save and restore Dn values. It certainly achieves the desired goal, but there are obvious snags. First, it can become messy and error prone in a complex program (where did I put A3 and D7...?). Second, there is a risk that a saved value might be inadvertently overwritten during some convoluted branching. Third, if you are sometimes saving bytes, sometimes saving words, and sometimes saving longwords, you have to pay attention to the odd/even address restrictions.

The M68000 provides two methods to simplify the saving and restoring of register values: the MOVEM instruction and the user stack.

MOVEM — MOVE MULTIPLE REGISTERS

MOVEM is a special version of MOVE offering a fast and economical way of saving any number of register values into consecutive memory locations, and then restoring them later as needed.

To save registers in memory the format is:

```
MOVEM.Z   <register list>,<destination>
```

To restore registers from memory the format is:

```
MOVEM.Z   <source>,<register list>
```

Note that Z can equal L or W only, so MOVEM.B is illegal.

The <register list> can specify up to 16 different registers (D0 through D7, A0 through A7) for saving or restoring, while the destination and source specify the starting memory location. MOVEM.L transfers all 32 bits, while MOVEM.W transfers only the lower word with some judicious sign-bit extensions when you restore. Program 5-1 could be written:

```
* Program 5-1A  MOVEM: Saving/Restoring Multiple Registers
* at Absolute Addresses

* We want to move a string without losing pointer values A0, A3.

        MOVEM.L   A0/A3,$4000    Save A0 and A3 at $4000
                                 and $4004
                                 <Copy string (A3) -> (A0)>
        MOVEM.L   $4000,A0/A3    Restore A0 and A3 from
                                 $4000 and $4004
```

Note how the <register list> is set up with a slash (/) between each register. To save consecutive registers you can list them as:

```
        MOVEM.L   D0-D5/A4-A6,$6000
```

which would save 9 registers, the 6 data registers D0 through D5 and the 3 address registers A4 through A6. The 9 register values would be stored in 9 longwords at memory locations $6000 through $6020. You would restore them all with:

```
        MOVEM.L   $6000,D0-D5/A4-A6
```

You have been saving your registers at absolute memory locations, but you can also save them by specifying a pointer (always providing you have a spare An) using the –(An) pre-decrement mode, in which case you must restore by using the (An)+ post-increment mode in the source operand. Again, you will notice how these two modes complement each other. Program 5-1B shows this variant:

```
* Program 5-1B  MOVEM--Saving/Restoring Multiple Registers
* Using Address Indirects -(An) and (An)+

* We want to move a string without losing pointer values A0, A3.
* A5 points to the last used address in our saving area in
* memory.
* Assume A5 = $4008.
```

```
        MOVEM.L    A0/A3,-(A5)

* Reduce A5 by 4. Save A3 first at $4004. Reduce A5 again by 4.
* Then save A0 at $4000. A5 now = $4000.
* Note that MOVEM conveniently reverses the saving order for you!

        <copy string (A3) -> (A0)>

        MOVEM.L    (A5)+,A0/A3

* Restore A0 first from $4000. Increment A5 by 4 then restore A3
* from $4004. Increment A5 by 4. A5 is again = $4008.
```

The MOVEM with –(An) and (An)+ is very flexible. As you will see in the next section, it is very similar to the stack concept.

STACKS

The stack solution to saving and restoring registers requires a brief preamble on stack jargon and mystique.

As shown in Figures 5-1 and 5-2, the address register A7 is designated as the USP (User Stack Pointer) and its job is to point to a special area of memory called the **user stack**. This stack "grows" downwards from a stack base address, from high to low memory as you save data, and "shrinks" upwards, back towards the stack base, from low to high memory as you restore.

It helps to stand on your head during this paragraph. Which recalls the famous box that arrived from Dublin, Ireland, with the following inscription: "This box must always be kept upside-down. To avoid any confusion the bottom has been marked 'Top.'"

The preferred term for saving is **pushing** data on the stack; you restore by **pulling** or **popping** data from the stack. Stacks are LIFO (Last In First Out) devices because when you pull off a stack you restore the most recently saved data. In contrast, a **queue** is a FIFO (First In First Out) device.

There is never any doubt about where you are saving stuff on the user stack. A7 always points to the last item saved, which is also the first candidate to be restored.

The sequence for pushing D1, say, on the stack is:

```
        MOVE.L    D1,-(A7)        Save D1 on stack

* Pre-decrement of A7 (by 4 because of the L) means moving the
* stack pointer down in memory.  (Down is the direction of stack
* growth.)
```

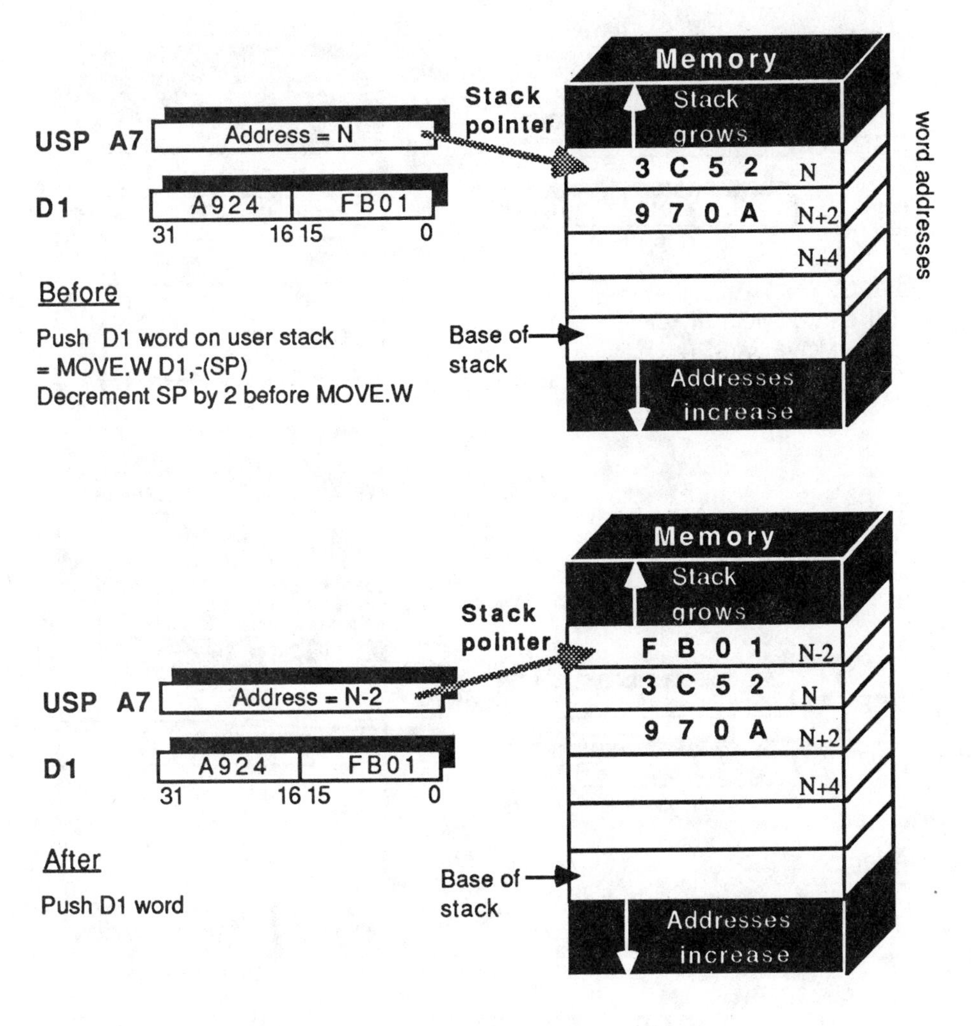

Fig. 5-1 User Stack Operation: Pushing

```
* Then save D1 at the new address in A7.  Stack pointer therefore
* points at item just saved.
```

Pulling D1 from the stack involves:

```
        MOVE.L    (A7)+,D1        Restore D1 from stack

* Previous D1 value is stored at A7, so move (A7) to D1, then
* post-increment A7 by 4 to shrink the stack.  A7 now points at
* the data (if any) that was pushed before D1.
```

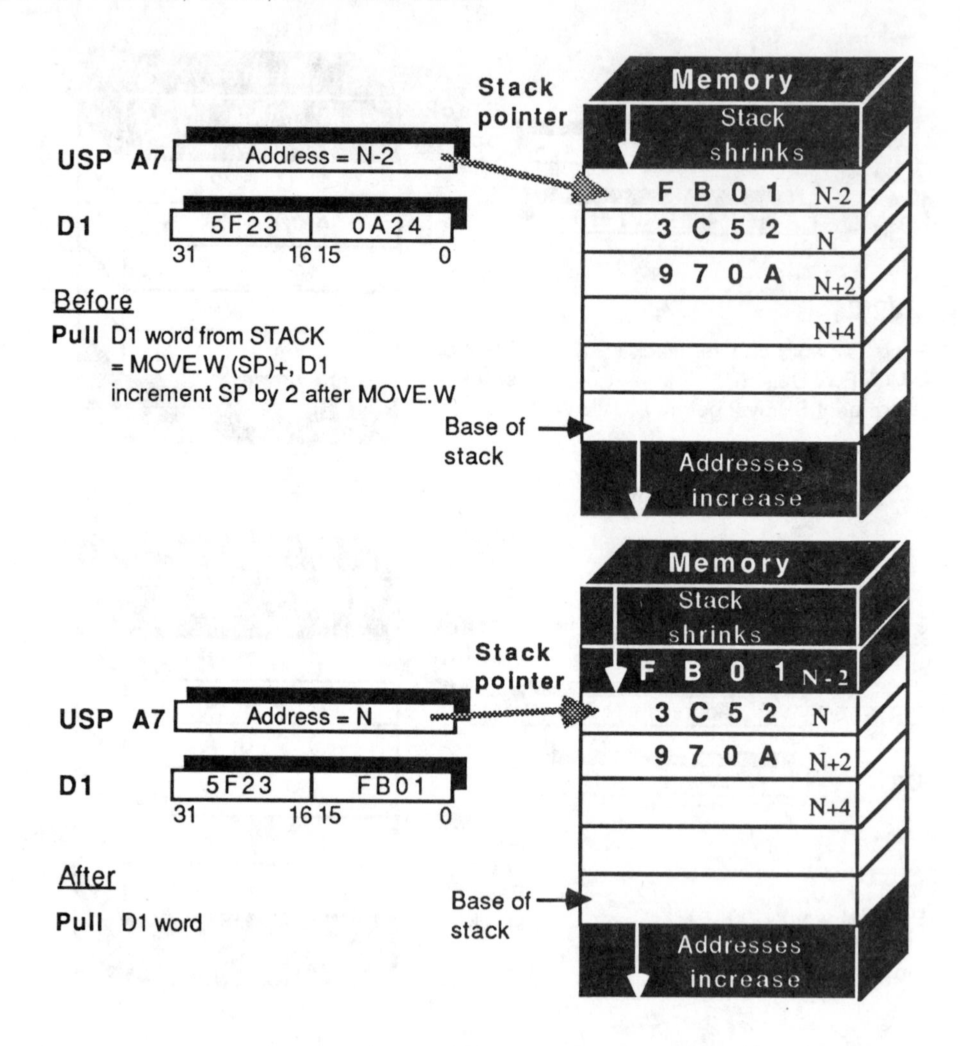

Fig. 5-2 User Stack Operation: Pulling

Standard syntax allows you to use the mnemonic SP (Stack Pointer) in place of A7:

```
MOVE.L    D1,-(SP)       Save D1 on stack
MOVE.L    (SP)+,D1       Restore D1 from stack
```

MOVEM AND THE STACK

You can use MOVEM to save multiple registers on a stack:

```
MOVEM.L   D0-D3/A0-A6,-(SP)
```

will push 11 register values and

```
MOVEM.L    (SP)+,D0-D3/A0-A6
```

will pop them all back.

MOVEM, however, saves only registers (L or W), whereas with MOVE you can also push memory data on the stack, including bytes.

PUSHING BYTES ON THE STACK

When you push a byte on the stack with, for example:

```
MOVE.B    D2,-(SP)      Save lower byte of D2 on
                         stack
```

the M68000 has a nice built-in trick to spare you the embarrassment of hitting odd-numbered memory boundaries if you subsequently wanted to push a word or longword. Figure 5-3 shows how this trick works.

Normally, the MOVE.B pre-decrements and post-increments An by 1, but with SP (= A7) the processor adjusts the pointer by 2 to preserve even-numbered addresses. All stack data, then, is aligned on word boundaries. When you push a byte, in fact, it goes into the upper half of the stack word, and the lower half is "wasted."

Having seen the stack invoked explicitly by MOVEs and SPs in the program, you will next see a situation where the M68000 makes use of the stack under its own steam, as it were, without a specific MOVE being required. First you need to understand the general concept of a subroutine.

SUBROUTINE — BRIEF DEFINITION

A **subroutine** is a specially constructed piece of program which can be called into operation from anywhere in the main program, and having performed its duty, will return control back to the place in the program that called it. Subroutines have identifying labels and calling a subroutine is rather like branching. Unlike the Bcc, which just branches you elsewhere, calling a subroutine requires a mechanism for remembering the line that called it, so that when the subroutine has concluded, the system knows where to resume.

Subroutines are vital in reducing the amount of code you need to write and debug. Almost any sequence of instructions that you find used several times in a program can be usefully made into one subroutine, and then called as often as you like from any line in your program. Let's see how subroutines are

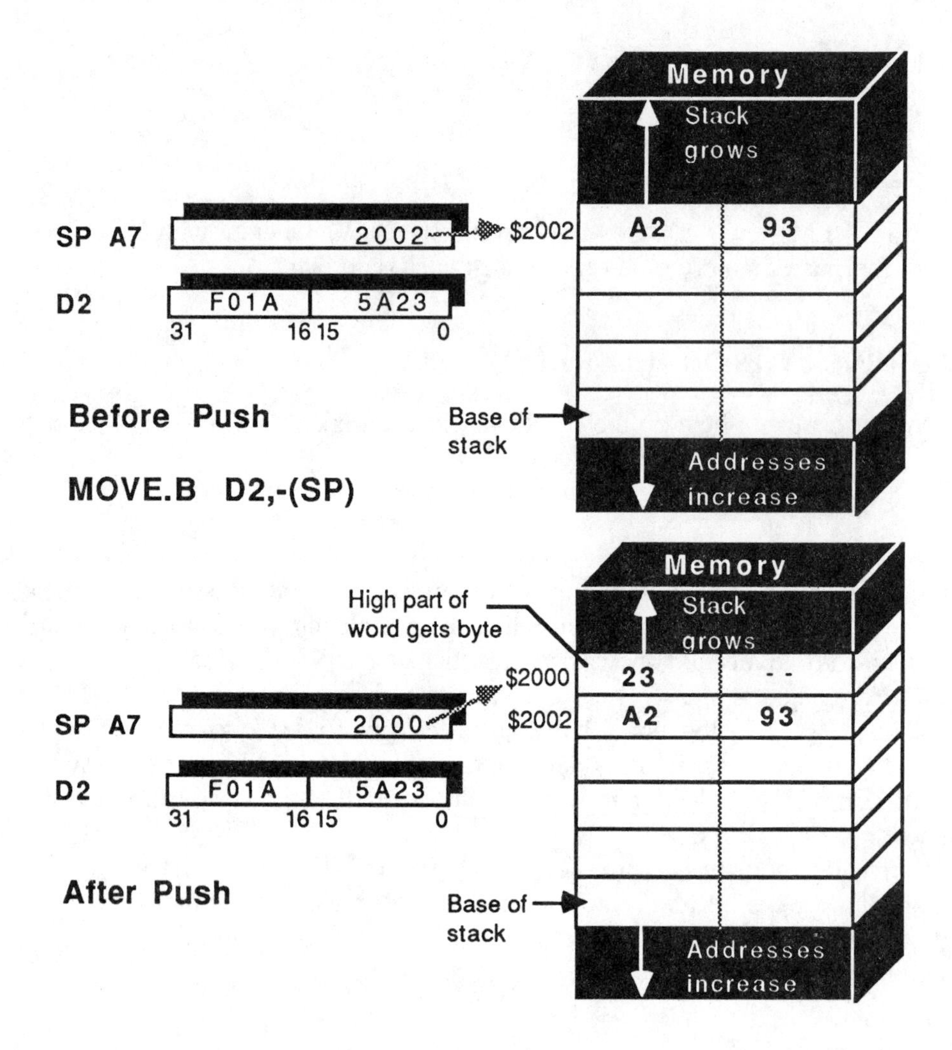

Fig. 5-3 Byte Operations on Stack

called, and how the stack is invoked automatically by the M68000 to ensure that the return address is saved.

BSR — BRANCH SUBROUTINE

Subroutines are called with a BSR instruction. The format for BSR is the same as Bcc:

```
BSR     <label>   Branch to SubRoutine at
                  <label>
```

At the line <label> we would find our subroutine, coded just like any other piece of program, but always concluded with an RTS, ReTurn from Subroutine. Here, step by step, is the sequence of operations BSR triggers:

1. Calculates the address of the next instruction and pushes this address on the user stack.
2. Branches (unconditionally like BRA) to the instruction labeled <label> by setting the PC to the <label> address.
3. The subroutine instructions at <label> are then obeyed sequentially until the RTS is encountered.
4. The PC is then loaded by pulling from the stack the address we saved there in step 1 above. In effect the processor internally performs a MOVE.L (A7)+,PC.
5. The processor takes its next instruction from the address in PC, so control passes back to the instruction following the BSR instruction.

The BSR, <label>, and RTS trio have combined to perform the neat trick we referred to, namely calling a subroutine. The chosen label should be, as usual, mnemonic, since we will usually talk about calling the "label" subroutine. A subroutine saves programming effort and reduces the length of a program, thereby conserving memory.

Neither BSR nor RTS affect the CCR condition flags directly, although the instructions in the subroutine itself will almost certainly change and make use of the CCR. Let's see BSR in action:

```
* Program 5-2  Calling a Subroutine Called ACCUM

* Program to add some numbers that are in memory
* D1 will be used as an accumulator.
* Subroutine ACCUM adds D0 to D1.

START    CLR.L    D1            Clear accumulator D1
         *   *    *             Do other things
MAIN     MOVE.L   (A1),D0       Set D0 from memory address A1
         BSR      ACCUM         Call ACCUM subroutine
         MOVE.L   (A2),D0       Set D0 from address A2
         BSR      ACCUM         Call ACCUM again
         <print grand total in D1>
         <conclude>
         *   *    *
* Subroutine section starts here.

ACCUM    ADD.L    D0,D1         This is a one line subroutine
         RTS                    called ACCUM
```

```
* ACCUM input  = longword D0 which is unchanged
        output = longword D1 = D1 + D0

          <possibly more subroutines follow here>
          *    *    *
```

Usually, of course, subroutines are longer and more useful than this example. However, it does illustrate the basic principles of subroutine calling.

Subroutines — Input and Output Parameters

You usually set up particular values using MOVE just prior to the BSR. Each subroutine will have its own set of required inputs or parameters. ACCUM has just one input, the value of D0, and one output, the total in D1. To maximize the usefulness of subroutines, these parameters and how they are affected should be well commented and documented. Subroutines are often designed as general purpose programs or utilities. Once they are thoroughly tested they can be added to a library of subroutines accessible to everyone using the system. Many assemblers allow such library files to be scanned during assembly; any subroutines referenced in the main program can be automatically copied into your program. The motivation is "never reinvent a perfectly good wheel." Once you understand the function of a particular subroutine you learn to treat it almost like a single instruction without being bogged down by the inner details.

Subroutine Side Effects on Registers

A well-designed subroutine for general use must guard against unwanted side effects. A complex subroutine may make use of many registers and, unless steps are taken, their orignal values could be lost to the calling program. The user stack turns out to be an excellent place to save and restore such values, in spite of the fact that BSR and RTS both use the stack to save and restore the subroutine return address (steps 1 and 4 above). The stack LIFO philosophy handles any number of pushes and pulls — provided your pulls and pushes are sequenced correctly. Here's a program using the user stack during a subroutine:

```
* Program 5-3 Subroutine CLRMEM

* A0 points to an area of memory which we want to CLeaR.
* D0 contains the number of words to be cleared.
* Subroutine CLRMEM must not alter A0 and D0.

MAIN      <do things>
          BSR       CLRMEM              Push return address
                                        then call CLRMEM
```

```
          <back here after subroutine> A0 and D0 unchanged
          *     *     *                Stack back to original
                                       state
* Subroutines start here
CLRMEN    MOVE.L    D0,-(SP)           Push D0 to save
          MOVE.L    A0,-(SP)           Push A0 to save
MLOOP     CLR.W     (A0)+              Clear (A0), inc A0 by 2
          SUBQ.L    #1,D0              Decrement counter
          BNE       MLOOP              If counter 0 exit MLOOP
          MOVE.L    (SP)+,A0           Pull A0 to restore
          MOVE.L    (SP)+,D0           Pull D0 to restore
          RTS                          Pull return address
          <more subroutines here possibly>
          *     *     *
```

The pulls from the stack (implicit and explicit) reverse the sequence of the pushes, leaving the stack in the state it was in before the BSR.

Subroutine Side Effects on the CCR

It is almost certain that the flags in the CCR will change during a subroutine and this could be a nuisance to the mainstream program. Quite often you will test a result and call one of three different subroutines depending on a result of zero, positive, or negative. When you return you may want to test again using the original CCR flags.

CONTEXT

Also, as you've seen, you may want to call the same subroutine under many different conditions, and a subroutine that changes the context of the main calling program reduces our flexibility and leads to errors that can prove difficult to diagnose.

Many other user and systems events can temporarily interrupt your program to do other things — so the general concept of "preserving the context" is fundamental to all modern computer operations.

Context simply means a list of all those registers and processor states (including the current PC) which we need to save somewhere so that when the time comes to resume our program (after a subroutine or interrupt or whatever) the entire status quo of our job can be restored. A very high proportion of all software bugs can be traced to the side effects of poor context handling. The M68000 instruction set, therefore, has many instructions (MOVEM is one good example) to simplify this problem. Depending on the situation, the saving of the context may either be the programmer's responsibility or it may be a task assigned to the operating system or the hardware.

Later we will see how the M68000 maintains an independent supervisor stack using the SSP (Supervisor Stack Pointer) accessible only in supervisor mode. The latter is a privileged mode intended to protect vital systems contexts held in the supervisor stack.

SAVING THE CCR

For user-supplied subroutines you can use the user stack to save the CCR flags rather as you did to preserve normal register values. Pushing the CCR on the user stack, however, differs between the MC68000 and the MC68010/68020 (for reasons we'll discuss in Chapter 7). The MC68000 has to use:

```
MOVE.W  SR,-(SP)          Push SR on stack
```

So, although you need to save only the CCR, you are forced to save both bytes of the Status Register (the upper system byte as well as the CCR).

The MC68010/20 allows the simpler:

```
MOVE.W  CCR,-(SP)         Push CCR on stack
```

which just saves the CCR byte on the stack (the other byte moved is all zeroes).

You can restore the CCR on all models with

```
MOVE.W  (SP)+,CCR         Pull CCR from stack
```

In all Chapter 5 examples we'll use the MC68000 version (MOVE from SR).

RTR — RETURN AND RESTORE CCR

A simpler way to restore the CCR is to use a special version of RTS called RTR (ReTurn from subroutine and Restore condition codes). RTR at the end of your subroutine will first pull the CCR from the stack, then perform an RTS. Using RTR when you have not earlier pushed the CCR is a dreadful mistake — your stack will be "out of synch" with weird results all round.

NESTING SUBROUTINES

Once you grasp the basic LIFO mechanism of the user stack, you will readily see that subroutines can themselves call subsubroutines and so on — a concept known as **nesting**. You just trust the stack to pull what was last pushed! The maximum depth of nesting allowed will depend on your particular OS and memory disposition — many systems do not allocate a fixed amount of memory for the stack; rather, the stack is allowed to "grow down" in free user memory until it "hits" occupied territory.

It is now time to introduce some more addressing modes. Excluding special modes on the MC68020 only, we have four more addressing modes to reveal in this chapter. They are all variants of the address register indirect.

ADDRESS REGISTER INDIRECT WITH OFFSET

This mode is written d16(An) where d16 represents the 16-bit offset (sometimes called the **displacement**) in bytes, which is added to the pointer value of An before the operand is fetched from memory. Unlike the –(An) and (An)+ modes, however, the value of An is unchanged by d16(An).

The offset can be any signed 16-bit number in the range -32,768 through +32,767 and we use the notation d16 to remind you of this limitation.

So d16(An) allows you to access memory within 32K bytes (above or below) of the pointer address, An. Its main use is to operate on data in a table where An points to the starting address (or **base**) of the table.

It is helpful to express the d16(An) mode in terms of an <ea> (effective address) calculation, namely: <ea> = d16 + An. This formula tells you how the processor determines the actual operand address. The d16 offset is, in fact, stored as one extension word, just as you saw earlier in the case of immediate data. The <ea> calculation time can range from 0 in the simple direct modes to as many as 17 clock cycles for a complex indirect mode. Let's look at the d16(An) mode in action.

Offset Mode — Applications

In Figure 5-4, A2 = $6000 points to a table of data consisting of 20 longwords, ($6000), ($6004), ($6008), ($600C), etc. To load D3 from the 4th table entry, we need

```
MOVE.L     12(A2),D3
```

since the source effective address = A2 + (3 longwords) = $3000 + 12 bytes = $300C. After the move A2 still = $3000. If we wanted to reverse the second and third entries in our table, one way would be as follows:

```
* Program 5-4  Swap Table Entries
```

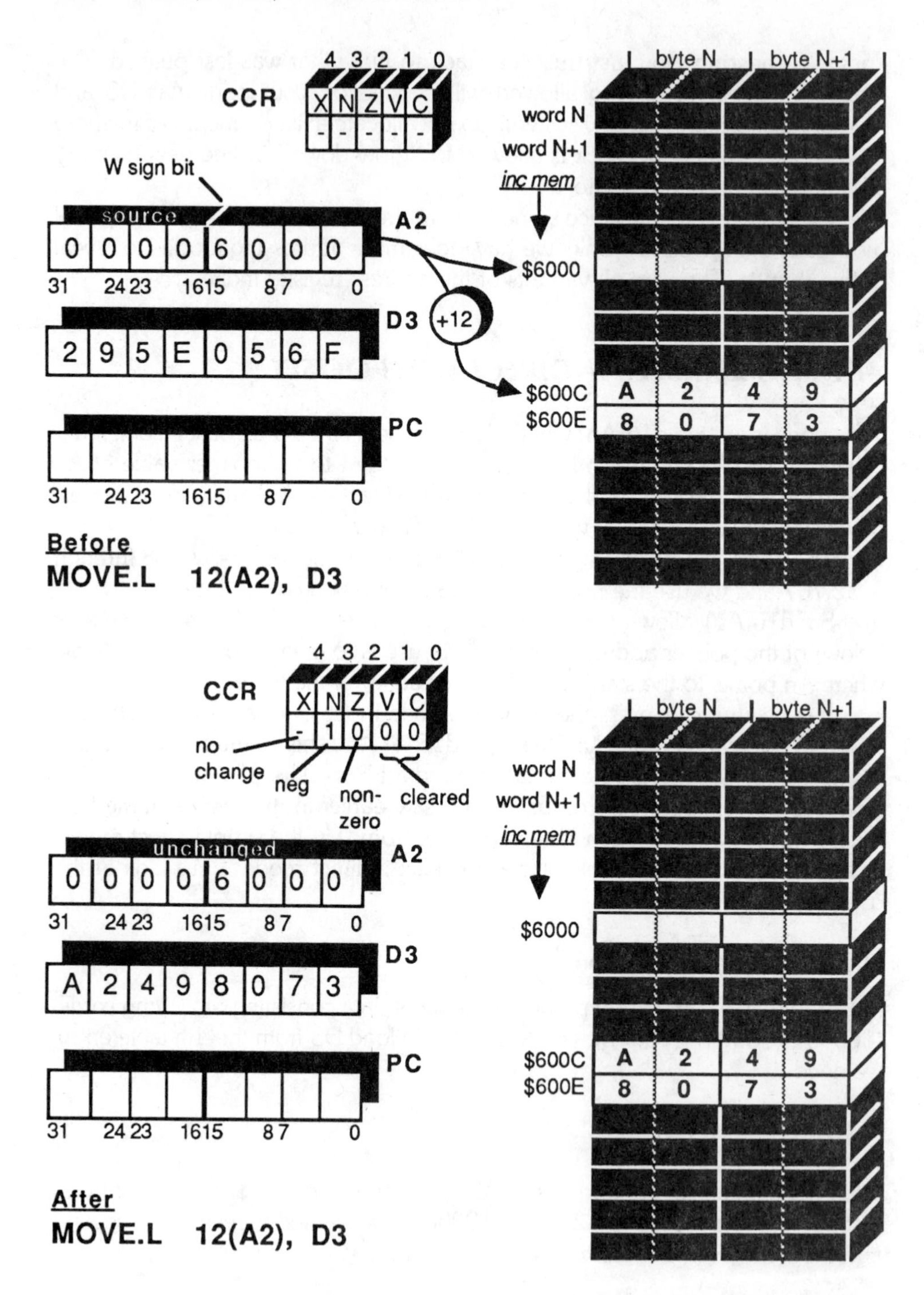

Fig. 5-4 MOVE.L 12(A2),D3

```
* Illustrate use of d16(An) mode in source and destination.
* A2 points to base of table of longword entries.
* Switch the 2nd and 3rd entries.

            MOVE.L    4(A2),D0        Save 2nd table entry
            MOVE.L    8(A2),4(A2)     Move 3rd to 2nd
            MOVE.L    D0,8(A2)        Move 2nd to 3rd
```

Three points to note when using this mode are:

1. For L and W operations the sum (d16 + An) must be even. For B operations the sum can be odd or even.
2. –1(An) should not be confused with –(An). For example, if A2 = $2001, MOVE.B –1(A2),D3 and MOVE.B –(A2),D3 both move byte ($2000) to lower byte of D3, but the –1(A2) move leaves A2 still = $2001. The pre-decrement –(A2) reduces A2 to $2000.
3. This mode often appears as TAG(An), for example, in real-life programs, where TAG is a symbolic (preferably mnemonic) offset which, as you saw with labels, gets equated to a numerical offset during assembly.

There are many situations where we need the flexibility of a variable offset to supplement the fixed offset of the d16(An) mode. Our next addressing mode supplies the solution.

ADDRESS REGISTER INDIRECT WITH OFFSET AND INDEX

This extension of the d16(An) mode allows an extra variable offset, known as an **index**, to be added from a register. For brevity we will call it the index mode. It is written as d8(An,Xi.Z) where d8 is a fixed offset in bytes (8-bit signed number) giving a range of –128 through +127; An holds the base address as in the d16(An) mode; Xi is any register (D0 – D7, A0 – A7), known here as the index register, and Z is a size code, L or W.

The effective address, <ea> is built up from three separate elements: <ea> = An + d8 + Xi.Z. In other words, the processor adds the offset d8 bytes, then gets the number from Xi.Z and adds that number of bytes as an additional offset to An. The contribution to this total from the index register, Xi, is either the full 32 bits for Xi.L, or just the lower 16 bits for Xi.W. The speed of the <ea> calculation is the same for L and W indexing.

As with the d16(An) mode, the actual value of An is unchanged. Also, we must watch that the <ea> we obtain is even for L and W operations.

We often abbreviate the index mode to d(An,Xi). If the fixed d offset is 0, this mode gives us a simple indexing mode as found in many 8- and 16-bit processors.

INDEX MODE — APPLICATIONS

The main application of the d(An,Xi) mode is accessing complex multidimensional arrays and tables of data in memory. With two offsets, for example, you can set An pointing to the base of a **spreadsheet**. If you set the offset d to the line number and move the column number to the index register Xi, d(An,Xi) is the effective address of the data-cell in the target box, the intersection of row d and column Xi.

Although the fixed offset d8 offers only –128 to +127 displacements, the addition of an index register is ample compensation. Xi.L can give you a range of 2 gigabytes on either side of the An pointer.

Using the data in Program 5-4, let's see the index mode in action, first with d8 = 0 to show simple indexing.

```
* Program 5-5  Swap Table Entries Using Index Mode

* Initial data as for Program 5-4
* Illustrate use of d8(An,Xi.Z) mode in source and destination.
* A2 points to base of table of longword entries.
* Switch the 2nd and 3rd entries.

        MOVEQ.L   #4,D1                    Set Index Reg D1 = 4
        MOVE.L    0(A2,D1.W),D0            Save 2nd table entry
        MOVEA.W   #8,A0                    Set index reg A0 = 8
        MOVE.L    0(A2,A0.W),0(A2,D1.W)    Move 3rd to 2nd
        MOVE.L    D0,0(A2,A0.W)            Move 2nd to 3rd

* Note that A2 is unchanged.
```

In Program 5-5 we have used both D1 and A0 as index registers just to remind you that any register can be used to index. The data registers are, in fact, more popular than address registers for indexing, simply because you can do more arithmetic on them. When you are scanning or searching a table using the d(An,Xi) mode, you often want to add, subtract, multiply, and even divide the offset sitting in Xi.

In Program 5-5, the table consisted of longwords, so we had to remember to adjust the index offset by multiples of 4 bytes. For tables of words the offsets would have to be multiples of 2 bytes. Naturally you can ask the M68000 to do these calculations for you. To obtain multiples, let us go forth and multiply!

MULTIPLICATION

There are two basic multiply instructions which use the same format:

```
MULS    <source>,Dn        MULtiply Signed
MULU    <source>,Dn        MULtiply Unsigned
```

They both multiply two 16-bit Words to give a 32-bit result. No data size code is needed since W is always implied. The source can be any addressing mode except An (Address Register Direct). What happens is this:

(word from source) times (lower word of destination Dn) = (32-bit result in Dn)

Just like ADD and SUB, the source is unchanged but the destination factor is overwritten by the answer. Unlike ADD and SUB, however, multiply needs separate versions: MULS for signed and MULU for unsigned operations. With ADD and SUB, you will recall, the V (oVerflow) and C (Carry) flags were set to warn you of erroneous signed or unsigned results. Multiply is different.

The inviolate laws of binary arithmetic tell us that whether you multiply 2 signed or 2 unsigned 16-bit numbers, the answer always fits in 32 bits without overflow or carry! Multiplying a signed number by an unsigned number is not a fruitful exercise and the M68000 assumes you know in advance the type of numbers you intend to multiply. You must therefore choose between MULS and MULU to get a sensible answer. Both MULS and MULU set the CCR thus:

Flag	X	N	Z	V	C
MULS/MULU	–	*	*	0	0

(To remind you of our notation: X unchanged; N set to sign-bit 31; Z set to 1 if result 0; V and C flags always cleared to 0.) MULS, of course, will correctly handle the sign of the result, for example, (−6) x (−2) = +12 and (−6) x (+2) = −12 so the N flag literally means "positive or negative." MULU is multiplying without regard to sign, so the N flag is simply telling you if there is a 0 or 1 in the most significant bit (position 31) of Dn after the multiplication.

We illustrate MULS with a simple (but essential) payroll example.

```
* Program 5-6  Payroll: Hours x Rate = Pay
```

```
* As in Program 4-1 D2 word contains hours worked in March = 138.
* D4 word holds the hourly rate in cents = 699.
* Calculate March gross salary and if positive save it in memory
* at longword absolute address $A200.  Preserve the values in D2
* and D4.

                MOVE.W   D4,-(SP)      Save D4 word on stack
                MULS     D2,D4         D4 now = D2 x D4
                                       = Hrs x Rate = Gross
                                       (D2 unchanged,D4 changed)
                BMI      DEBIT         If result negative branch
                                       to label DEBIT
                                       (Branch if MInus)
                BEQ      NOPAY         If result zero branch to
                                       label NOPAY
                MOVE.L   D4,$A200      Save Gross in memory
                MOVE.W   (SP)+,D4      Restore D4 from stack
                <carry on--normal payroll>
                *    *    *
                BRA      OVER          Skip to end
DEBIT           MOVE.W   (SP)+,D4      Restore D4 from stack
                <check negative gross> (see note 2 below)
                *    *    *
                BRA      OVER          Skip to end
NOPAY           MOVE.W   (SP)+,D4      Restore D4 from stack
                <check zero gross>     (see note 2 below)
                *    *    *
OVER            <conclude program>

* Gross pay for March = 96462 cents is stored at $A200.
* D2 unchanged and D4 restored.
```

1. We used MULS rather than MULU because in most financial applications we would be allowing for negative amounts (refunds, adjustments, etc). MULS permits us to use BMI (Branch Minus) meaningfully, since BMI tests the N flag.
2. We must remember to keep the stack "tidy." Since we pushed D4, we must pull it sooner or later. We could not pull it before our tests BMI and BEQ, since MOVE alters the N and Z flags.
3. We have a typical use of BRA (Unconditional Branch) to bypass irrelevant sections of a program. Without the first BRA OVER, for example, the main program would "run on" into the DEBIT section — a common source of program misfortune.

DIVISION

Just like multiply, there are two divide instructions:

```
DIVS    <source>,Dn     DIVide Signed
DIVU    <source>,Dn     DIVide Unsigned
```

Both divide the 32-bit destination Dn (dividend) by the 16-bit word source (divisor), to give a 16-bit quotient in the lower Dn word and a 16-bit remainder in the upper Dn word. The source can be any addressing mode except An, so we can divide a data register by another data register or by a word in memory. As we have found in other arithmetic operations, the source (divisor) is unchanged but the destination (dividend) is "lost" — overwritten by the results. Divide, then, performs as follows:

(Destination Dn = 32-bit dividend) divided by (16-bit word source divisor)

gives (upper Dn word = remainder),(lower Dn word = quotient). Here is a quick example:

```
* Program 5-7  Payroll: Average Daily Earnings Using DIVS
* Using the data in Program 5-6: D4 holds March gross pay =
* 96462 cents. Calculate the average daily earnings and store in
* 2nd word of a table with base pointer A2. Save the remainder in
* the 6th word of this table. Preserve value in D4.

          MOVE.L    D4,D7       Save D4 in D7
          DIVS      #31,D4      Divide D4 by 31 (immediate)
                                Lower D4 = quotient
                                Upper D4 = remainder
          MOVE.W    D4,2(A2)    Save quotient in table
          SWAP      D4          Reverse words in D4
                                Remainder now lower word of D4
                                Quotient now upper word of D4
          MOVE.W    D4,10(A2)   Save remainder in table
          MOVE.L    D7,D4       Restore D4 from D7

* 2(A2) now holds 3111 and 10(A2) holds 21.
* 96462/31 = 3111 and 21 over.
```

SWAP Dn is a simple but useful instruction which reverses the upper and lower half words of a data register only. Notice that in the Program 5-7, you cannot immediately use MOVE to save the remainder, since MOVE.W moves the lower word and MOVE.L moves the whole word. Later, you'll see more exotic ways of manipulating portions of a register, using shifts and rotates – but here you see the motivation for such operations: the need to "isolate" and access part of a register.

We used DIVS for the same reason we used MULS in Program 5-6. DIVS gives the correct signed answer, for example, (–24)/(–2) = +12 and (24)/(–2) = –12, and so on. The N and Z flags in the CCR reflect the state of the quotient, because the remainder takes the same sign as the dividend (unless the remainder is 0). For example,

$$(25)/(-2) = (-12) \text{ with remainder } +1$$
$$(-25)/(+2) = (-12) \text{ with remainder } -1$$
$$(-25)/(+25) = (-1) \text{ with remainder } +0$$

Unlike MULS, though, DIVS and DIVU can run into two snags. The first snag is "Divide by 0". If your program doesn't test and take avoiding action, then the M68000 will TRAP this error (to avoid the horrors of an infinitely long calculation). TRAPs belong to a class of exceptions (some of which you can control, others of which are controlled by the system) that put the M68000 into the supervisor mode (which we mentioned in Chapter 3). In this privileged mode the operating system can take appropriate action.

Briefly, TRAPs, such as the "TRAP on zero divide", guide the processor to a table in system memory (addresses $000 – $3FF) called the exception vector table, where it finds the address of a routine for handling the exception. The M68000 therefore has tremendous flexibility in coping with conditions that on less thoughtful chips would result in crashes, chaos, or both.

The second snag is this: DIVS and DIVU can give rise to overflow, when the dividend is so large in relation to the divisor that the quotient exceeds the 16-bit capacity (signed = –32,767 to +32,768 or unsigned 65,536). To protect you, then, DIVS and DIVU both set the V flag in the CCR if overflow occurs.

If your numbers are likely to stray into these ranges you can use BVS (Branch if oVerflow Set) immediately after the division, just as we did earlier to test an ADD.

Alternatively, there is a special TRAP instruction called TRAPV (TRAP on oVerflow) which, like the trap on zero divide (except that TRAPV is voluntary), takes the system into the exception vector table to select the chosen remedy.

DIVS and DIVU change the CCR thus:

Flag	X	N	Z	V	C
DIVS/DIVU	–	*	*	*	0

which is the same as MULS/MULU except for the V flag.

In Program 5-7 we used immediate mode source, #31, as our divisor — the number of days in March. A more practical program would allow for other months in the year! For example, we could set up a small table holding the days in each month. Such a table would be useful in many financial applications — calculating elapsed days between dates for interest charges, and so on. The index mode is tailor-made for accessing such tables. Our next example also shows how you can do arithmetic on the index register to simplify the location of a table entry.

```
* Program 5-8  Average Daily Earnings for Any Month

* Month number M (Jan=1, Feb=2, etc) is in lower word D0.
* D4 holds gross pay in cents for that month.
* A0 points to base of table MDAYS in memory holding 12 words.
* (A0) = 31; 2(A0) = 28; 4(A0) = 31; 6(A0) = 30
* 8(A0) = 31;10(A0) = 30;...........;12(A0) = 31
* Hence number of days in month M is in word {2 x <M-1>}(A0).
* We ignore leap years for the moment.
* Calculate average daily earnings to 1 decimal place and put
* result in word D6.
* Save register values of D0,D4.
* We use <> as brackets to avoid confusion with indirect address
* brackets ().

        MOVEM.L   D0/D4,-(SP)      Stack 'em
        SUBQ.W    #1,D0            Word D0 = M - 1
        MULU      #2,D0            D0 = 2 x <M - 1>
        MULS      #100,D4          Multiply gross by 100
        DIVS      0(A0,D0.W),D4    Divide D4 by days in month M
        MOVE.W    D4,D6            Ignore upper word D4 = remainder
                                   lower word D6 = average x 100
        MOVEM.L   (SP)+,D0/D4      Unstack 'em

* For the familiar month of March, M = 3, so D0 index register
* contains 2 x <3-1> = 4. Source operand divisor for DIVS is
* therefore word at address 0 + A0 + 4 = 4(A0), that is, 3rd
* entry in MDAYS table which = 31.  D6 now contains our average x
* 100.  We can round this off to 1 place later.
```

An alternative method of multiplication is to use shifts, which we discuss next.

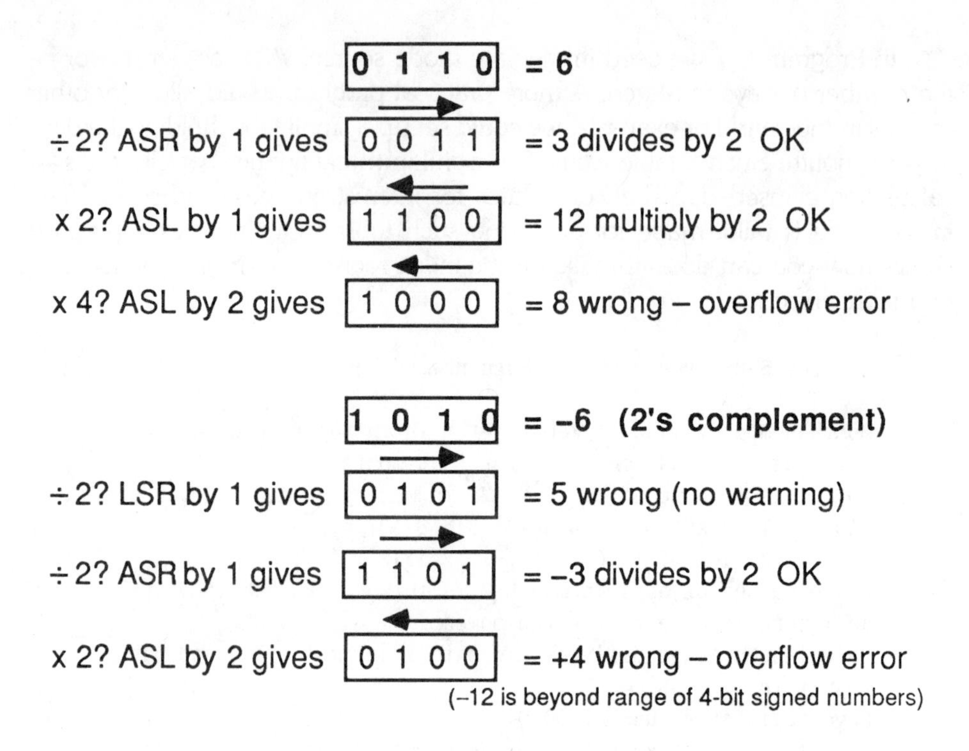

Fig. 5-5 Shifting to Multiply and Divide

ASL — ARITHMETIC SHIFT LEFT

We used MULU in the first multiplication because we are dealing with small known positive integers (and it is slightly faster than MULS). In fact, there is a much quicker way to multiply by 2, 4, 8, or any small power of 2. We can use

```
ASL.z       #<d3>,Dn
```

which does an arithmetic shift left on Dn. The number of places shifted is determined by the 3-bit number in <d3>, giving a shift count in the range of 1 to 8. The z determines which portion of Dn is shifted, L, W, or B. Figure 5-5 shows how ASL can be used to multiply by 2.

Each shift left of the bit pattern in the L, W, or B of Dn is equivalent to doubling the value of that part of Dn. So, an ASL of 1 can double just the lower byte or word of Dn without affecting the rest of Dn. Zeroes are "pushed" into Dn from the right as the shift takes place, and bits get "pushed" out at the other end.

In Program 5-8 we can replace:

```
MULU      #2,D0      Longword D0 = {word D0 x 2}
```

with any of these:

```
ASL.L     #1,D0      Longword D0 = {longword D0 x 2}
ASL.W     #1,D0      Word D0 = {word D0 x 2}
ASL.B     #1,D0      Byte D0 = {byte D0 x 2}
```

All the ASLs above work the same as MULU in our example since the maximum value in D0 is 22, well within the signed capacity of D0's lower byte. For larger numbers, of course, you would need to decide the safest size code to use. Unlike MULS/MULU, ASL can cause overflow — and the CCR should be tested if there is any danger of exceeding the L, W, or B range of Dn.

ASL is about three to five times faster than the equivalent MULS or MULU.

If you need to shift more than 8 positions or shift a variable number of positions, you can use the format

```
ASL.z     Dm,Dn      Shift Dn Left, Dm times (max 63)
```

where the lower 6 bits of the source data register Dm contains the shift count.

Finally, you can ASL a memory operand, but the shift count is restricted to 1:

```
ASL.z     <memory operand>    Single left shift memory operand.
```

In Chapter 6 we will expand on the whole subject of shifts and rotates, so for now we briefly mention an obvious variant on ASL — ASR, which lets you shift Right.

ASR — ARITHMETIC SHIFT RIGHT

As shown in Figure 5-5, shifting a register to the right is the same as dividing by a power of 2. To preserve the sign of the number you are shifting, ASR "pushes" the sign-bit into the left-hand side as the register is shifted to the right.

ASR formats are the same as ASL formats:

```
ASR.z     #<d3>,Dn          Shift Dn Right, <d3> times
ASR.z     Dm,Dn             Shift Dn Right, Dn times (max 63)
ASR.z     <memory operand>  Single right shift memory operand
```

INDEX MODE SUMMARY

The index mode allows us to set pointers to structured data in memory. Positive or negative offsets to a base address held in An can be calculated in many ways using arithmetical operations on any register, designated as the index register, Xi, in the d(An,Xi) mode.

We now conclude our examination of the basic M68000 addressing modes by looking at the two relative modes.

RELATIVE MODES — MOTIVATION

In previous examples we have often made use of data located at absolute memory addresses, for example, "hours YTD is stored at address $6000 or HRSYTD". In real-world applications programming we seldom know in advance the absolute address of anything — programs or data. In fact, we often take special pains to ensure that our programs will work wherever they are loaded in memory.

Such programs are said to be **relocatable** or **position independent**. Indeed, some operating systems (such as the Alpha Micro AMOS running on its MC68000-based AM100L) require that all programs be relocatable. Other operating systems may place restrictions or require special loading software for nonrelocatable code.

In a relocatable program most memory references must be made relative to addresses within the program itself, which are not known in advance. Obvious exceptions to this rule are memory references to fixed locations such as memory-mapped I/O locations and systems areas like the exception vector tables.

When a program is loaded in memory and running, of course, the instructions must have enough information to enable the processor to calculate the effective address of each operand, so it can locate, fetch, and update correctly.

THE ROLE OF THE PROGRAM COUNTER

The key to all this is PC, the Program Counter, which we have already seen as a rather special address register holding the absolute address of the current instruction. Wherever our program ends up in memory, we can regard the succession of addresses in the PC rather like the arrows you see on public signs that say, "You are Here!"

So, if we have a way of referring to memory operands, not in absolute address terms, but relatively as, say, "420 bytes beyond (or behind) the current

PC, grab the YTD hours for March," we can boldly relocate such instructions without restriction.

The two relative addressing modes, PC Offset and PC Index, give us this ability. They make use of PC in the same way as the d16(An) Offset and d8(An,Xi.Z) index modes make use of An.

RELATIVE ADDRESSING—PROGRAM COUNTER ADDRESSING WITH OFFSET

This mode is written symbolically as d16(PC), which looks just like the d16(An) mode with PC playing the role of An. You'll recall that d16 is a signed 16-bit offset or displacement, held in an extension word, and offering a range of plus/minus 32K bytes.

The effective address is calculated by adding d16 to the address held in PC: <ea> = d16 + PC, allowing access to source memory addresses within 32K bytes on either side of the current PC value. The offset is stored as a single extension word following the instruction and, strictly speaking, it is the address of this extension word which represents the value of PC when the <ea> is calculated. This is hardly surprising if you remember that the processor has to fetch the d16 word from memory, so PC has advanced beyond the instruction itself.

Although the d16(PC) mode, so far, looks like the d16(An) mode, there is one fundamental exception.

Relative modes can only be used as source operands.

Any combination of op code/operand in which d16(PC) is an alterable destination operand is illegal. The reason is simply to discourage you from modifying or writing over your own program. We will elaborate on this later.

Relative mode operands cannot be altered.

The d16(An) mode can be used as source or destination, but the d16(PC) mode is source only.

It may seem at this point that the d16(PC) mode could prove irksome in practice — how on earth can we supply values for d16? How many bytes beyond or behind my current instruction is my target operand's <ea>? The answer is that by using label operands we can delegate the chore of displacement calculation to the assembler. This trick is somewhat similar to the one we saw in action with Bcc <label> in Chapter 4.

LABELS AS RELATIVE OPERANDS

We saw in Chapter 4 that the ORG directive forces the assembler to assign absolute addresses to label operands.

There is another assembler directive called RORG (relative origin). In a RORG section of a program, the assembler automatically translates the label operand into d16(PC) addressing mode. It then calculates the relative offset (plus or minus) in bytes between the current instruction and the label address and sets this value into the d16 extension word.

At this stage the assembler does not know what value the PC will hold when the instruction is eventually decoded during a run. All the assembler needs to determine is the relative offset, the "distance" in bytes between any instruction using a label and the label itself.

Most assemblers are **multipass**, that is, they scan the source code several times, allowing them to establish the relative positions of all labels, and then compute and store the correct d16 offsets.

Let's look at a typical situation. We introduce the JMP (JuMP) instruction, which is simply a more versatile version of the unconditional branch instruction BRA. There is also a JSR (Jump SubRoutine) corresponding to BSR (Branch SubRoutine). In normal computer jargon jumping and branching are identical concepts. In M68000 parlance, however, there is a technical distinction. JMP and JSR can accept a wider class of destination operands than BRA and BSR, as we'll see when we cover <control effective addresses> at the end of this section.

```
            RORG                Following program is Relative

            *    *    *         Do something
            JMP  LOOP           JUMP to LOOP
            *    *    *         600 bytes worth of instructions
LOOP        <do more>
            *    *    *
```

The two words of the assembled JMP instruction would look like this:

Bit	15	14	13	12	11	10	9	8	7	6	5	4	3	2	1	0	
											m	m	m	r	r	r	
JMP	0	1	0	0	1	1	1	0	1	1	1	1	1	0	1	0	
d16	0	0	0	0	0	0	1	0	0	1	0	1	0	1	1	0	= +598

Bits 6 through 15 encode the JMP instruction, while bits 0 through 5 encode the d16(PC) addressing mode. The extension word holds the calculated offset to the instruction labeled LOOP. This offset is positive because we are jumping forward.

When this instruction is decoded during execution, the processor, following the rigid rules of d16(PC) mode, fetches the extension word and calculates the effective address of the operand as follows: <ea> = PC + 598 bytes. The PC currently holds the address of the extension word, so, <ea> = address of JMP + 600 bytes, which is the address of the LOOP line. The JMP instruction then places the calculated <ea> into the PC. The processor therefore takes its next instruction from the memory address of LOOP. In other words, we have jumped to LOOP.

The assembler automatically calculates: offset d16 = "<label> – PC" bytes, while the processor calculates: <ea> = PC + offset d16, with a real, known address in PC to obtain the effective address of <label>.

Labels in an ORG section equal absolute address mode. Labels in a RORG section equal PC relative with offset address mode.

You will seldom code d16(PC) directly, but each time you use a label in a RORG section of a program, you now know that you are invoking PC relative addressing with offset.

In addition to the use of labels with branch and jump, labels can be used as source operands in many ways. RORG allows the DC (Define Constant) and DS (Define Storage) directives with PC relative labels. The data areas are relocatable because of the PC relative mode. For example:

```
                RORG

TABLE           DC.W        $34A2,$00B7
```

sets up 2 words of data at an address TABLE that can be accessed as a source operand no matter where the program is in memory.

```
                MOVE.W      TABLE,D1
```

will move $34A2 to the lower word of D1. To achieve this the assembler sets up a d16 offset in an extension word to the MOVE instruction and the source operand is encoded as d16(PC) mode. When the instruction is decoded and executed the offset + PC gives the correct effective address for the data stored at TABLE.

We can now look at yet another method of accessing memory using the important LEA (Load Effective Address) and PEA (Push Effective Address) instructions.

LEA is a two-operand instruction with the following format:

```
LEA <source>, An
```

LEA calculates the effective address of the source operand and places this address in the register An. All 32 bits of An are affected, even if the chip uses fewer address bits.

PEA is a one-operand instruction: PEA <source> performs the LEA calculation and pushes the effective address on to the user or supervisor stack (whichever is active). PEA is equivalent in effect to:

```
        LEA  <source>, An
        MOVE.L    An, -(SP)
```

(although no intermediate An is involved).

We can illustrate one use for LEA with labeled data areas:

```
* Program 5-9  Use of LEA

* Calculate the average (arithmetic mean) of two numbers in TABLE

          RORG

TABLE     DC.W      $34A2,$00B6     Define 2-word data area at
                                    address TABLE

          CLR.L     D1              Clear accumulator register
          LEA       TABLE,A3        Load <ea> of TABLE in A3
          MOVE.W    (A3)+,D1        D1 = 1st word. Inc A3 by 2
          ADD.W     (A3),D1         Add 2nd word to D1
          ASR.W     #1,D1           Divide sum by 2

* Answer is in D1 lower word = <$34A2 + $00B6>/2 = $1AAC
```

Using LEA can often save time. If a complex operand needs to be accessed several times during a program, it pays to use LEA first to get the operand's <ea> into an address register. For example, suppose we have done some heavy calculations to establish values for An and Xi prior to using d8(An,Xi) mode to access a complex array. Each time we use d8(An,Xi) as an operand we force the processor to calculate the <ea> (taking from 8 to 14 clock cycles). But if we use

```
          LEA  d8(An,Xi),Am          Load Am with <ea> = d8+An+Xi
```

we have Am as a pointer for all subsequent processing.

Alternatively, if we were about to call a subroutine which needed our d8(An,Xi) operand, we could

```
PEA  d8(An,Xi)        Push d8+An+Xi on stack
```

before the BSR or JSR. The stack would then hold

```
at address SP         Return address for subroutine (2 words)
at address SP+4       <ea> from the PEA (2 words)
```

During the subroutine we can "recover" this <ea> using

```
MOVEA.L  4(SP),Am     Load Am from SP+4
```

Conceptually, LEA is the converse of the () indirection brackets.

An points to data (An).

The <ea> of (An) is An.

LEA (An),Am sets Am equal to An.

Next we look briefly at the remaining relative mode, PC relative with offset and index.

RELATIVE ADDRESSING—PROGRAM COUNTER WITH OFFSET AND INDEX

We will call this PC index mode for short. This mode is written as d8(PC,Xi.Z) from which you can correctly deduce that it follows the format and rules for the normal index d8(An,Xi.Z) mode, replacing An with PC. The operand effective address is calculated as

```
<ea> = d8 + PC + Xi.Z
```

where d8 is a signed 8-bit offset (–128 to +127 bytes), and Xi.Z is any register selected as the index register. The data size code Z can be L or W, and this dictates whether 32 or 16 bits (sign-extended to 32) of Xi (signed) are used as the additional indexing offset to PC. The d8 offset and codes specifying the register Xi and size Z are all located in a single extension word.

To simplify our formats we sometimes write this mode as d(PC,Xi). We repeat the warning we gave for PC offset d16(PC):

Relative modes can only be used as source operands.

Any combination of op code/operand in which d(PC,Xi) is an alterable destination operand is illegal.

From our discussion of relocatable code, it will be clear that PC index mode allows us to set up and access labeled tables and arrays. Let's revamp Program 5-9 to show a very simple use of PC index with our TABLE data.

```
* Program 5-10  Version of 5-9 Using PC Index Mode

* Calculate the average (arithmetic mean) of two numbers in TABLE

         RORG

         CLR.L      D1                     Clear accumulator register
         MOVEQ.W    #0,D0                  Set index reg D0 to 0
         MOVE.W     TABLE(PC,D0.W),D1      D1 = 1st word in TABLE
         ADDQ.W     #2,D0                  Inc index D0 by 2 bytes
         ADD.W      TABLE(PC,D0.W),D1      Add 2nd word to D1
         ASR.W      #1,D1                  Divide sum by 2
         <conclude program>

* Define a data area at relative address TABLE

TABLE               DC.W       $34A2,$00B6,$56F9,$11CC
                    <continue table ad lib>

* Answer is in D1 lower word = <$34A2 + $00B6>/2 = $1AAC
```

As with our earlier RORG/label examples, the assembler establishes the offset value from PC to TABLE. This offset, though, is limited to a d8 signed value, so Program 5-9 works only if TABLE starts within –128 or +127 bytes of our MOVE and ADD instructions. The TABLE, though, can be as long as we need — so with this in mind we have repositioned the TABLE data compared with Program 5-9. We use D0 as an index register, allowing us to pull out any entry in TABLE.

Before the instruction

```
ADD.W TABLE(PC,D0.W),D1
```

D0 has been set to 2, so the <ea> calculation for the source operand is

$$
\begin{aligned}
<ea> &= PC + d8 + D0 \\
&= PC + <TABLE - PC> + 2 \\
&= TABLE + 2
\end{aligned}
$$

What we add therefore is the second word in the TABLE.

RELATIVE MODE — SOURCE ONLY RESTRICTION

As we have stated twice, relative mode is illegal as a destination operand. This was a deliberate design decision by Motorola to reduce the risk of a program (especially a relocatable one) inadvertently writing over itself. For example,

```
MOVE.W    D0,8(PC)        (illegal)
```

if allowed, would replace the instruction (or a part of it) that lies 4 words (8 bytes) ahead, with whatever is held in D0's lower word. There is a high probability of chaos when the instruction decoder reaches this word and blindly attempts to obey it. Of course, you could be extremely clever and deliberately set D0's bit-pattern to correspond with a valid instruction! Self-modifying programs do have a role to play, but the M68000 forces you to take special action, as it were, to make sure you know what you are doing.

One side effect of this restriction is that great care is needed when using labels:

```
MOVE.W    D0,TABLE        Legal for ORG sections
MOVE.W    D0,TABLE        Illegal for RORG sections
```

Although these two instructions look the same, their addressing modes differ. TABLE in ORG is an absolute address, and therefore valid as a destination. TABLE in RORG is a relative mode — d16(PC) and invalid as a destination.

One of the ways to beat the RORG restriction is:

```
LEA       TABLE,A1        <ea> of TABLE to A1
MOVE.W    D0,(A1)         Move D0 word to TABLE
```

ADDRESSING MODES — GRAND SUMMARY

We have now visited all 12 of the basic M68000 addressing modes (the MC68020 has 6 more which we cover in Chapter 8). We have, of necessity, glossed over many of the subtleties in order to give you a general picture.

In describing some of the instructions, we have occasionally indicated that the source and/or destination operands are restricted to certain addressing modes. These various limitations can appear quite arbitrary and confusing, even to experienced programmers. Much of the existing M68000 technical literature compounds this feeling by using inconsistent and conflicting terms for classes of addressing modes.

In Appendix B, part of which we reproduce below, we have attempted a logical classification of the addressing modes that will, hopefully, clarify when and why certain modes are valid. Appendix C lists all the op codes with their permissible source and destination modes.

M68000 ADDRESSING MODE TYPES

Each addressing mode can belong to some or all of the following nine overlapping groups.

<ea> = Any effective address
<rea> = Register effective address
<dea> = Data effective address
<mea> = Memory effective address
<cea> = Control effective address
<aea> = Alterable effective address (data or memory)
<adea> = Alterable data effective address
<amea> = Alterable memory effective address
<acea> = Alterable control effective address

An * in the table below indicates the groups for each mode (and the modes for each group).

Mode	*ea*	*rea*	*dea*	*mea*	*cea*	*aea*	*adea*	*amea*	*acea*	
Dn	*	*	*			*	*			
An	*	*				*				
(An)	*		*	*	*	*	*	*	*	
(An)+	*		*	*		*	*	*		
–(An)	*		*	*		*	*	*		
d(An)	*		*	*	*	*	*	*	*	
d(An,Xi)	*		*	*	*	*	*	*	*	
Abs.W	*		*	*	*	*	*	*	*	
Abs.L	*		*	*	*	*	*	*	*	
d(PC)	*		*	*	*					
d(PC,Xi)	*		*	*	*					
Immed	*		*	*						
bd(An,Xi)	*		*	*	*	*	*	*	*	68020
bd(PC,Xi)	*		*	*	*					68020

Mode	*ea*	*rea*	*dea*	*mea*	*cea*	*aea*	*adea*	*amea*	*acea*	
[bd,An],Xi,od	*		*	*	*	*	*	*	*	68020
[bd,An,Xi],od	*		*	*	*	*	*	*	*	68020
[bd,PC],Xi,od	*		*	*	*					68020
[bd,PC,Xi],od	*		*	*	*					68020

The MC68020 modes are a sneak preview of Chapter 8.

Mode Description:

Dn	Data register direct } Jointly called register direct
An	Address register direct }
(An)	Address register indirect
(An)+	Address register indirect with post-increment
–(An)	Address register indirect with pre-decrement
d16(An)	Address register indirect with offset—also written as d(An)
d8(An,Xi.Z)	Address register indirect with offset and index—also written as d(An,Xi)
Abs.W	Absolute short address—also written as xxx.W or label
Abs.L	Absolute long address—also written as xxx.L or label
d16(PC)	Program counter with offset (relative mode)—also written as d(PC) or label
d8(PC,Xi.Z)	Program counter with offset and index (relative mode)—also written as d(PC,Xi) or label (PC,Xi)
Immed	Immediate data operand—also written as #<data>

MC68020 Only (see Chapter 8 for detailed explanation):

bd(An,Xi.Z*s)	Address register indirect with base displacement and index (similar to d(An,Xi) but bd can be d16 or d32)
bd(PC,Xi.Z*s)	Program counter with base displacement and index (similar to d(PC,Xi) but bd can be d16 or d32)
[bd,An],Xi.Z*s,od	Memory indirect post-indexed
[bd,An,Xi.Z*s],od	Memory indirect pre-indexed
[bd,PC],Xi.Z*s,od	PC memory indirect post-indexed
[bd,PC,Xi,Z*s],od	PC Memory indirect pre-indexed

Abbreviations:

Dn	Any data register, D0 – D7
An	Any address register, A0 – A7
Xi	Any Dn or An used as an index register
z	Data size code (L, W, or B)
Z	Data size code (L or W)
s	Scale factor (1, 2, 4 or 8)
PC	Program Counter (20, 24, or 32 bits)
SR	Status Register
SP	Stack Pointer
CCR	Condition Code Register
d	A 2's complement or sign-extended offset (displacement); d16, d8, d3, etc. indicates the number of bits
bd	A 2's complement base displacement (16 or 32 bits)
od	A 2's complement outer displacement (16 or 32 bits)
xxx	Any valid absolute address

MODE GROUPS — DEFINITIONS

Let's pick out a few modes/groups to indicate why they are associated as shown.

<dea> *data effective address*: Includes all modes except An. As we saw, An allows only restricted arithmetic; it is not classified as a true data operand.

<mea> *memory effective address*: Excludes just the two direct register modes in <rea>, Dn and An, that are nonmemory operands.

<adea> *alterable data-effective addresses*: All those <dea>s which can be valid destinations, subject to change by an instruction. Clearly immediate data cannot be an alterable destination, so immediate mode is a <dea> but not an <adea>. Similarly, we have seen that the two relative modes are not alterable. Finally, An is not <adea> because it is not <dea>.

<amea> *alterable memory effective addresses*: All those <mea>s which can be destinations subject to change.

<aea> *alterable effective addresses*: Simply a combination of <adea> and <amea> together with An.

<cea> *control effective address*: A subset of <mea> representing just those memory addresses to which control can be passed, for example by JMP (JuMP) or JSR (Jump SubRoutine).

INSTRUCTION FORMATS USING MODE GROUPS

These mode groupings allow you to specify the permissible op code/operand combinations concisely and precisely. Here are some examples using instructions that we have already seen (see Appendix C for a complete listing):

MOVE.z <ea>,<adea>

Source	<ea>	All addressing modes are legal.
Destination	<adea>	Only alterable data effective address modes legal. Excludes An, all relative and immediate modes.

MOVEA.Z <ea>,An

Source	<ea>	All addressing modes are legal.
Destination	An	Only address register direct legal.

ADD.z <ea>,Dn
ADD.z Dn,<amea>

Either

Source		All modes
Destination		Dn only.

Or

Source		Dn.
Destination	<amea>	Only alterable memory effective address modes legal. Excludes Dn, An, all relative and immediate modes.

ADDI.z #<data>,<adea>

Source	#<data>	Immediate mode only.
Destination	<adea>	Only alterable data effective address modes legal. Excludes An, all relative and immediate modes.

ADDQ.z #<data>,<aea>

Source	#<data>	Immediate mode only.
Destination	<aea>	Only alterable effective address modes legal. z = L,W only for An. Excludes all relative and immediate modes.

MULS <dea>, Dn

Source	<dea>	Data effective address modes legal; all modes except An.
Destination	Dn	Only data register direct legal.

BRA LABEL

Source	none	
Destination	LABEL	Relative modes d(PC) and d(PC,Xi) only.

JMP <cea>

Source	None	
Destination	<cea>	Control effective address modes legal. Excludes Dn,An, (An)+,–(An) and immediate mode.

The above schema can be extended to cover all but a handful of instructions, like MOVEM, that have unusual operands.

IMPLICIT OPERANDS

To complete the picture we note that some instructions make use of miscellaneous systems registers without specific mention in the operand field. Examples we have already seen are:

Instruction		*Implicit Operand(s)*
BRA	Branch always	PC
JMP	Jump always	PC
Bcc	Branch conditionally	PC
BSR	Branch subroutine	PC,SP
JSR	Jump subroutine	PC,SP
RTS	Return from subroutine	PC,SP
RTR	Return sub/restore	PC,SP,CCR
MOVE to CCR		CCR
MOVE from SR		SR

CONCLUSION

There you have it, and we trust your basic understanding of the M68000 instruction set has been enriched. In the next chapter, we will cover several miscellaneous groups of instructions before we proceed to discuss the MC68010 and MC68020.

6

Miscellaneous M68000 Instructions

In this chapter we look at some miscellaneous M68000 instructions grouped by function. We will use the mode groups listed in Chapter 5 and Appendix B to simplify our discussion of legal operand addressing modes.

NOP — NO OPERATION

The NOP is a one-word instruction which advances the PC to the next instruction. No CCR flags are changed and there are no complicated rules for the source and destination operands, because there are no such operands. However, it is definitely a useful instruction to know about if you are developing assembly language programs, especially if your editing/debugging facilities are primitive. It is often useful to reserve space in your program (each NOP = 1 word) for subsequent insertions; similarly you can delete instructions by replacing them with NOPs. The machine-level (object) code for NOP is $4E71, and on some systems you can delete by slotting $4E71 directly into your object code without reassembling.

BIT MANIPULATION

Our first major group of miscellaneous instructions allows you to handle bits and groups of bits within registers, special registers, and memory.

Table 6-1 Summary of Logical Instructions

Opcode	*Operand*	*CCR Changes*
AND.L/W/B OR.L/W/B	<dea>,Dn or Dn,<amea>	X_ N* Z* V0 C0
NOT.L/W/B	<adea>	X_ N* Z* V0 C0
EOR.L/W/B	Dn, <adea> [NO MEM SRC]	X_ N* Z* V0 C0
ANDI{.B} ORI{.B} EORI{.B}	#xxx,CCR	X* N* Z* V* C*
ANDI{.W} ORI{.W} EORI{.W}	#xxx,SR (PRIVILEGED)	X* N* Z* V* C*

<dea> = data addressing modes = ALL except An
<amea> = memory alterable addressing modes = (An), (An)+, −(An) d(An), d(An,Xi), Abs.W, Abs.L
<adea> = data alterable addressing modes = <amea> + Dn

{z} means data size IMPLIED

CCR symbols: _means unchanged, * means changed according to CCR rules, 0 means always set to 0

As we have already seen, most instructions have L, W, and B variants for manipulating selected parts of the operands. There are many occasions when we need to isolate other portions of the operand; perhaps we need to access the top or middle bytes of a Long word. Also, it is often useful to set up our own private status or condition registers — for example, in a payroll program you might find an "employee status byte" with the 8 bits representing: sex (1 bit), marital status (2 bits), and so on. The operating system, too, often communicates to the programmer by setting or clearing flags in designated locations.

Many of the M68000 bit-handling instructions are therefore aimed at simplifying the task of testing, setting, and clearing bits that have a logical rather than an arithmetical significance. So, first let us review the basic logical operators.

LOGICAL OPERATIONS

The M68000 provides four basic logical instructions: NOT, AND, OR, and EOR which we summarize in Table 6-1. They are used in many situations, such as setting and changing flag bits, and for masking or extracting data fields in registers or memory. We shall first recap what each basic instruction does, then we shall show them in action.

NOT

Logical NOT means reversing each bit, from 0 to 1 and from 1 to 0, throughout the designated operand. Mathematically, this is the same as forming the 1's complement of the operand, so "NOT 01011010" –> 10100101. NOT requires just one operand, which serves as source and destination. The format is:

```
NOT.z       <adea>
```

where <adea> stands for any alterable data-effective address, that is, any address mode except An, d(PC), d(PC,Xi), and Immediate. As usual, the z data size code dictates whether 32, 16, or 8 bits of the operand are NOTted.

For example,

```
NOT.B       D1
```

in Figure 6-1 reverses the lower byte of D1 without affecting the upper 3 bytes. The CCR changes just like a MOVE as shown in Table 6-1.

AND

AND requires a source and a destination operand. The basis for a logical AND is the following truth table.

Source	0	0	1	1
Destination	0	1	0	1
AND	0	0	0	1 → New destination

In other words, AND operates bit by bit, checking the bit values in the source and destination, and forming a new bit in the destination according to the rules above. Unless both source and destination have 1's in the same position, the AND sets a 0 in that position. There are two legal formats:

```
AND.z       <dea>,Dn
AND.z       Dn,<amea>
```

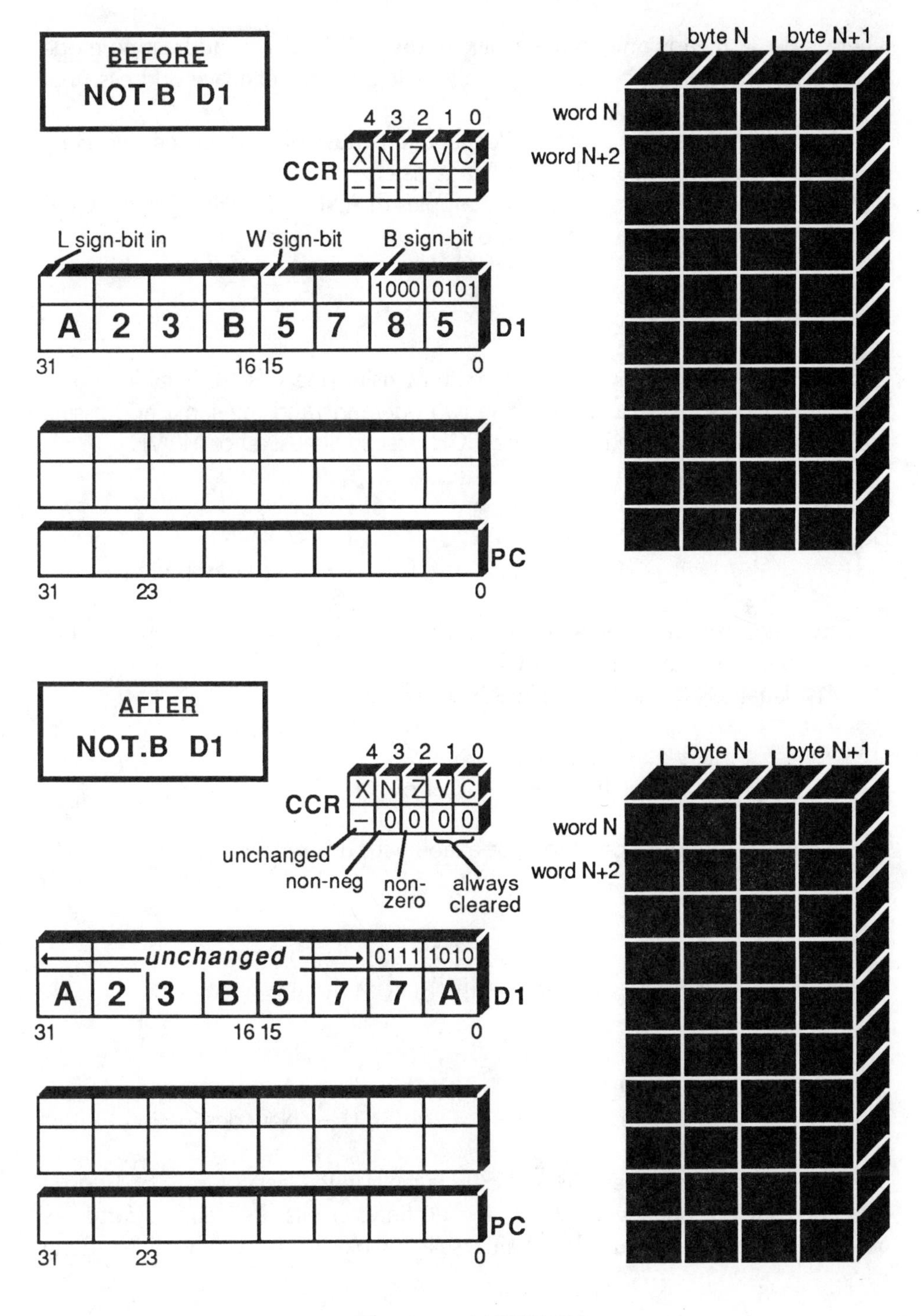

Fig. 6-1 NOT.B D1

where <dea> means any data effective address, that is, any addressing mode except An, and <amea> means any alterable memory effective address (that is, any <adea> except Dn).

Note that either the source or destination must be a data register. Both source and destination can also be data registers.

Figures 6-2 and 6-3 shows two examples of AND. AND changes the CCR just like a MOVE, as shown in Table 6-1.

OR

Logical OR is the inclusive OR. Apart from using the OR truth table shown below, OR works just like AND, using two operands and the same addressing modes and data sizes, and it sets the CCR exactly like AND or MOVE.

Source	0	0	1	1
Destination	0	1	0	1
OR	0	1	1	1 → New destination

Here you notice that OR sets a 1 if either or both source and destination bits are 1 — hence the term inclusive OR.

The legal OR formats, just like AND, are:

```
OR.z        <dea>,Dn
OR.z        Dn,<amea>
```

Figures 6-4 and 6-5 show OR in action with different operands.

EOR

EOR is the exclusive OR, as shown in the EOR truth table:

Source	0	0	1	1
Destination	0	1	0	1
EOR	0	1	1	0 → New destination

The key difference between OR and EOR is the 0 in the last column. EOR looks for either but not both when it sets the destination bits. Its claim to fame, as we'll see, is that it can be used to reverse selected bits in a field without disturbing

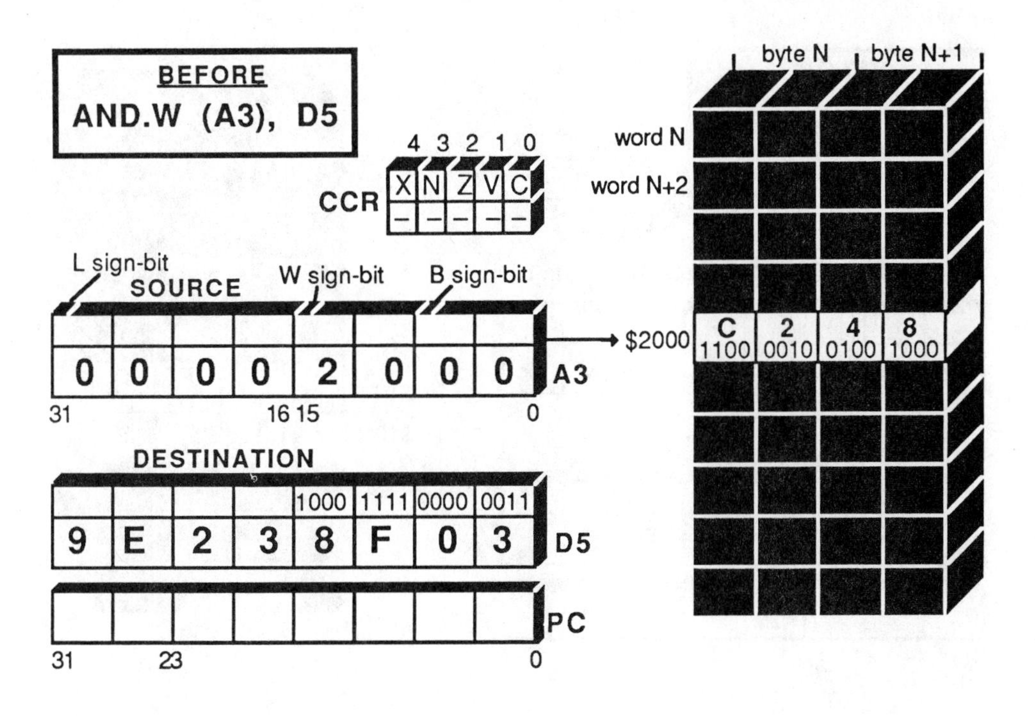

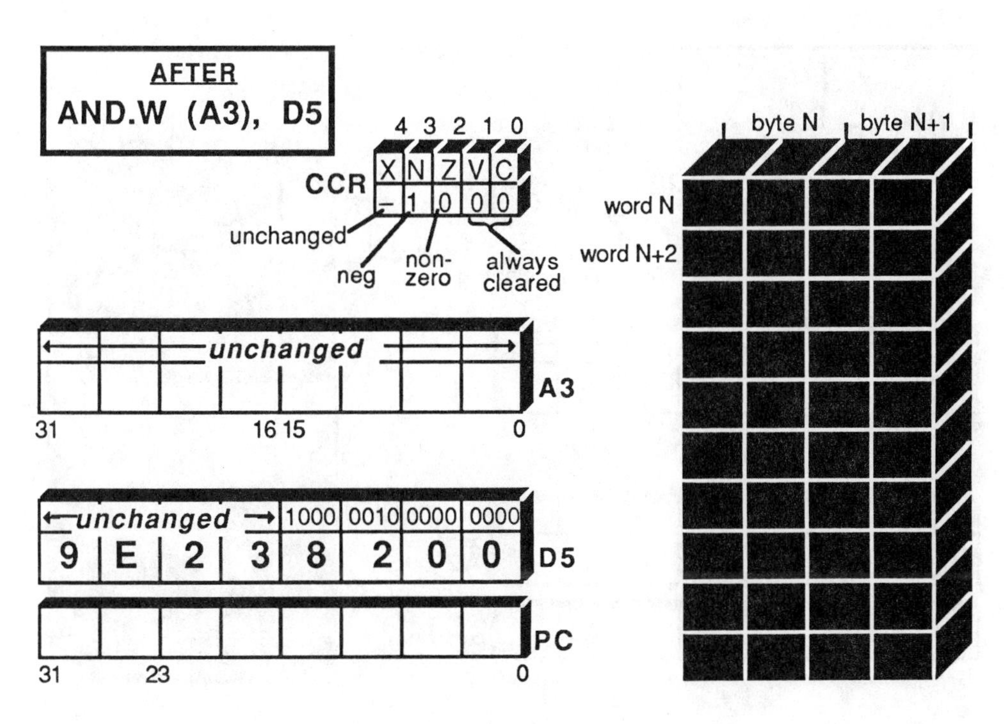

Fig. 6-2 AND.W (A3),D5

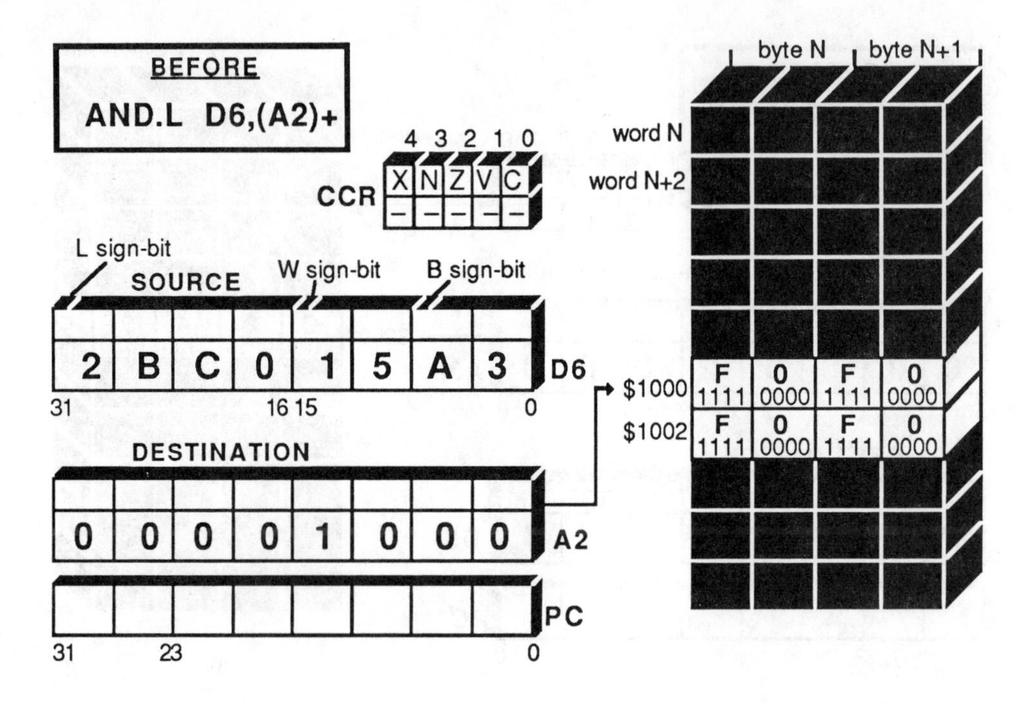

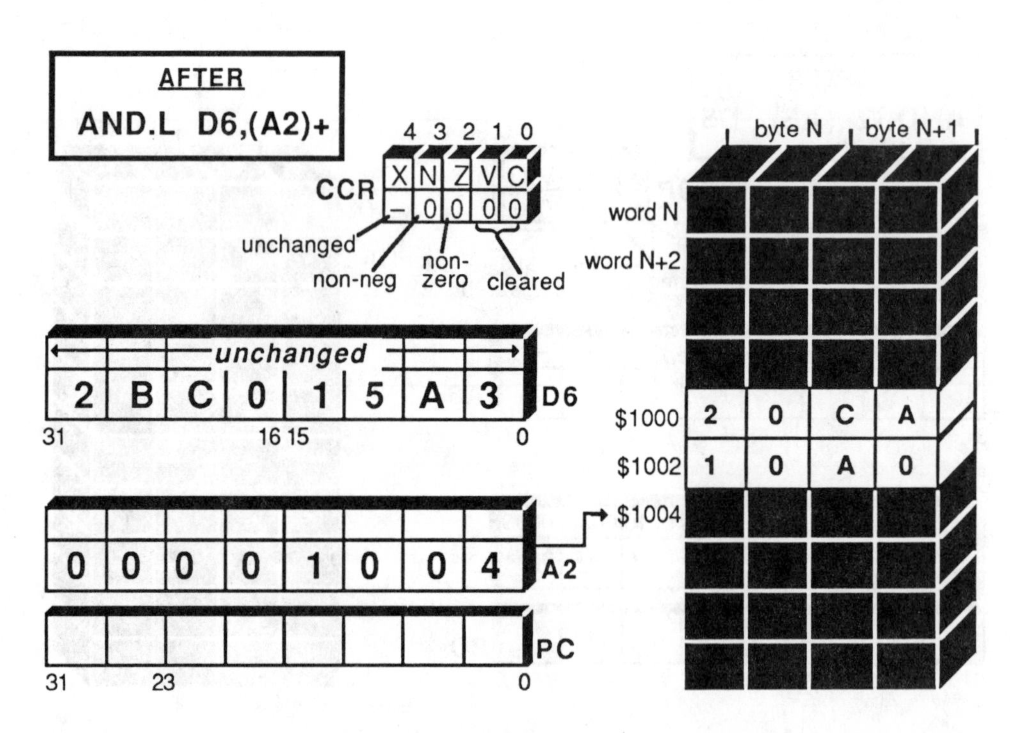

Fig. 6-3 AND.L D6,(A2)+

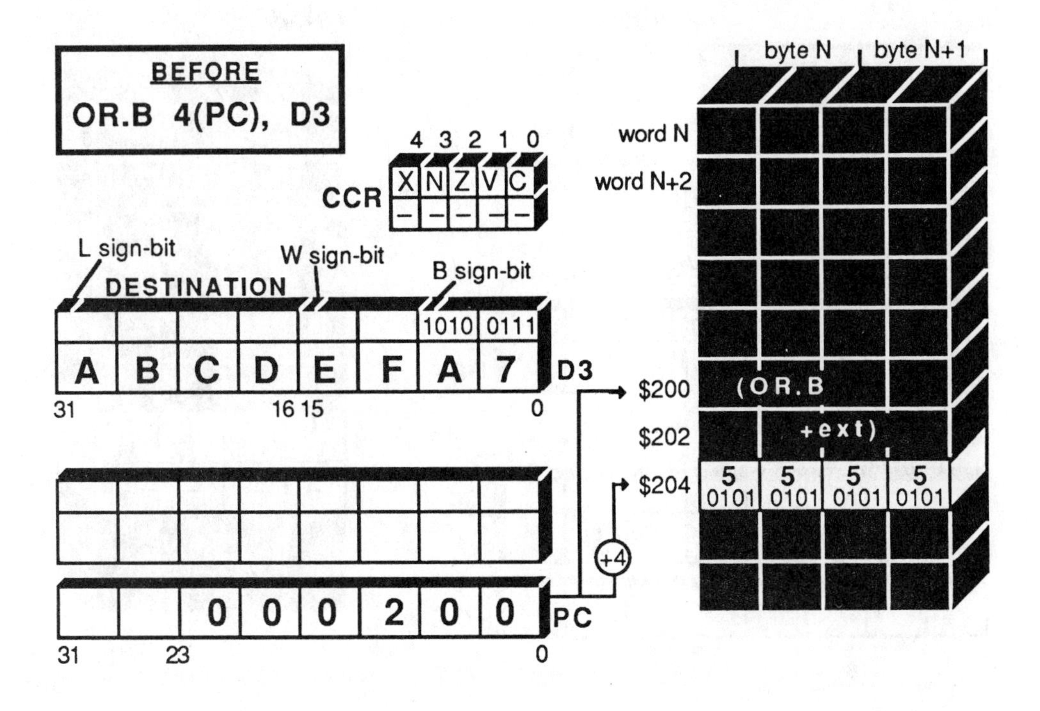

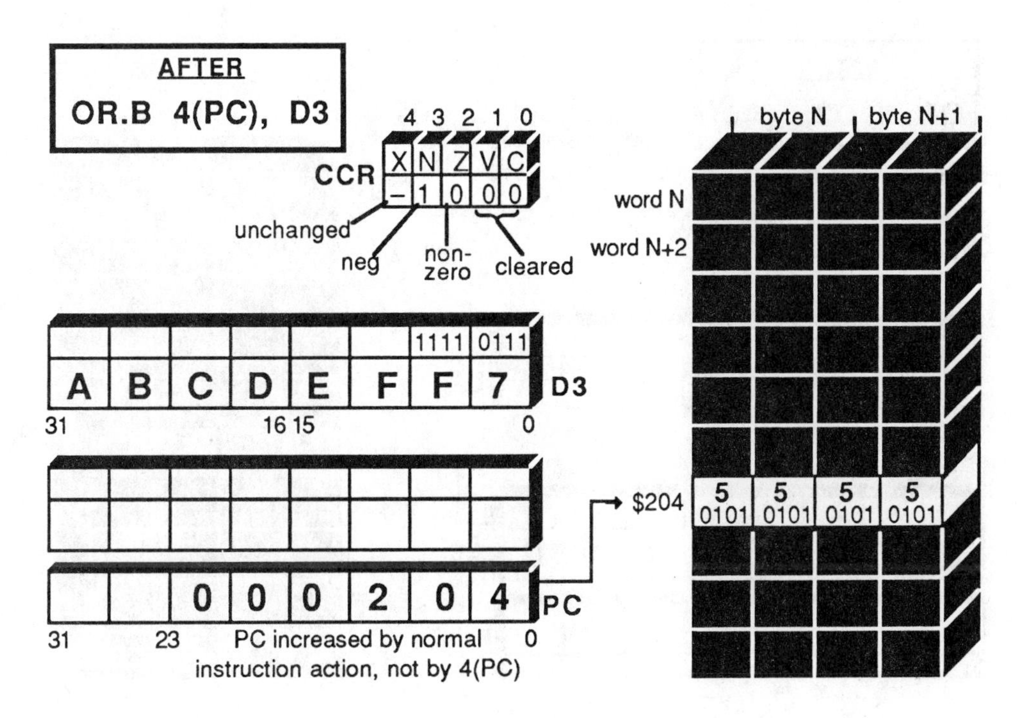

Fig. 6-4 OR.B 4(PC),D3

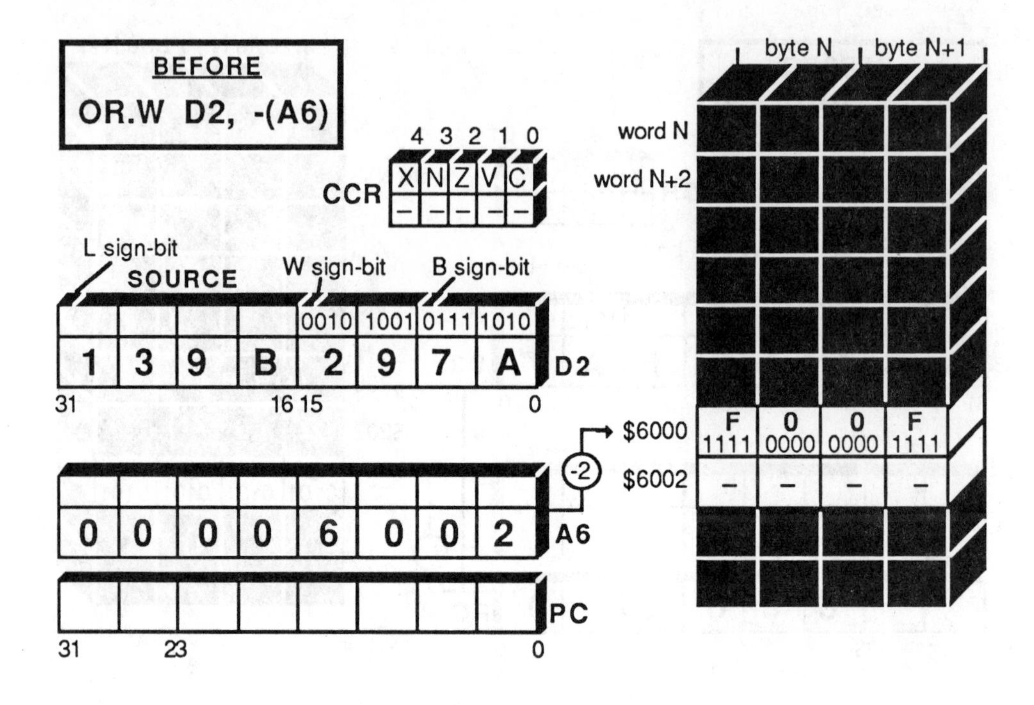

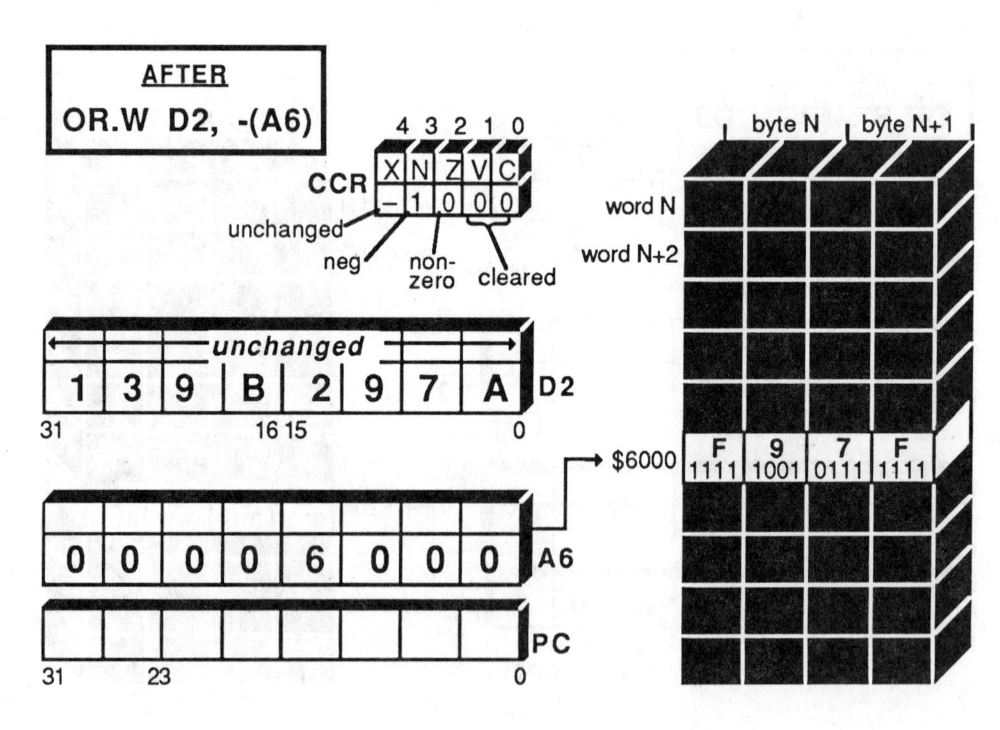

Fig. 6-5 OR.W D2, – (A6)

the other bits — unlike NOT, which reverses every bit. Unlike AND and OR, EOR allows only one legal format:

```
EOR.z       Dn,<adea>
```

You cannot have a memory address mode for EOR source.

EOR changes the CCR exactly like AND, OR, and MOVE, as shown in Figure 6-6.

LOGICAL INSTRUCTIONS — IMMEDIATE MODE VARIATIONS

With the exception of NOT, the logical instructions have Immediate source mode formats, ANDI, ORI, and EORI that all follow the same format:

```
ANDI.z
ORI.z         #<data>,<adea>
EORI.z
```

The size of #<data> should be d32, d16, or d8 depending on the size code z used (L, W, or B). The instruction takes on one or two extension words to store the immediate data.

The use of immediate source mode with AND is very common. To mask or isolate a destination operand, you create a #<mask> with 1's in the "selected" bit positions, and 0's in the "discarded" bit positions. Since #3 = 00000011, the AND.B in Figure 6-7 clears all but the lower 2 bits in D2.

With EORI.W, the #<mask> is chosen so that 1's select the bit positions for reversal, while 0's leave the corresponding destination positions unchanged. In Figure 6-8 the bits in the lower byte of memory at (A1) are all reversed by the "FF" while the upper byte is unchanged.

CHANGING THE CCR

A special format for the immediate logical instructions allows you to change any or all of the flags in the CCR byte:

```
ANDI.B
ORI.B         #<d8>,CCR
EORI.B
```

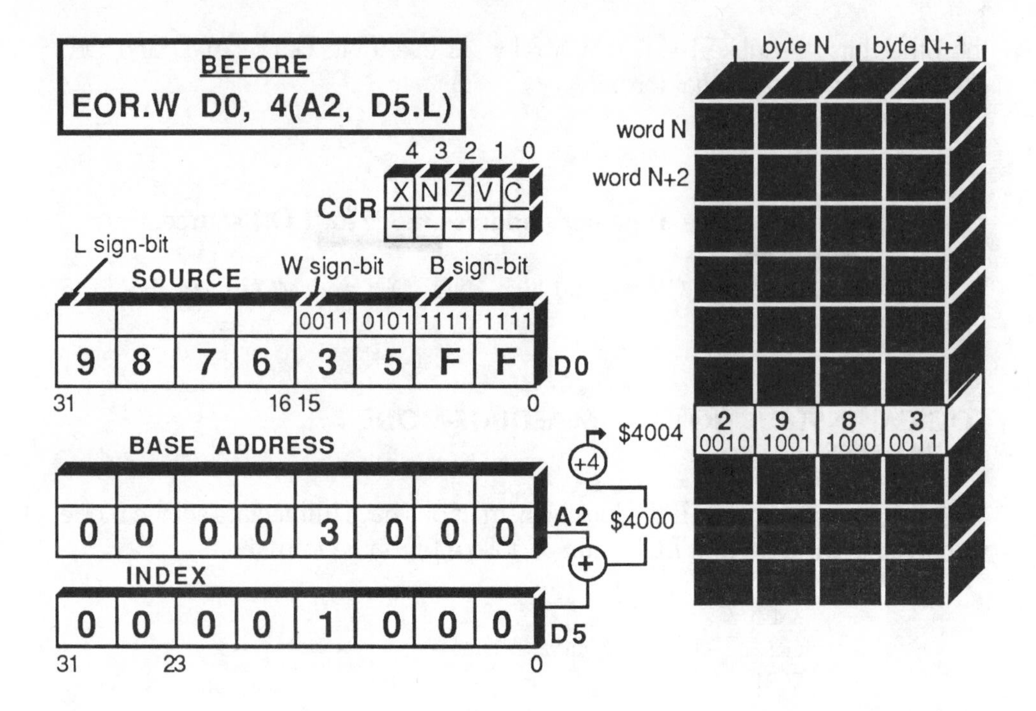

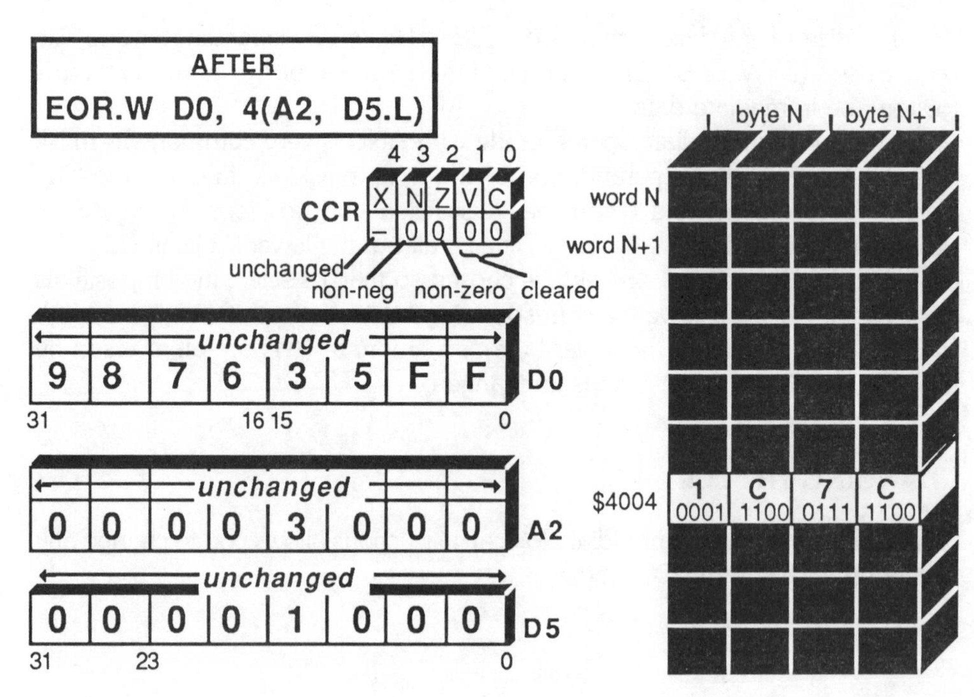

Fig. 6-6 EOR.W DO,4(A2,D5.L)

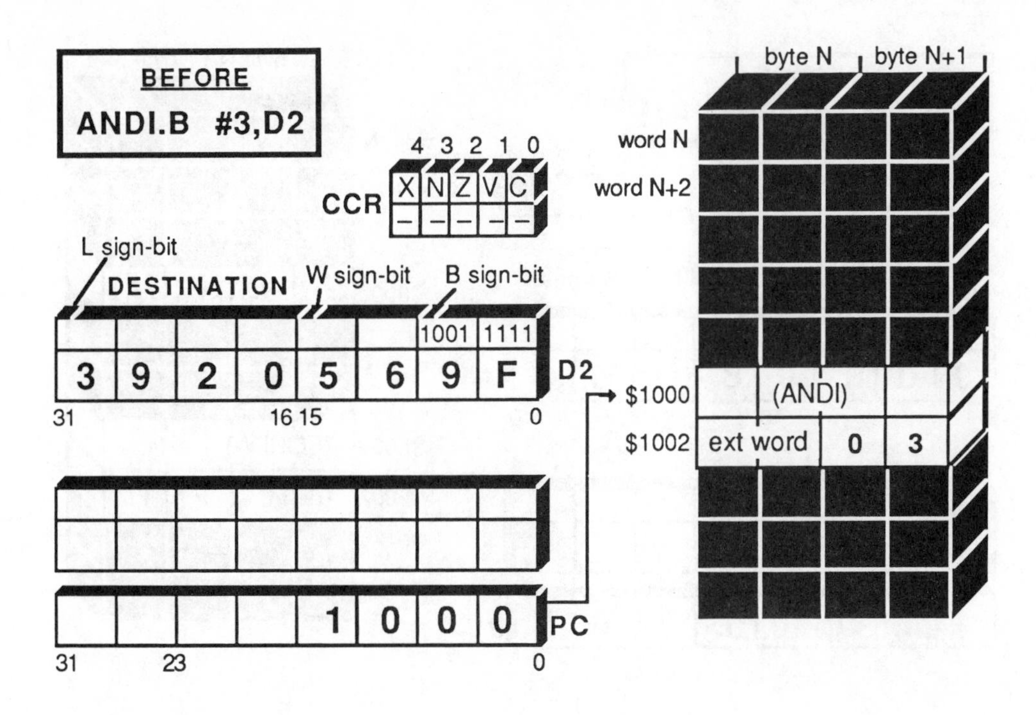

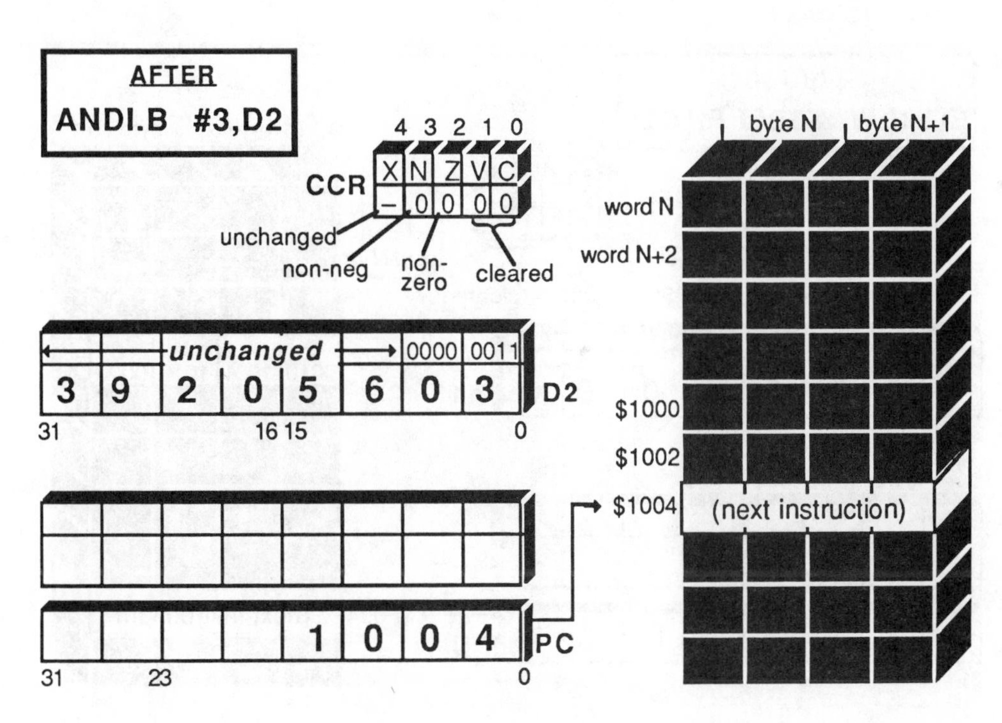

Fig. 6-7 ANDI.B #3,D2

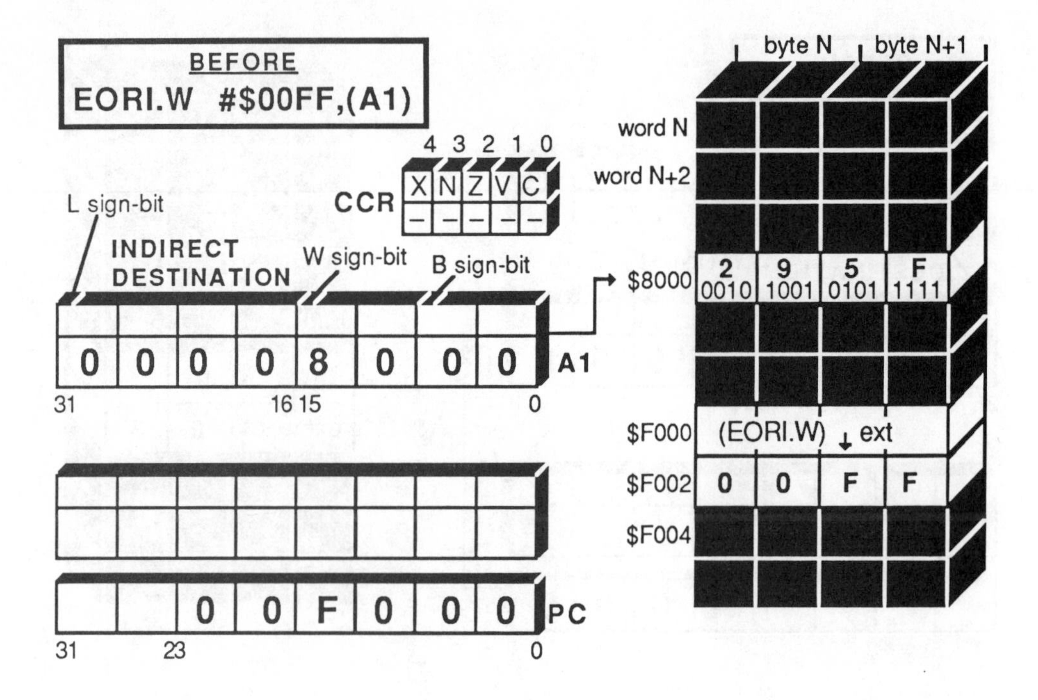

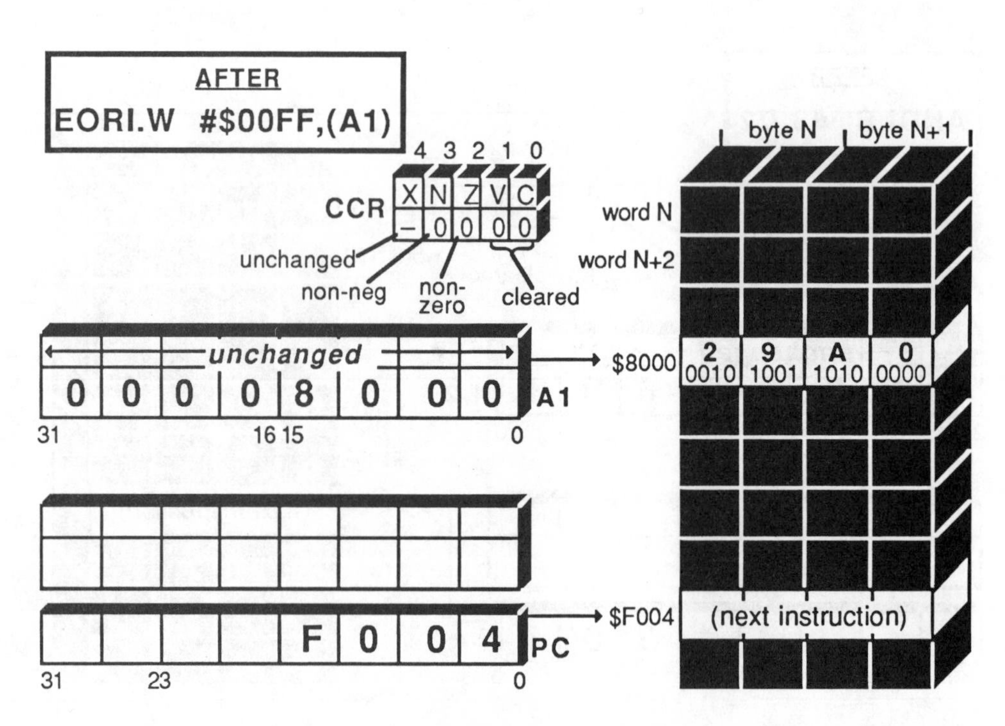

Fig. 6-8 EORI.W #$00FF,(A1)

Note that the destination is simply written as CCR, and that only z = Byte operations are allowed. The B is optional, but we'll use it to remind you what's going on. To use this format you need to recall that:

Bit 0 = C flag
Bit 1 = V flag
Bit 2 = Z flag
Bit 3 = N flag
Bit 4 = X flag
Bits 5-7 not used

A common application is to clear the X flag without disturbing the other CCR flags. We use:

```
        ANDI.B          #$EF,CCR
```

since $EF = 11101111. This is mandatory before embarking on calculations involving extended arithmetic, for reasons we'll explain later in this chapter in the section on multi-precision mathematics. It is instructive to compare the ANDI-to-CCR method of changing the CCR with the MOVE-to-CCR method.

```
        MOVE.W          #$EF,CCR        Only a byte is moved in spite
                                        of the W data size
```

would certainly clear the X flag, but the other flags would be set to 1.

CHANGING THE SR (STATUS REGISTER)

In the supervisor mode only, you can change both bytes of the SR, the upper system byte, and the CCR (= lower user byte). For this we use the formats:

```
        ANDI.W
        ORI.W           #<d16>,SR       Privileged instructions
        EORI.W                          (Supervisor mode only)
```

The system byte contains the ST (State and Trace) flags as well as the 3-bit interrupt mask — hence the need for privilege protection! (MOVE-to-SR is similarly privileged.) We cover this subject in detail later, in the section "More on Privilege."

LOGICAL OPERATIONS — SUMMARY

By proper choice of the source mask operand, selected bits or flags in the destination can be altered. The rules are:

NOT	Every bit reversed (NOTted) in destination
AND	0 in source—Clears (to 0) selected bit in destination 1 in source—Selected bit unchanged in destination
OR	0 in source—Selected bit unchanged in destination 1 in source—Sets (to 1) selected bit in destination
EOR	0 in source—Selected bit unchanged in destination 1 in source—Selected bit reversed (NOTted) in destination

PRACTICAL APPLICATION

Problem: Clear the 8th bit (bit position 7) of each byte in a string of ASCII characters in memory.

Background: In some systems the 7-bit ASCII character set (see Appendix F) is extended by using the eighth bit (bit position 7) for nonstandard control functions. On other occasions the eighth bit may be used as a parity bit (see Program 6-2 for example). This eighth bit is sometimes a nuisance and must be suppressed.

Given: A non-empty ASCII string starting at the memory address stored in A6, that is to say, the first byte of the string is byte (A6). The end of the string is signaled by a null byte $00.

Solution: Program 6-1

```
LOOP     ANDI.B    #$7F,(A6)+     Immediate source is
                                  "01111111"
                                  A6 is post-incremented
                                  to "next byte"
         TST.B       (A6)         Is next byte null?
         BNE.S       LOOP         No -- so loop
         <rest of program>        Yes -- we've reached
                                  end of string.
```

Program Notes: We are using $7F as a #<mask> — it has 1's in all the bit positions (0 through 6) we do not wish to disturb, and a 0 in the bit position we want to suppress. The underpinning logic is:

1 AND x = x (x unchanged)
0 AND x = 0 (x cleared)

Notice the power of the (A6)+ addressing mode when used in conjunction with the null byte string terminator. The latter is a widely used technique when dealing with variable length objects such as strings. The single ANDI.B line clears the 8th bit in the byte at address A6 and then increments A6 by 1 for the next byte address. TST.B simply tests this next byte (without incrementing) — and BNE says Branch Not Equal to zero. We therefore keep looping through the string until the final null byte is reached.

SHIFT AND ROTATE INSTRUCTIONS

There are eight shift and rotate instructions that let you move the bit patterns in data registers or memory to the left or right. By setting the shift count, which determines the number of shifts, you can effectively relocate bits within bytes, bytes within words, and words within longwords. Shifts also have an arithmetical function.

We saw in Chapter 4 that in simple binary arithmetic, shifting a bit pattern once to the left is equivalent to multiplying by 2, while shifting once to the right is the same as dividing by 2. So one obvious use of shifting instructions is as an easy and fast way of multiplying and dividing by powers of 2.

However, before we rush around shifting bit patterns left and right, we must know if they represent *signed* or *unsigned* numbers. Recall that in signed 2's complement numbers the most significant bit is a sign bit. If we lose this while shifting our answer may be wrong. Because of this problem the M68000 offers two types of shift: logical shift and arithmetic shift. These differ in the way they handle the sign bit. Let's look at logical shifts first, since these are the easiest to grasp.

LOGICAL SHIFT INSTRUCTIONS

A logical shift is mainly used on unsigned numbers. It moves the bit patterns in a data register or memory a certain number of positions to the left (LSL) or right (LSR) by pushing in 0's from one end or the other. As you push in a 0, you can imagine the other bits in the register being displaced, nudging each other along, with one poor bit falling out at the other end! Figures 6-9 and 6-10 show two typical word logical shifts.

The number of shifts performed, known as the **shift count**, is specified here by an immediate source operand, indicated as always with the # symbol. So in our examples, the contents of the lower word of D1 get 3 left shifts and 2 right shifts. Immediate shift counts are allowed in the range #1 to #8. This obviously means that the immediate shift count maximum is #8.

To shift more than 8 times, you need the format

```
LSL.z     Dm,Dn
```

or

```
LSR.z     Dm,Dn
```

where the source data register Dm holds the shift count. With this format you can shift from 1 to 64 times, left or right. Only the bottom 6 bits (bits 0 through 5) of Dm are used to determine the shift count (which explains the limit of 64 for shift counts using this format). The correct technical term for this, which will save us much verbiage later, is: **data register source shift count** = Dm modulo 64 (often abbreviated to Dm mod 64). For example, if

Dm = 3 or 67 or 131, then shift count = Dm mod 64 = 3

or if

Dm = 63 or 127 or 191, then shift count = Dm mod 64 = 63

The rule is: keep dividing Dm by 64 until the remainder is less than 64. Most clocks run on an (hours mod 12) basis, so the concept is everpresent.

Using Dm as the shift count allows greater flexibility than using the immediate data shift count — for example, the shift count can be varied dynamically during a program. Immediate data shifts are for small fixed shifts. If the shift count ever happens to be 0, by accident or design, note that no shift occurs, but the CCR is affected (see list below).

The data size code z specifies how many bits of the destination register will be affected by the shift. In our LSL.W example, the lower 16 bits (word) of D1 were shifted. Had we used L or B the shifting would have included all 32 bits or would have been confined to the lower 8 bits of D1.

LOGICAL SHIFTS AND THE CCR

What happens to the bits that get pushed out of the register as we shift? As Figures 6-9 and 6-10 showed, they move after each shift into both the C (Carry)

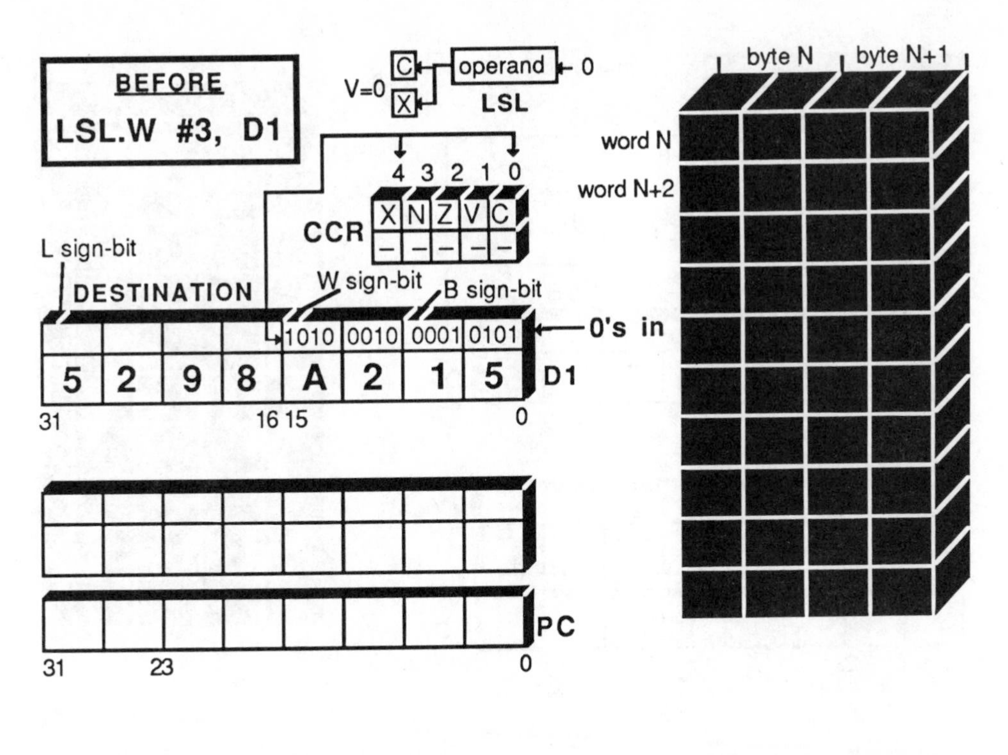

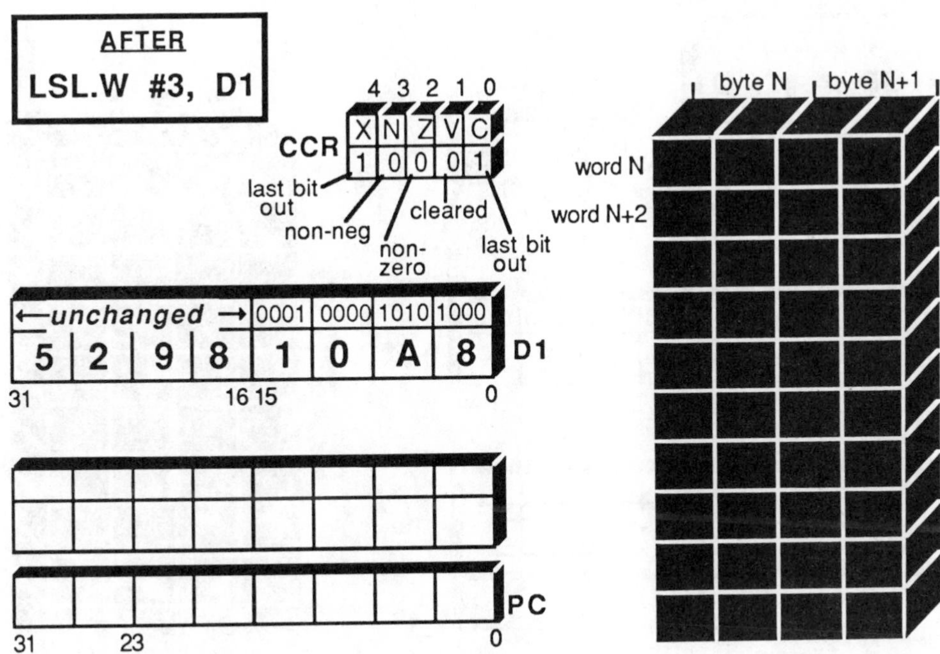

Fig. 6-9 LSL.W #3,D1

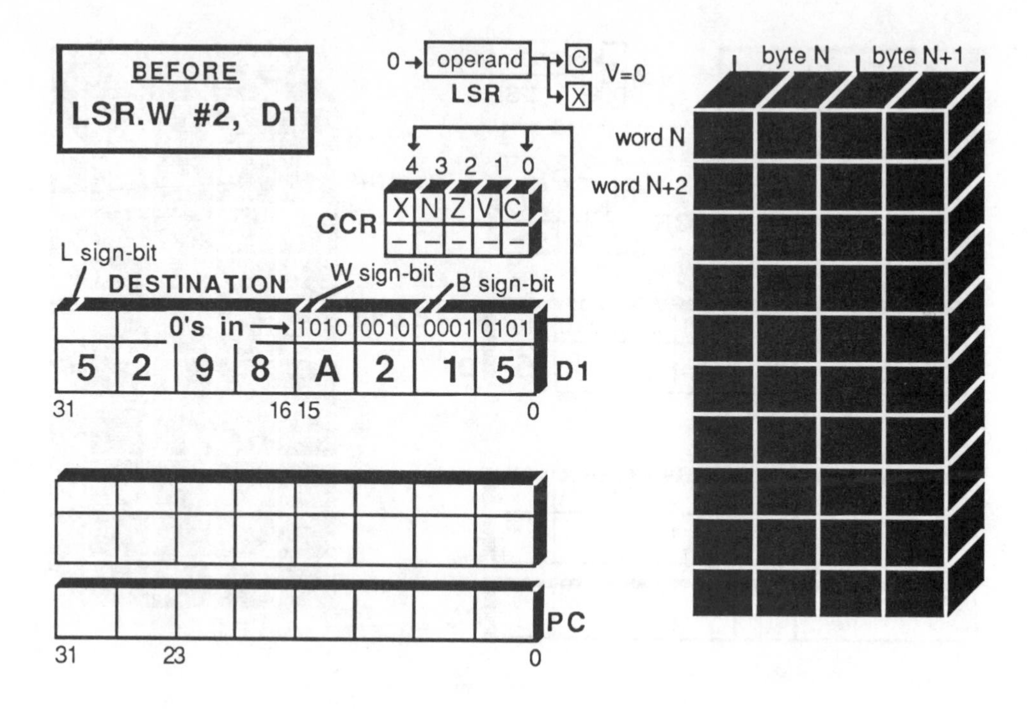

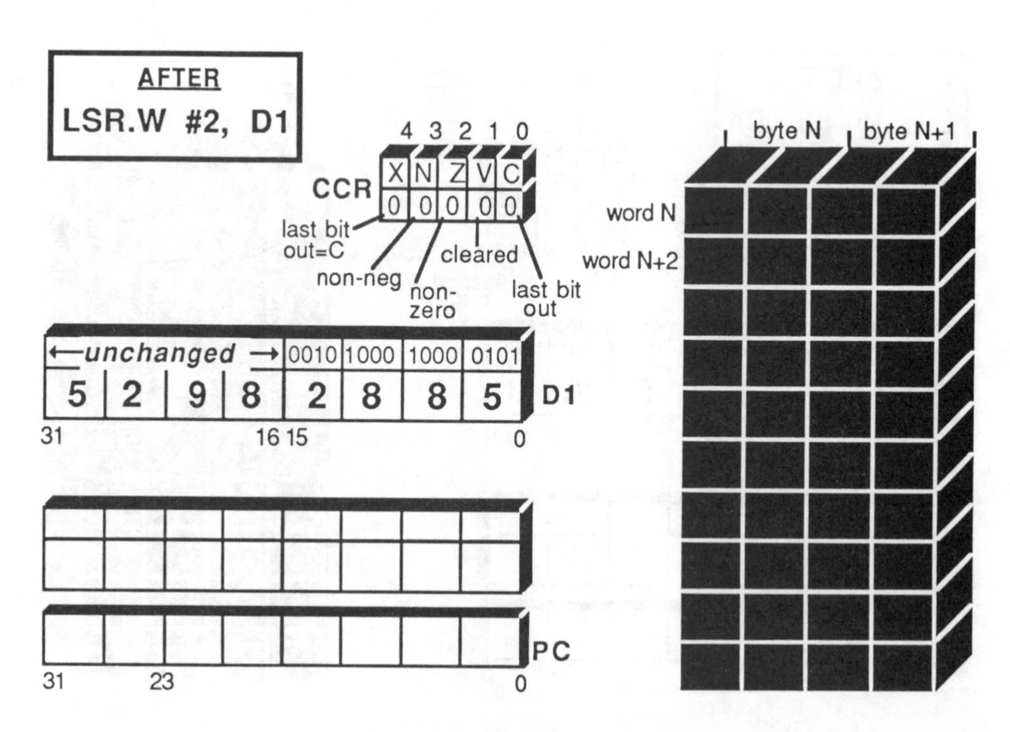

Fig. 6-10 LSR.W #2,D1

and X (eXtend) flags of the CCR (Condition Code Register). If you look at the C or X flag after the shift instruction is completed, it tells you the value, 0 or 1, of the last bit that was pushed out. The N (Negative) and Z (Zero) flags tell you whether the bits left in D1 *after* the shift represent a negative or zero value. Remember that if we are dealing with unsigned operands, the N flag is simply reporting the state of the most significant bit, rather than the sign of the operand. The V (oVerflow) flag is always cleared to 0. The following list sums up the CCR changes.

X flag: Set to the value of the last bit shifted out of destination word. Unaffected if the shift count is 0, that is, if no actual shift is performed.

N flag: Set to 1 if Dn is negative after shift, otherwise cleared to 0.

Z flag: Set to 1 if Dn is zero after shift.

V flag: Always cleared to 0.

C flag: Set same as X flag, but cleared to 0 if the shift count is 0, that is, no actual shift performed.

LOGICAL SHIFT FOR MEMORY OPERANDS

Logical shifts of bit patterns in memory are restricted in two ways. Only words in memory can be shifted, and the shift count must be 1.

The format for memory operand shifting is:

```
LSL.W  <amea>
LSR.W  <amea>
```

where <amea> is any alterable memory effective address mode.

The shift count is always 1, so it is not explicitly listed as a source operand.

The CCR changes just like a register logical shift:

X flag: Set to the value of the last bit shifted out of destination word.

N flag: Set to 1 if memory word is negative after shift, that is, if bit position 15 is 1 — otherwise cleared to 0.

Z flag: Set to 1 if memory word is zero after shift.

V flag: Always cleared to 0.

C flag: Set same as X flag (because shift count is never 0).

In Figure 6-11 we shift the word at (A6) one to the left. Note the changes in the CCR.

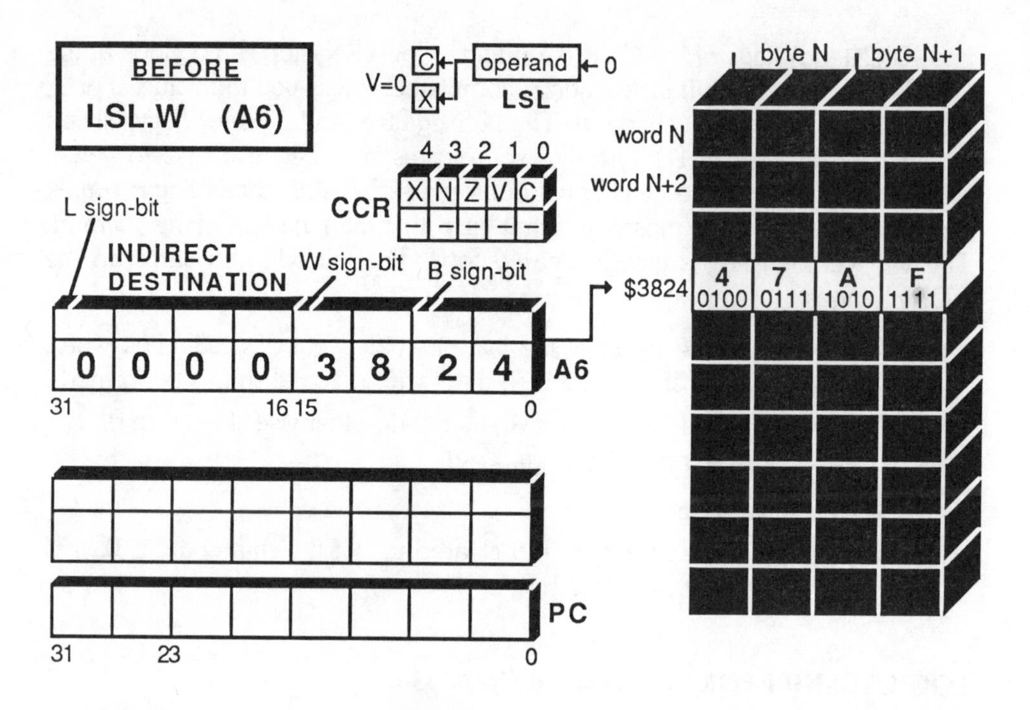

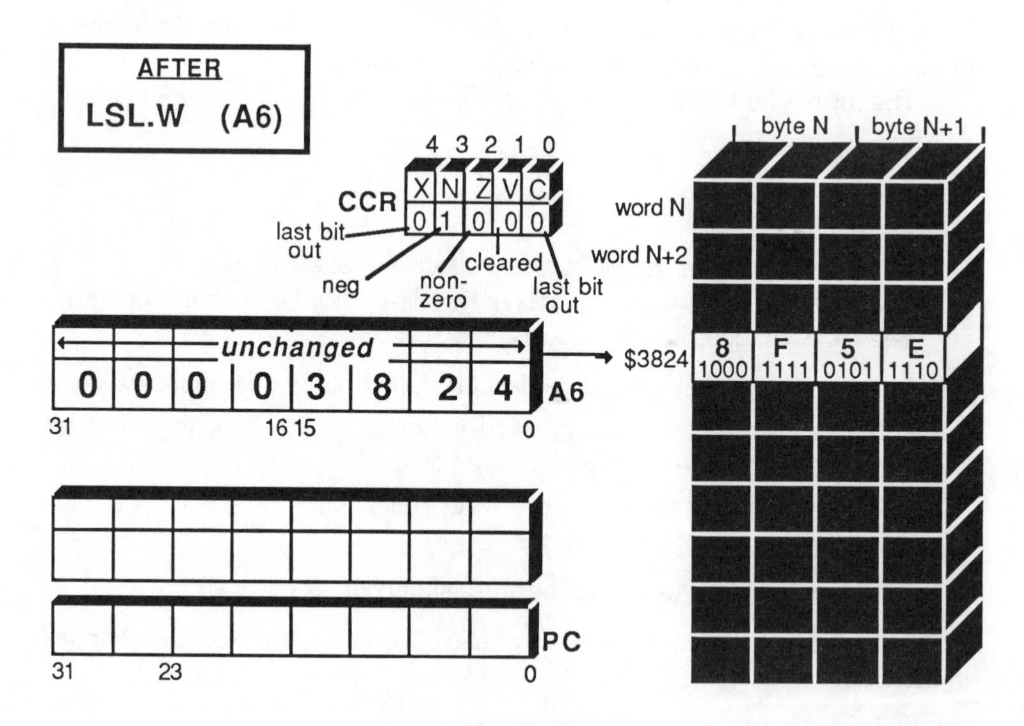

Fig. 6-11 LSL.W (A6)

PRACTICAL APPLICATION

Problem: Check the parity of an 8-bit ASCII character. Count the 1's in the ASCII code and set D3 byte = 0 if even parity; set D3 byte = 1 if odd parity (error condition).

Background: The standard 7-bit (bits 0-6) ASCII set shown in Appendix F assigns characters to each of the 128 7-bit combinations \$00 thru \$7F. As a check on the accuracy of transmission, an 8th parity bit (bit 7) is sometimes added to each code. The rule is:

If the number of 1's in the 7-bit code is odd, set bit 7 = 1

If the number of 1's in the 7-bit code is even, clear bit 7 = 0

Hence all valid 8-bit ASCII codes will have an even number of 1's — and we call this an **even parity check**. As each character is received we can check to see if a bit has been dropped (or added) during the transmission. There are more elaborate checking methods available, but the even-odd parity check is adequate for many situations. Its chief advantage is that any odd number of bit corruptions will change a valid ASCII code into an invalid and therefore detectable code. The worst kind of errors are those that leave no immediate trace. For example, the 7-bit ASCII code for numeral 5 is \$35. If the 1 in bit 0 gets "lost" we will receive \$34, which is the numeral 4. This type of error may not be detected until you come to balance your checkbook. The 8-bit even parity ASCII code would immediately pick up this error:

0110101 = \$35 = "5"	0110100 = \$34 = "4"	7-bit ASCII
Dropping bit 0 from "5" gives	0110100 = \$34 = "4"	
00110101 = \$35 = "5"	10110100 = \$B4 = "4"	8-bit ASCII
Dropping bit 0 from "5" gives	00110100 = \$34 = INVALID	(wrong parity)

Given: An 8-bit ASCII character in lower Byte of D1.

Cases:

D1 byte = \$A2 = 10100010 will give D3 = 1 (3 1's in D1 = odd)

D1 byte = \$47 = 01000111 will give D3 = 0 (4 1's in D1 = even)

Solution: Program 6-2

```
                CLR.B     D3              set D3 byte = 0
      SHIFT     TST.B     D1              Is D1 byte all 0's?
                BEQ.S     OVER            If yes we have finished
```

```
        LSL.B    #1,D1       If no we do one logical
                             shift left of the byte in D1
        BCC.S    SHIFT       did a 1 get pushed out?
                             If no then carry is clear
                             and we branch to SHIFT
                             If yes we have to alter D3
        EORI.B   #1,D3       Reverse bit 0 in D3
                             ie if D3=0 set D3=1
                                if D3=1 set D3=0
        BRA.S    SHIFT       Branch again to SHIFT
OVER    TST.B    D3          Is D3=0?
        BNE      ERROR       If no branch to ERROR
        <rest of program. Parity OK>
        *   *   *
        BRA      NEXT_JOB    Go to other things
ERROR   <take appropriate action for parity error>
        *   *   *
```

Program Notes: Some of the branch instructions have the optional .S modifier, which selects the short 8-bit displacement. When making short branches (-128 to +127 bytes) this option saves an extension word in the assembled instruction.

ARITHMETIC SHIFT INSTRUCTIONS

Figure 6-12 illustrates the arithmetic shift. As you can see arithmetic shifts are very similar to the logical shifts of the previous section. In fact, they use the same source and destination formats and they shift destination bit patterns to left or right according to the given data size and shift count. (ASL equals Arithmetic Shift Left and ASR equals Arithmetic Shift Right.) The difference is that when signed numbers are shifted arithmetically, the processor protects you against changes in the sign bit that might lead to erroneous results. For example, if you want to divide −4 by 2 using a right shift, the logical shift right is wrong! Here's why:

In 2's complement −4 = **11111100** (in byte format)

Logical shift right −4 = **01111110** = +126

Correct arithmetic shift right should be −2 = **11111110**

The situation gets worse if you try to divide −4 by 4 using a logical shift right with a shift count of 2.

The problem is that when LSR pushes a 0 in at the left (most significant) position of any negative number, it not only alters the sign bit (from 1 to 0), it also moves the previous sign bit down to bit position 6 — and the resulting

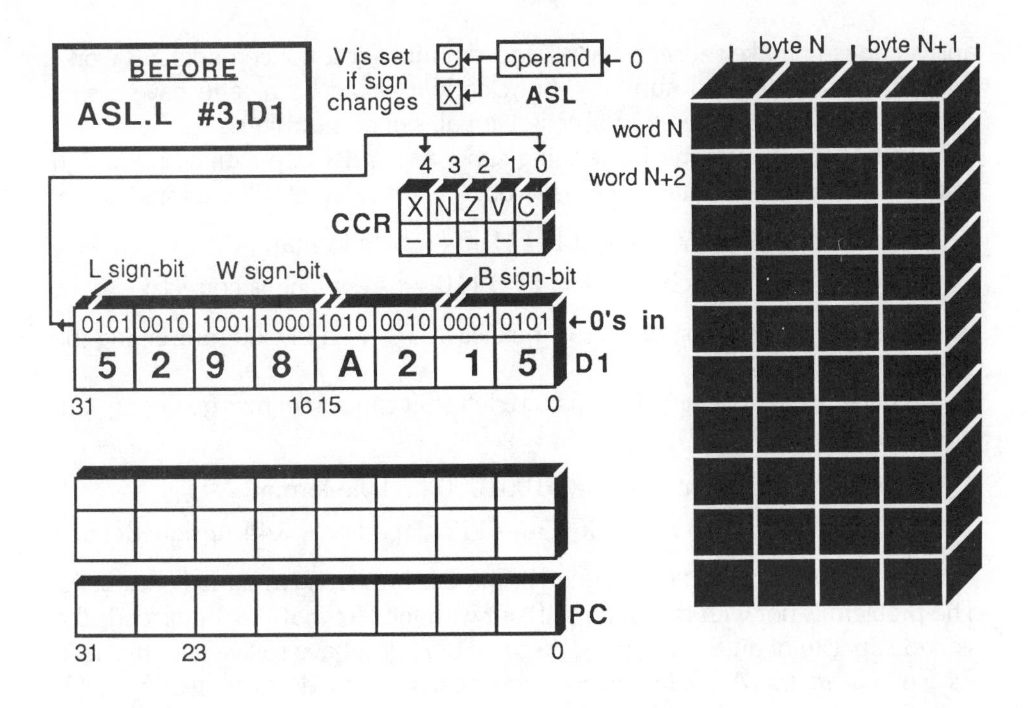

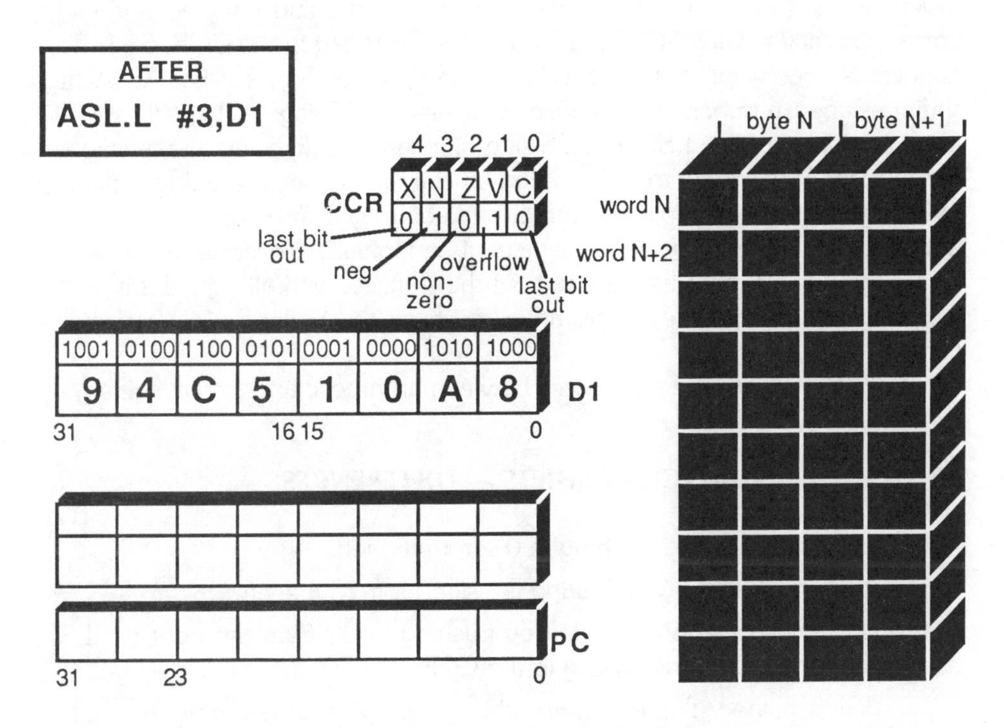

Fig. 6-12 ASL.L #3,D1

answer doesn't make sense, as far as signed arithmetic is concerned. LSR works fine with positive signed numbers, but clearly it would be nice to have a shift right (divide by 2) that works correctly with all signed numbers.

The ASR achieves this by pushing either a 0 or a 1 depending on the sign of the number to be shifted. Let's take our "−4 divided by 2" example again:

In 2's complement −4 = **1**1111100 (in byte format)

Arithmetic shift right −4 = **11**111110 = −2 which is correct

Because −4 has a sign bit of 1, ASR pushes in a 1 from the left, preserving the sign of the dividend.

Similarly, multiplication by 2 using a left shift can sometimes go wrong with signed numbers:

In 2's complement +72 = **0**1001000 (in byte format)

Shift left +72 = **1**001000**0** = −112 signed or +144 unsigned

Here the answer is correct in unsigned arithmetic but wrong in signed arithmetic. The problem is not with the shift itself, but with the fact that +144 exceeds the signed capacity of an 8-bit byte (−126 to +127). We have to live with this fact. As we saw in the ADD instruction, the best we can do is to watch the V (oVerflow) flag in the CCR — this is our warning against signed arithmetic errors. You may recall that LSL always clears the V flag in the CCR. So LSL is dangerous if you want to shift signed numbers. The solution is to use ASL when shifting signed numbers — because ASL sets the V flag. ASL pushes in 0's from the right, just like LSL, but if a sign bit change is detected at any stage in the shift, the V flag is set to 1. If no sign bit change occurs, the V flag is cleared to 0. Note that in a multiple left shift the sign bit may change several times, and may actually end up with the same value it had initially. Nevertheless, V will be set to 1 and will remain at 1 throughout the shift. As with all signed arithmetic the obligation falls to the programmer to check the V flag — a V=1 spells danger.

Let's summarize the differences between arithmetic and logical shifts:

ARITHMETIC AND LOGICAL SHIFTS — DIFFERENCES

LSR shifts right by pushing in 0's from the left.

ASR shifts right by replicating the sign bit from the left.

LSL and ASL both shift left by pushing in 0's from the right but LSL clears the V (oVerflow) flag in the CCR.

ASL sets the V flag to 1 if any change of sign occurs during the shift.

Now let's summarize the similarities between arithmetic and logical shifts.

ARITHMETIC AND LOGICAL SHIFTS — SIMILARITIES

Arithmetic and logical shifts share the same operand addressing modes:

```
ASL.z  #<d3>,Dn     Immediate shift count from 1-8
ASL.z  Dm,Dn        Shift count Dm mod 64
ASL.W  <amea>       Memory shift count = 1

ASR.z  #<d3>,Dn
ASR.z  Dm,Dn
ASR.W  <amea>
```

Logical and arithmetic shifts both push out bits at either end into the C and X flags, and they both set the N and Z flags in the same way. Figure 6-12, a few pages back, and Figure 6-13 show two typical arithmetic shifts.

ARITHMETIC SHIFTS AND THE CCR

Summing up the CCR changes:

X flag: Set to the value of the last bit shifted out of destination. Unaffected if the shift count is 0, that is, if no actual shift performed.

N flag: Set to 1 if destination is negative after shift — otherwise cleared to 0.

Z flag: Set to 1 if destination is zero after shift.

V flag: Set to 1 if any change occurs to the sign bit at any stage of the shift.

C flag: Set same as X flag, but cleared to 0 if the shift count is 0, that is, no actual shift performed.

PRACTICAL APPLICATION

Problem: Calculate the arithmetic mean of two signed numbers, D0 and D1, to the nearest whole number, and place the answer in lower word of D3. Signal an error if signed range is exceeded.

Background: The arithmetic mean, sometimes known as the average, is found by adding the two numbers together and dividing by 2. The mean is exactly halfway between the two numbers. A very common application is found in binary searches of a sorted file. We locate a target record by splitting the file into two equal parts. Comparing our target with the middle record tells us which half of

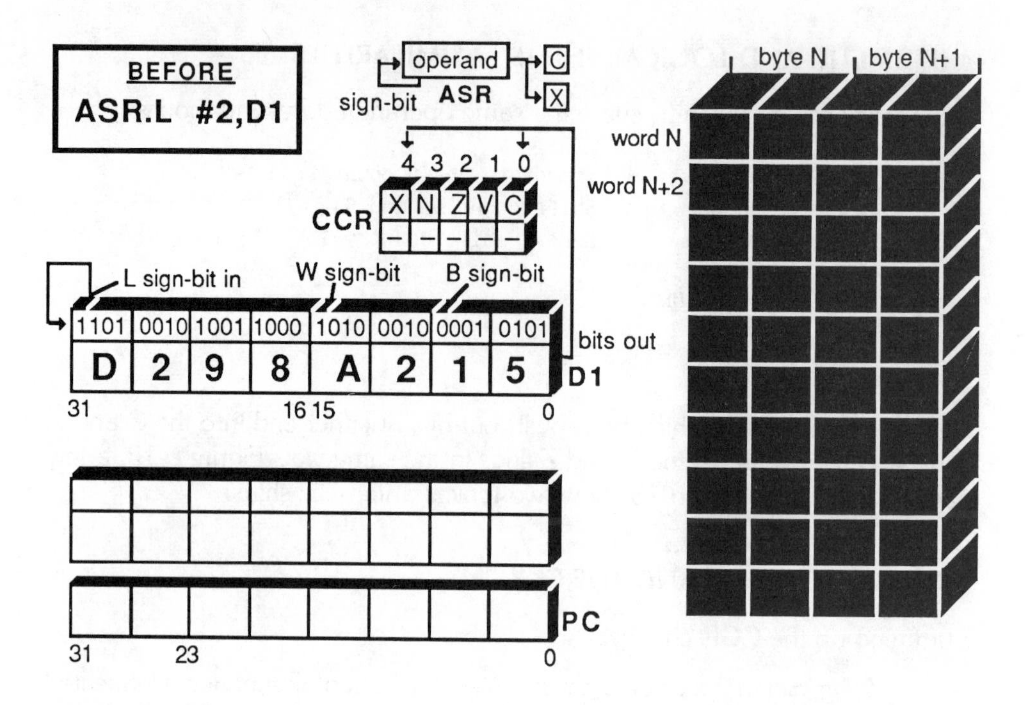

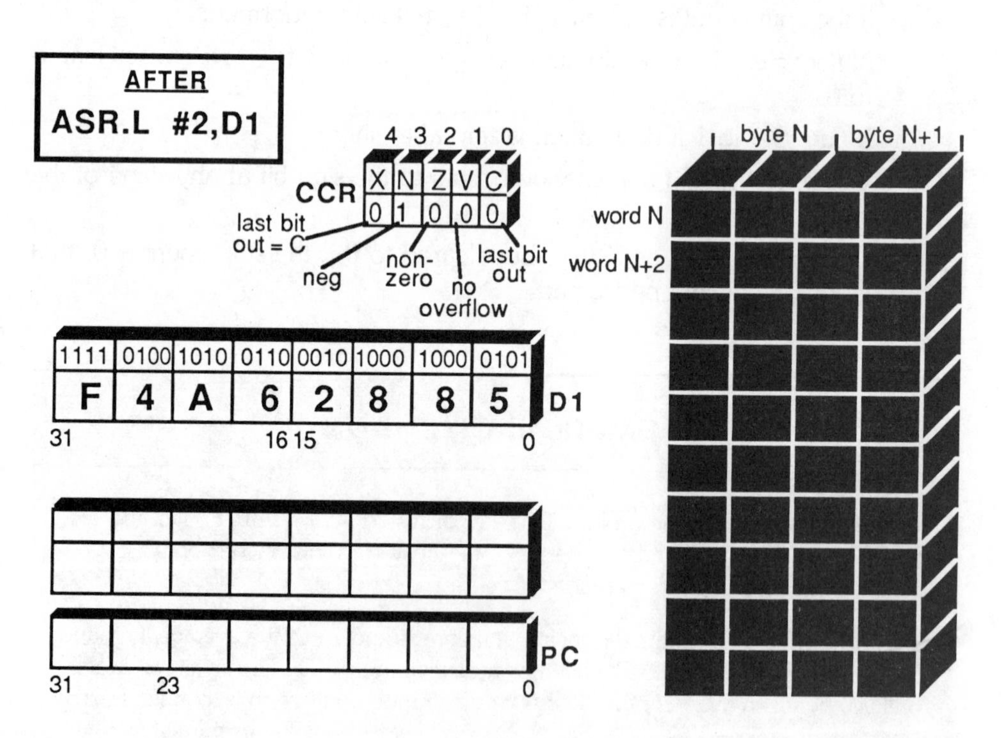

Fig. 6-13 ASR.L #2,D1

the file contains the target. We then split that half of the file in two, and so on until we "home" in on the desired record. At each stage of the binary search we need to calculate the mean of two record numbers in order to locate the midway record.

Given: Two 16-bit signed numbers in D0 and D1.

Cases:

D0 = 2979 = $0BA3 D1 = 4261 = $10A5
D0 + D1 = 7240 = $1C48 (no overflow)
D3 = 1/2 x 7240 = 3620 = $0E24

D0 = –3 = $FFFD D1 = –5 = $FFFB
D0 + D1 = –8 = $FFF8 (no overflow)
D3 = 1/2 x –8 = –4 = $FFFC

D0 = 43981 = $ABCD D1 = 26341 = $66E5
D0 + D1 = 70322 = $112B2 (overflow error)

Solution: Program 6-3

```
         MOVE.W    D0,D3     D0 word now in D3 word
         ADD.W     D1,D3     D3 word = D0 + D1
         BVS       ERROR     Branch to ERROR if V flag set
         ASR.W     #1,D3     Divide D3 word by 2
                             Ignore any remainder
                             D3 now has mean of D0,D1
                             (nearest whole number)
                             with correct sign.
         <rest of program>
         *    *    *
         BRA       NEXT_JOB  Go on to other things
ERROR    <signal an error>
         <take appropriate action>
         *    *    *
         END
```

Program Notes: If D0 + D1 is even, the mean formed in D3 is exact but if D0 + D1 is odd, the mean in D3 will be 0.5 too low. Our simplified problem called for the nearest whole number, so we have ignored any remainder when dividing by 2. There is an easy way to distinguish these two cases. When you ASR an even number the bit pushed out is a 0, but when you ASR an odd number the bit pushed out is a 1. Since the bit is pushed out into the C and X flags of the CCR, we can easily test the C flag with a BCS or BCC and take appropriate action.

Table 6-2 Summary of Shift Instructions

Opcode	*Operand*	*CCR Changes*
ASL.L/W/B ASR.L/W/B	Dm,Dn or #<d3>,Dn	X* N* Z* V* C*
ASL.W ASR.W	<amea>	X* N* Z* V* C*
LSL.L/W/B LSR.L/W/B	Dm,Dn or #<d3>,Dn	X* N* Z* V0 C*
LSL.W LSR.W	<amea>	X* N* Z* V0 C*

<amea> = alterable memory addressing modes = (An), (An)+, −(An) d(An), d(An,Xi), Abs.W, Abs.L

#<d3> = 3 bits immediate data = Shift Count range 1 - 8

CCR symbols: _means unchanged, *means changed according to CCR rules, 0 means always set to 0

Table 6-2 gives a concise summary of all the shift instructions and how the CCR is affected.

ROTATES

Rotating the bits in a register is very much like logical shifting as described above, except that the displaced bits that get pushed out at either end are entered back into the register at the other end. As the word "rotate" suggests, you can imagine the register bit patterns moving clockwise (rotate left) or counterclockwise (rotate right). As with shifts you can specify the number of times the bits are rotated, using either immediate data or a data register to set the shift count. The rotate instruction formats for source/destination are identical to those for shifting. The big difference is what happens to the displaced bits as they rotate. Table 6-3 summarizes the four Rotate variants.

ROR — ROtate Right

ROL — ROtate Left

Table 6-3 Summary of Rotate Instructions

Opcode	*Operand*	*CCR Changes*
ROL.L/W/B ROR.L/W/B	Dm,Dn or #<d3>,Dn	X_ N* Z* V0 C*
ROL.W ROR.W	<amea>	X_ N* Z* V0 C*
ROXL.L/W/B ROXR.L/W/B	Dm,Dn or #<d3>,Dn	X* N* Z* V0 C*
ROXL.W ROXR.W	<amea>	X* N* Z* V0 C*

<amea> = memory alterable addressing modes = (An), (An)+, −(An)
d(An), d(An,Xi), Abs.W, Abs.L

#<d3> = 3 bits immediate date = Shift Count range 1 - 8

CCR symbols: _means unchanged, *means changed according to CCR rules, 0 means always set to 0

ROXR — ROtate with eXtend Right

ROXL — ROtate with eXtend Left

They all accept the three formats we gave for shifts, which are:

```
ROR.z    Dm,Dn      Rotate Dn{.z} Right (Dm mod 64) times
ROR.z    #<d3>,Dn   Rotate Dn{.z} Right d3 times (1 - 8)
ROR.z    <amea>     Rotate memory{.z} Right once only
```

Figure 6-14 illustrates how the displaced bits always pass into the C flag of the CCR. In the ROR/ROL variants, the displaced bits also move directly into the other end of the register, and the X flag is unchanged.

In the ROXR/ROXL variants, the displaced bit moves into both the C and X flags. The previous X flag bit gets pushed back into the register. The X flag is, as usual, playing the role of an additional register bit, so:

ROXR/ROXL.L rotates 33 bits (longword plus X)

ROXR/ROXL.W rotates 17 bits (word plus X)

ROXR/ROXL.B rotates 9 bits (byte plus X)

All rotates, like logical shifts, clear the V flag — so you get no warning of signed arithmetical errors.

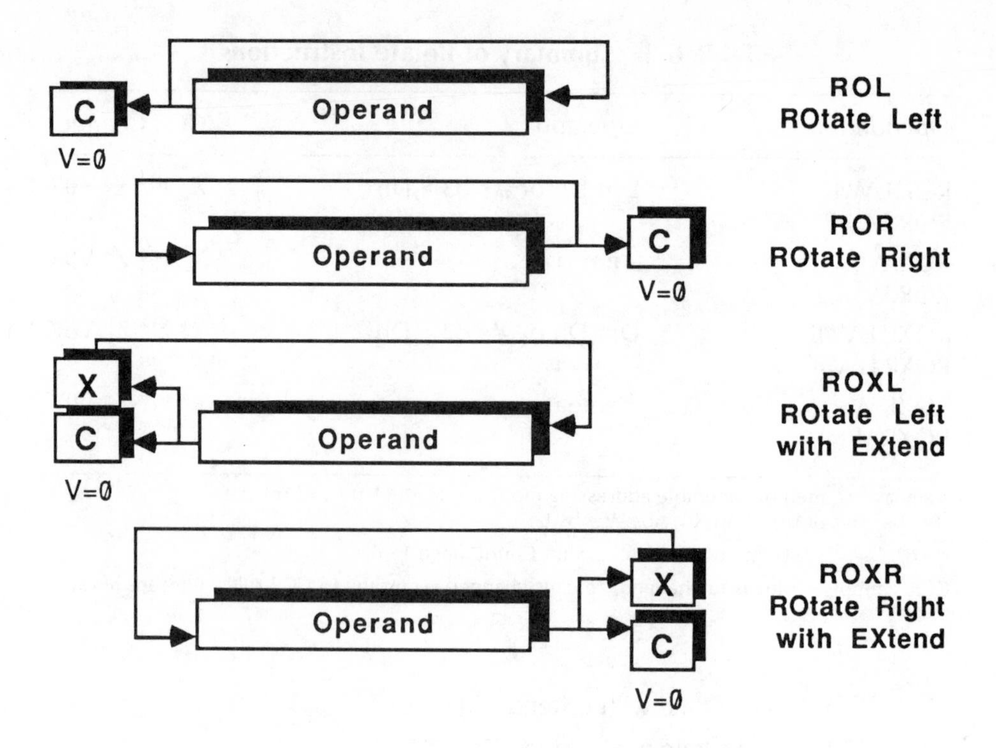

Fig. 6-14 Rotates: General Diagrams

Here is an application to further illuminate the nature of rotates.

```
* Program 6-4   Add the 4 Signed Bytes in a Longword

* D0 contains 4 bytes each representing signed numbers:
* Byte 1 = bits 0-7 (lower-lower byte)
* Byte 2 = bits 8-15 (upper-lower byte)
* Byte 3 = bits 16-23 (lower-upper byte)
* Byte 4 = bits 24-31 (upper-upper byte)
* Place the sum of these 4 numbers in D1.
* Use D3 as temp (scratch) register.
* Preserve value of D0 and D3.

        MOVE.L   D3,-(SP)   Save scratch register D3
        CLR.L    D3         Clear longword D3
        CLR.L    D1         Clear longword D1
        MOVE.B   D0,D1      Byte 1 to D1
        ROR.L    #8,D0      Byte 2 to lower-lower byte position
                            (Byte 3 to upper-lower byte of D0)
```

```
                            (Byte 4 to lower-upper byte of D0)
                            (Byte 1 to upper-upper byte of D0)
        MOVE.B      D0,D3   Byte 2 to D3
        ADD.W       D3,D1   Add byte 2 to byte 1 = D1
        ROR.L       #8,D0   Byte 3 to lower-lower byte position
                            (Byte 4 to upper-lower byte of D0)
                            (Byte 1 to lower-upper byte of D0)
                            (Byte 2 to upper-upper byte of D0)
        MOVE.B      D0,D3   Byte 3 to D3
        ADD.W       D3,D1   Add byte 3 to D1
        ROR.L       #8,D0   Byte 4 to lower-lower byte position
                            (Byte 1 to upper-lower byte of D0)
                            (Byte 2 to lower-upper byte of D0)
                            (Byte 3 to upper-upper byte of D0)
        MOVE.B      D0,D3   Byte 4 to D3
        ADD.W       D3,D1   Add byte 4 to word D1
        ROR.L       #8,D0   Byte 1 to lower-lower byte position
                            (Byte 2 to upper-lower byte of D0)
                            (Byte 3 to lower-upper byte of D0)
                            (Byte 4 to upper-upper byte of D0)
        MOVE.L      (SP)+,D3 Restore D3 from stack

* D0, after a total of 32 rotates, has original value restored.
* D1 contains sum of bytes 1-4.
```

We used D3 and ADD.W to avoid the dangers of overflow. Summing four signed bytes cannot exceed the 16-bit signed range but can exceed the 8-bit signed range — so we cannot use

```
        ADD.B       D0,D1
```

immediately after the ROR unless we check for overflow.

There are, of course, many different ways of "isolating" the bytes or words in a longword. SWAP, for example, is often used in conjunction with a rotate. (We'll see more of SWAP later in this chapter.) Let's revamp Program 6-4 using SWAP to add just bytes 1, 3, and 4.

```
* Program 6-5   Add Bytes 1, 3, and 4 of a Longword

* D0 contains 4 bytes each representing signed numbers.
* Byte 1 = bits 0-7 (lower-lower byte).
* Byte 2 = bits 8-15 (upper-lower byte).
* Byte 3 = bits 16-23 (lower-upper byte).
* Byte 4 = bits 24-31 (upper-upper byte).
```

```
* Place the sum of bytes 1, 3, and 4 numbers in D1.
* Use D3 as temp (scratch) register.
* Preserve value of D0 and D3.

        MOVEM.L   D0/D3,-(SP)  Stack 'em
        CLR.L     D3           Clear long word D3
        CLR.L     D1           Clear long word D1
        MOVE.B    D0,D1        Byte 1 to D1
        SWAP      D0           Reverse words of D0
                               Byte 3 is now lower-lower byte D0
                               Byte 4 is upper-lower byte D0
                               (Byte 2 is upper-upper byte D0)
                               (Byte 1 is lower-upper byte D0)
        MOVE.B    D0,D3        Byte 3 to D3
        ADD.W     D3,D1        Add Byte 3 to Byte 1 = D1
        ROR.L     #8,D0        Byte 4 to lower-lower byte position
                               (Byte 1 to upper-lower byte of D0)
                               (Byte 2 to lower-upper byte of D0)
                               (Byte 3 to upper-upper byte of D0)
        MOVE.B    D0,D3        Byte 4 to D3
        ADD.W     D3,D1        Add Byte 4 to D1
        MOVEM.L    (SP)+,D0/D3  Restore D0,D3 from stack

* D1 contains sum of bytes 1, 3, and 4.
```

BIT TESTING AND SETTING

In Chapter 4 we met the TST.z instruction, which tested the whole operand (L, W, or B) for zero and set the CCR flags accordingly. In the next group of instructions we refine this idea to include testing of individual bits in a variety of situations.

BTST — TEST A BIT

BTST allows you to test any bit in a data register, or any bit in a byte of memory. The result of the test, just as with TST, is reflected in the Z flag of the CCR:

Tested bit = 0 sets Z flag to 1
Tested bit = 1 clears Z flag to 0

The other flags in the CCR are unchanged.

TST, as we saw in Chapter 4, tests a whole byte, word, or longword for zero, whereas BTST tests only a single bit. BTST has the following formats:

```
BTST.L    Dm,Dn           Test the (Dm mod 32)th bit of Dn
BTST.L    #<d5>,Dn        Test the (d5)th bit of Dn
BTST.B    Dm,<mea>        Test the (Dm mod 8)th bit of <mea> byte
BTST.B    #<d3>,<mea>     Test the (d3)th bit of <mea> byte
```

<d5> represents a 5-bit number, 0-31. <d3> is a 3-bit number, 0-7.

Note that <mea> here excludes immediate mode as a valid destination. Since the destination is not altered by BTST, relative mode destinations are allowed.

The source operand, indicating the position of the bit to be tested, can either be a number in a data register or an immediate constant. Remember that bit position 0 is the first, least significant bit in all cases.

The actual range limits for bit position are obviously (0-31) for registers and (0-7) for memory bytes, and this is reflected in the formats. If you try to test a bit position outside these ranges, the processor will simply reduce modulo 32 or modulo 8 as we have indicated above.

Since only memory bytes can be tested with BTST, it may sometimes be necessary to move from memory to a Dn for more elaborate tests.

The data size codes are implied by the format, and therefore optional for most assemblers. We prefer to use them in order to clarify our intent.

Here are two simple examples of using BTST.

```
* Program 6-6   Testing for Odd or Even Using BTST

* D3 contains an unsigned number.  If it is even, leave it alone.
* If it is odd, add 1 to make it even.

          BTST.L    #0,D3     Is bit 0 of D3 = 0?
          BEQ       EVEN      If Yes D3 is even - so branch
          ADDQ.L    #1,D3     If No D3 is odd - so add 1
          BCS       ERROR     D3 too big for 32-bit
                              unsigned. Carry detected.
EVEN      <rest of program>
            *    *    *
ERROR     <deal with range error>
```

Program 6-6 relies on the elementary fact that the least significant bit of an even binary number is 0. Making odd numbers even is a useful trick for adjusting M68000 addresses to the nearest word boundary.

```
* Program 6-7   Test Employee Status Using BTST

* A0 points to employee record in memory.  Word 1 of record has
* employee ID.  Lower byte of word 2 is employee status byte:
*    Bit 0 = 0 for male; 1 for female
*    Bit 1 = 0 for FT (full time); 1 for PT (part time)
*    Bit 2 = 0 for HO (head office) staff; 1 for branch staff
* Increase D6 counter by 1 if employee is female/FT/HO
* When we enter this program segment, D6 contains subtotal of
* such employees.

         BTST.B   #0,2(A0)   Test sex bit
         BEQ      IGNORE     Bypass male i.e. if bit 0 = 0
         BTST.B   #1,2(A0)   Test FT/PT
         BNE      IGNORE     Bypass PT i.e. if bit 1 = 1
         BTST.B   #2,2(A0)   Test HO/Branch
         BNE      IGNORE     Bypass Branch i.e. if bit 2 = 1
         ADDQ.L   #1,D6      Add 1 for target employee
IGNORE   <rest of program>
* This would form part of a general program for counting the
* number of employees in each category.
```

Here we are testing the byte in memory at address A0+2, hence the destination operand is 2(A0). For repeated tests of 2(A0), we would probably find it quicker to move 2(A0) to a data register since we would save on <ea> calculations and memory fetches.

TEST AND CHANGE A BIT

Three variants of BTST are:

- BCLR — Test a bit and clear
- BSET — Test a bit and set
- BCHG — Test a bit and change

They not only test the specified bit and set the Z flag just like BTST, but they then proceed to unconditionally modify the tested bit as indicated by the mnemonic.

The formats differ slightly from BTST insofar as only alterable memory operands are allowed — which is natural when you consider that BCLR/BSET/BCHG actually alter the destination:

```
BCLR.L   Dm,Dn        Test the (Dm mod 32)th bit of Dn
BCLR.L   #<d6>,Dn     Test the (d6 mod 32)th bit of Dn
```

```
BCLR.B    Dm,<amea>         Test the (Dm mod 8)th bit of <amea> byte
BCLR.B    #<d3>,<amea>      Test the (d3)th bit of <amea> byte
```

Having adjusted the Z flag, BCLR clears the specified destination bit to 0.

```
BSET.L    Dm,Dn             Test the (Dm mod 32)th bit of Dn
BSET.L    #<d6>,Dn          Test the (d6 mod 32)th bit of Dn
BSET.B    Dm,<amea>         Test the (Dm mod 8)th bit of <amea> byte
BSET.B    #<d3>,<amea>      Test the (d3)th bit of <amea> byte
```

Having adjusted the Z flag, BSET sets the specified destination bit to 1.

```
BCHG.L    Dm,Dn             Test the (Dm mod 32)th bit of Dn
BCHG.L    #<d6>,Dn          Test the (d6 mod 32)th bit of Dn
BCHG.B    Dm,<amea>         Test the (Dm mod 8)th bit of <amea> byte
BCHG.B    #<d3>,<amea>      Test the (d3)th bit of <amea> byte
```

Having adjusted the Z flag, BCHG reverses the specified destination bit, 1→0 or 0→1.

The three bit test and set instructions are commonly used simply to reset selected bits, ignoring the test aspect altogether.

Using the data for Program 6-7, let us transfer someone to head office by changing the employee status byte.

```
* Program 6-8   Change Employee Status Using BCLR

* A0 points to employee record in memory.  Word 1 of record has
* employee ID.  Lower byte of word 2 is employee status byte:
* Bit 0 = 0 for male; 1 for female
* Bit 1 = 0 for FT (full time); 1 for PT (part time)
* Bit 2 = 0 for HO staff; 1 for branch staff
* Demote employee to head office by clearing bit 2

          BCLR.B    #2,2(A0)  Bit 2 of byte 2(A0) ->0
          BEQ       WHOOPS    Employee was HO already
          <rest of program>
          *    *    *
WHOOPS    <check our records>

* BCLR tests bit 2 before clearing it.  BEQ will branch if bit 2
* was already 0 -- revealing a possible error in our employee
* selection or records.
```

BCHG is useful for controlling activity during loops, acting as a flip-flop or switch. For example:

```
* Program 6-8A   Alternating Jobs Using BSET and BCHG

         BSET.L    #0,D2      Start with bit 0 of D2 = 1
LOOP     BCHG.L    #0,D2      Flip 0->1 or 1->0
         BEQ       JOB0       Do job0 on even numbered loops
         <do job1>            Do job1 on odd numbered loops
         BRA       LOOP
JOB0     <do job0>
         BRA       LOOP

* Each time we reach LOOP we test bit 0 of D2 and set or clear
* the Z flag.  We next flip bit 0 from 0 to 1, or 1 to 0. Then we test
* the Z flag and do either job0 or job1.  The jobs therefore
* alternate as we loop.  To avoid endless looping we assume that
* one or another job contains some test for loop exit.
```

Scc — SET ON CONDITION

Scc is a set of single-operand, byte-only instructions, all using the format

```
Scc{.B} <adea>
```

The byte at <adea> is set to $FF (all 1's) if condition cc is true, and set to $00 (all 0's) if condition cc is false. Since the destination is altered by Scc, only <adea> modes are permitted.

Scc has 16 variations corresponding to the condition mnemonics given by the letters cc. Each condition is based on the state of the CCR flags at the time the test is made. We have already seen some of these in Chapter 4 under the section on Bcc (Branch on Condition). Table 6-4 shows the complete list of the cc codes as used with Scc, Bcc and DBcc (which we will learn more about later).

The essential function of Scc is to store the result of a CCR test, so you can use the result later in the program after the original CCR has been subject to change. We have seen that most instructions alter the CCR in some way or other. This can be a nuisance if you want to delay a conditional action.

HOW THE cc's WORK

The various cc conditions range from simple one-flag CCR conditions to complex Boolean expressions based on several flags.

Table 6-4 Conditon Codes for Bcc, DBcc and Scc

cc Mnemonic	*Condition*	*Boolean Formula*	*Relevant Number Mode*
CC	Carry Clear	$\sim C$	unsigned
CS	Carry Set	C	unsigned
EQ	Equal to	Z	all
F	False	0	all *
GE	Greater or equal	$(N \wedge V) + (\sim N \wedge \sim V)$	signed
GT	Greater than	$(N \wedge V \wedge \sim Z) + (\sim N \wedge \sim V \wedge \sim Z)$	signed
HI	Higher than	$\sim C \wedge \sim Z$	unsigned
LE	Less or equal	$Z + (N \wedge \sim V) + (\sim N \wedge V)$	signed
LS	Lower or same	$C + Z$	unsigned
LT	less than	$(N \wedge \sim V) + (\sim N \wedge V)$	signed
MI	Minus	N	signed
NE	Not equal	$\sim Z$	all
PL	Plus	$\sim N$	signed
T	True	1	all *
VC	Overflow Clear	$\sim V$	signed
VS	Overflow Set	V	signed

Legend: $\sim$ = logical NOT, $+$ = logical OR, $\wedge$ = logical AND, * F and T not used with Bcc

The single flag conditions have already been explained under Bcc. These 8 basic conditions rely on the state of just one of the N, Z, V, or C flags. These flags can be considered to be Boolean variables taking the value 1 for true and 0 for false. They can be combined as shown to represent more complex conditions. Table 6-4 shows the logical calculations performed by the M68000 to determine true or false to the typical questions we pose regarding the relations between numbers — greater, less, equal, and so on.

A TYPICAL MULTI-FLAG cc DISSECTED

Take, for example, the condition HI (HIgher [than]), listed in our table as an unsigned mode condition. If you want to compare two unsigned numbers in D0 and D1, you can write

```
        SUB.L     D0,D1
```

This subtracts D0 from D1, sets the CCR flags, and replaces D1 by the difference between D1 and D0. Or, as we'll detail later, you can write

```
        CMP.L       D0,D1
```

which performs the subtraction and sets the CCR flags, but does not alter D1.

To answer the question "Is unsigned D1 higher than unsigned D0?" we need to look at the C and Z flags after a SUB or CMP. If Z = 1 then we have a zero difference, so D1 = D0, hence HI is false. Likewise, if C = 1 we must have had a borrow, meaning that D1 is lower than D0, so HI is again false. Hence the HI condition is true only if (C = 0 and Z = 0) and this explains our Boolean formula: HI = $\sim C \wedge \sim Z$ which we read as NOT-C and NOT-Z.

The effect of

```
        SHI  D5         Set D5 if HIgher
```

for example, is:

> If (C=0 AND Z=0) place $FF in lower byte of D5.
> Otherwise place $00 in lower byte of D5.

D5 lower byte therefore remembers the result of the HI test, and can be consulted later. Similarly,

```
        BHI  <label>         Branch if HIgher
```

says branch to <label> only if (C=0 AND Z=0).

The processor performs such tests blindly regardless of what your previous program steps have done. It is up to you, in fact, to provide meaning to the condition HI by a previous SUB or CMP step using the two unsigned numbers you wish to compare.

Each of the other compound conditions can be analyzed in the same way, looking at the various flags following a SUB or CMP operation on the two numbers being compared.

SIGNED AND UNSIGNED cc's

It should be clear that questions like "greater than?" or "less than?" can only be resolved when you know which number mode is involved: signed or unsigned. Is "10000000" greater than "00000111"? The answer is yes for unsigned, but no for signed numbers.

On the other hand the questions "equal?" and "zero?" can be answered regardless of number mode. The final column of Table 6-4 indicates which conditions apply to which mode. Note that Motorola has chosen "higher/lower/same" for unsigned comparisons, and "greater/less" for signed comparisons.

You can try out the Boolean formulas by subtracting various signed and unsigned numbers and noting the CCR flags, (C=0, N=1, etc.). Then substitute the flag values, 0 or 1, in each Boolean formula, by applying the following rules:

$0 + 0 = 0$	False OR false = false
$1 + 0 = 1$	True OR false = true
$0 \wedge 0 = 0$	False AND false = false
$1 \wedge 0 = 0$	True AND false = false
$1 \wedge 1 = 1$	True AND true = true
$\sim 0 = 1$	NOT false = true
$\sim 1 = 0$	NOT true = false

$\sim(A + B) = (\sim A \wedge \sim B)$	NOT (A OR B) = (NOT−A AND NOT−B)
$\sim(A \wedge B) = (\sim A + \sim B)$	NOT (A AND B) = (NOT−A OR NOT−B)

Each cc condition will reduce to 0 (false) or 1 (true), and Scc will record this fact in any chosen register or memory location.

The rules expressed so concisely in Boolean algebra merit close study. They are worth whole chapters on the meaning of carry and overflow. Once you have convinced yourself that all of the rules work, you can relax and leave the M68000 to do the Boolean evaluations for you. It's rather good at this.

ST AND SF

Two of the cc's, T and F, are actually unconditional.

```
ST   <adea>   Always sets <adea> to $FF (true)
SF   <adea>   Always sets <adea> to $00 (false)
```

Note that we do not use T or F with Bcc. BRA is used for BT (Branch Always), while BF (Never Branch) is a structured programmer's slogan rather than an instruction.

TAS — INDIVISIBLE TEST AND SET OPERAND

Our final instruction in the bit manipulation group is TAS (Test And Set operand) which hides a subtle trick beneath its simple exterior:

```
TAS{.B}    <adea>
```

This line first tests the byte at <adea> and then sets the Z and N flags in the CCR (Z=1 if byte is zero, N=1 if sign bit 7 is 1). Finally, TAS unconditionally sets the destination sign bit 7 to 1 — forcing the byte to be negative.

The unusual trick built into this instruction is that the TAS operation is indivisible — meaning that a special read-modify-write memory cycle is employed, which cannot be interrupted, and no other program, processor, or device in the system can access the operand until TAS is finished. Even the normal bus error routines are modified to keep TAS indivisible. Why all this trickery just to test and set a byte?

The reason is the need to provide control and synchronization in various delicate situations that can occur in today's complex M68000-based multitasking and multiprocessing systems. The general idea is that a resource, which can be almost anything — from a disk file or bank of memory to an I/O device, or even an entire microprocessor — can be shared by different user jobs. Both hardware and software methods are used to regulate this sharing. Various flags, semaphores, and priority and queuing algorithms are employed to control who gets what and when and for how long. Typically, the program grabbing a resource flags it as "in use" by setting an agreed value in an assigned status bit or byte. The resource is eventually relinquished by clearing the status flag so that other jobs are free to access it.

Suppose, for example, that we have assigned a byte at address $1000, which signals to all user programs as follows:

($1000) = $00 means employee file free to be updated

($1000) nonzero means employee file in use – keep off

Such a byte might be given a fancy name such as employee file access status byte. We have suggested an absolute address so that there is a fixed place where any user program can test the file status.

Without TAS, our program might proceed as follows.

```
* Program 6-9  File Locking without TAS

      WAIT      TST.B     $1000          Is file free?
                BNE.S     WAIT           No -- keep trying
```

```
            ST        $1000           "Grab" file by putting $FF
                                      in byte ($1000)
                                      This warns others that
                                      file is busy

* ST is equivalent to MOVE.B #$FF,$1000

            <process file>
            CLR.B     $1000           Relinquish file by
                                      clearing ($1000) to $00
            <rest of program>
```

This seems fine, but what if an interrupt occurs just before the ST $1000 instruction? The interrupting program or process may well do a TST.B $1000 and, finding the file free, set ($1000) to busy, then proceed to update the file. When our program resumes at ST $1000, we also attempt to modify the file, unaware of the file status change — with possibly dire consequences.

Let's see how TAS helps.

```
* Program 6-10  File Locking with TAS

WAIT        TAS       $1000           Test ($1000) and adjust
                                      the CCR. Then set ($1000)
                                      negative = $80
            BNE       WAIT            File is busy elsewhere so
                                      try again
            <process file>            File was free, but we have
                                      grabbed it. It is flagged
                                      busy to others.
            CLR.B     $1000           Relinquish file
                                      by setting status byte = $00
            <rest of program>
```

The CLR.B is vital. Without it, jobs can cycle endlessly waiting to access the file — and the sooner you can CLR.B, the better. The TAS solution, unlike the TST/ST approach, ensures that the sequence of testing and setting the status flag cannot be interrupted. It is important to note that the BNE WAIT line is effectively testing the status byte as it was before TAS set it to $80. Any interrupts or exceptions occurring after TAS but before the BNE would not affect the BNE test, since the CCR is always saved and restored (as part of the interrupted program's context).

In real-world time-sharing applications, the simple file-locking procedure outlined above would naturally be more sophisticated, including such concepts as read-only files, public-restricted files, file-locking by record, and so on. Since

TAS sets just bit 7 (the sign-bit) of the operand (status byte) to signal "busy", the other six bits of the byte can be used to signal other properties of the shared resource. If so, the BNE (Branch Not Equal zero) after TAS can be replaced by BMI (Branch MInus), which tests the N flag.

COMPARE WITH THE CMP FAMILY OF INSTRUCTIONS

The next group of instructions allows you to compare the source and destination operands.

The key notion in the CMP instructions is that the processor goes through the motions of SUB (that is, subtract source from destination) but does not alter the destination. Recall that SUB replaces the destination with the calculated difference. All that CMP does, in fact, is to change the CCR flags (N, Z, V, and C) as though it had performed a SUB. After CMP, or its variants, you can use any of the conditional instructions which depend on the cc conditions shown in Table 6-4.

There are two points to remember concerning cc and CMP. First, we are always testing "destination <condition> source", where <condition> says, for example, higher than, less than, etc. It is not uncommon for programmers to get this the wrong way round, because instructions are written: source,destination.

There are four CMP formats, used according to the type of operands being compared:

```
CMP.z  <ea>,Dn         Compare anything with value in z of Dn
CMPA.Z <ea>,An         Compare any L or W source with An
CMPI.z #<data>,<adea> Compare immediate data with destination
CMPM.z (Am)+, (An)+    Compare successive memory addresses
```

CCR changes as does SUB, except CMP does not change the X flag.

Here are some examples:

```
* Program 6-11  Compare Unsigned Longwords

            CMP.L    D3,D4    Compare D3 and D4 longwords
            BEQ      SAME     Branch to SAME if D3 = D4
                              From here on we know D3,D4
                              are unequal
            BHI      D4HI     Branch to D4HI if D4 unsigned
                              is higher than D3 unsigned
                              From here on we know D4 is not
                              higher
```

```
                BCS       D3HI       Branch to D3HI if D4 unsigned
                                     is lower than D3
                <we should never reach here!>
                <see comments below>
      SAME      <D3=D4 case processed here>
                *    *    *
      D4HI      <D4 higher case processed here>
                *    *    *
      D3HI      <D3 higher case processed here>
                *    *    *

* The BLS branch would test "lower/same"; BNE would test
* "unequal" -- so there are plenty of overlapping choices after a
* CMP on unsigned numbers.  In the above sequence of conditional
* branches, we actually cover all possible relations between D3
* and D4.  Often you can avoid a conditional branch because
* previous branches have excluded all but one remaining
* possibility.  In the above, BCS could be replaced with BRA.
* Recall that the C flag after CMP or SUB means "borrow" rather
* than "carry" -- so BCS tests source higher than destination.


* Program 6-12  Compare Immediate: Signed Bytes

          CMPI.B   #-1,$4000        Is signed byte at address $4000
                                    greater/less/equal to -1?
          BLE      FROZEN           Branch if less or equal
          <process here if ($4000) byte greater than -1>
          *    *    *
FROZEN    <process here if ($4000) byte less than or equal to -1>
          *    *    *

* Signed comparisons use BEQ/BGE/BGT/BLE.  See Table 6-4
* CMPI source #<data> will be stored in one or two extension
* words depending on size data code.


* Program 6-13  Compare Two ASCII Strings in Memory

* ASCII string 1 has pointer A1; ASCII String 2 has pointer A2.
* Both strings terminate with an ASCII NUL ($00)
* Byte D6 is set to $00 if mismatch, $FF if strings identical
* Word D7 counts number of matched characters

          ST       D6               Set $FF in indicator byte D6
          CLR.W    D7               Clear matched character count
```

```
LOOP      CMPM.B    (A1)+,(A2)+    Compare bytes/inc pointer
          BNE       MISMAT         Bytes differ
          TST.B     -1(A1)         NUL reached?
          BEQ       ENDOK          Yes -- both bytes NUL
          ADDQ.W    #1,D7          Increase match count
          BRA       LOOP           On to next characters
MISMAT    CLR.B     D6             Set $00 in indicator byte D6
ENDOK     <rest of program>

* The bytes we are comparing are simply tested for NE (Not
* Equal), so we are not concerned with signed/unsigned
* interpretations.  If we were interested in lexicographic
* sequencing, e.g. Is string 1 ahead of string 2 in the dictionary?,
* we could test with BHI or BLS (unsigned) and set some
* indication in D6 when a mismatch occurs.
* Note the TST.B -1(A1) which tests the byte just compared.
* Since (A1)+ has incremented the pointer A1 by 1 (byte), we use
* an offset of -1 with a d(A1) operand.  -1(A1) is not to be
* confused with -(A1).  The latter would move our pointer back
* with bizarre results.
```

CMPA — COMPARE ADDRESS

The CMPA variant of CMP, like the SUBA variant of SUB, is used only when the destination is an address register. However, there is a subtle but important difference between CMPA and SUBA. SUBA, as with all purely arithmetic operations on An's, does not affect the CCR — but CMPA would not make any sense unless the CCR reflected the various N, Z, V, and C changes. Without these we would be unable to test the **cc** conditions, such as, are these two addresses greater/equal/less? So CMPA breaks the rules and sets up the CCR for us.

CMPA does not allow a byte data size code, and when you do a CMPA.W comparison, the word source is sign-bit extended to 32 bits before the subtraction is performed. In spite of this, remember that addresses are essentially positive unsigned values and, as we will see in the next example, we normally use the unsigned cc tests after CMPA.

CMPA is most useful when we need to check if an address pointer is within bounds. We have seen several examples of An being incremented/decremented in various ways, using (An)+, –(An), ADDA, SUBA, and stack operations. In many cases we must guard against An pointing over or below certain memory limits. A simple example follows.

```
* Program 6-14  CMPA: Private User Stack Limit Check

* We have established a small private stack with stack pointer
* A2.  A0 points to the base of this stack.  A1 points to the
* limit of the stack. The stack grows down in memory from A0 to
* A1 as we push on it.  Provide simple checks that A2 does not
* exceed the stack limits.  Normally A0 >= A2 >= A1.

          MOVE.W    D1,-(A2)       typical PUSH
          CMPA.L    A1,A2          Is stack full?
          BEQ       FULL           Yes, just -- so branch
          BCS       ERROR_2        "Below" stack base error
          <stack OK -- continue>
          MOVE.L    (A2)+,D7       typical PULL
          CMPA.L    A2,A0          Reached stack base?
          BCS       ERROR_2        ``Below" stack base error
          <stack OK -- continue>
FULL      <warning stack full>
          *    *    *
ERROR_1   <recover last save and adjust stack>
          *    *    *
ERROR_2   <check last restore and adjust stack>

* The first CMPA does {A2 - A1} so Z is set (BEQ) only if A2=A1,
* meaning that the stack is exactly full. C is set (=borrow) only
* if A1 is higher than A2, meaning that stack pointer is beyond
* limit.  BEQ test alone is inadequate since pushing can
* decrement A2 by 2 or 4.
* The second CMPA does {A0 - A2}, so BCS means that A2 is
* higher than A0, hence we have somehow managed to pull more than
* we pushed!  Getting "below" the stack base indicates a
* programming error, whereas getting "above" the stack limit
* simply means over-usage.
```

Closely associated with CMP and conditional branching is a composite instruction called DBcc, which gives the M68000 yet another edge over the competition. Let's see why.

DBcc — TEST cc, DECREMENT, AND BRANCH

The format is:

```
DBcc      Dn,<label>     Test cc, decrement Dn, conditionally
                         branch to <loop>
```

There are three elements to define in DBcc. The first is the cc condition code. The cc part is the familiar condition code, as used in Scc, and listed in Table 6-4. Thus we find DBEQ, DBHI, etc. The second is the Dn loop counter. Dn here represents the lower 16-bit word of Dn, and we call this the **loop execution counter**, or just loop counter, for short. The third element is the <label>. This defines the start of the loop we want to execute. As in the long version of the Bcc, <label> ends up as a 16-bit PC-relative displacement stored in an extension word. However, DBcc displacements allow only backword branches from DBcc to <label>, a maximum of $7FFE (32,766) bytes. The <label> must come before the DBcc.

DBcc SEQUENCE OF EVENTS

The sequence of events is as follows:

> If condition cc is true, do not branch but carry on with the next instruction.
>
> If condition cc is false, decrement word Dn by 1; that is, Dn → Dn – 1.
>
> Now test Dn. If Dn = –1 go on to next instruction. If Dn not = –1 branch to <label>.

As the implications start firming up and making sense, DBcc becomes an extremely useful composite instruction. A large percentage of assembly language programming effort is the tedious job of establishing loop controls, either by counting or by condition testing or both. DBcc reduces the tedium by combining all the normal looping requirements into one powerful instruction.

DBcc IN ACTION

Let's see the simplest count only version of DBcc using DBF (that is to say, where cc = F or always false.

```
* Program 6-15  DBF:  Simple Count Only Loop

* Perform jobA exactly 24,765 times then rest!

          MOVE.W    #24764,D0        Set D0 to {loop count - 1}
MORE      <jobA program here...>
          DBF  D0,MORE               Branch to MORE until D0 = -1
          <rest>

* The first time we meet DBF, condition is false (by definition)
* so we decrement D0 to 24,763 and loop (because D0 does not yet
```

```
* equal -1).  If you keep count of this process, you'll discover that
* the jobA is performed exactly 24,765 times before D0 hits -1.
* At this point we stop looping and "drop through" to the next
* line marked <rest>.
* Since jobA is performed once when we first enter the loop, and
* since we count until D0 is -1 we must remember to set loop
* counter = one less than number of loops needed.
```

Using DBF effectively removes the condition testing aspect of DBcc, leaving us with the counting element. Even so, if you compare this example to the normal non-DBcc counting loop, you will see considerable saving of programming effort.

DBT (with cc = always true) actually exists, but if you follow the sequence given above, you will see that

```
            DBT        Dn,<label>
```

immediately drops through to the next instruction. So, DBT in effect does nothing. It is mentioned only to check your grasp of the logic behind DBcc. If you are in any doubt, reread the DBcc sequence of events.

When we have a "proper" cc condition, like PL (Plus) or CC (Carry Clear), the DBcc becomes the equivalent of the DO – UNTIL <condition cc is true> construct, much prized in structured programming languages. Within this DO-UNTIL-condition-loop we have a further test: DO – UNTIL <Dn loop counter = –1>, which allows us to set a limit to the number of loop iterations. The next two programs should clarify this.

```
* Program 6-16  DBMI: Find First Negative Entry in Table

* A2 points to the base of a table of 100 signed words.
* Scan the table and place the first negative nonzero entry in
* lower word of D4. Record its table position (1 - 100) in D5.
* If no negatives found set D5 to -1 and D4 word = 0.

        CLR.W    D4          Clear D4 word
        MOVE.W   #99,D5      Set DB counter to {100-1}
SCAN    TST.W    (A2)+       Is (A2) word negative?
        DBMI     D5,SCAN     SCAN until (A2) -ve
                             or until 100 entries
                              tested
        TST.W    D5          Is D5 negative (= -1)?
        BMI      NOFIND      If yes -- all entries +ve
                             so branch to NOFIND with
                             D5 = -1.
```

```
                MOVE.W    -2(A2),D4       Save first -ve entry
                                          in D4
                SUBQ.W    #100,D5         D5 = D5 - 100
                NEG.W     D5              D5 = -D5 = {100 - counter}
                                          D5 now = table position
NOFIND          <rest of program>

* TST.W sets Z and N flags according to value of word (A2).
* CMPI.W #0,(A2)+ would do the same, but takes a few cycles more.
* Each non-negative number we read (MI = false) will decrement
* D5 and test for D5 = -1 which signals end of table and NOFIND.
* The first negative number (MI = true) (if any) takes us out of
* the loop to TST.W D5. D5 will only be -ve (-1) if whole table
* was scanned unsuccessfully.  If D5 is in the range 0 - 99, we
* can calculate the table position of the find from {100 - D5}.
* NEG.W is a common trick to get {a - Dn} by negating {Dn - a}.
* Note the -2(A2) to get at the previous word, since (A2)+ has
* already advanced A2 to the next word.
```

You can use this type of DBcc loop to pick out all kinds of numbers from a table. For example:

```
SCAN            CMPI.W    #3000,(A2)+
                DBLE      D5,SCAN         Loop ends if (A2)<=3000
                *    *    *
```

would locate the first (if any) entry less than or equal to 3000.

Variable length tables or strings can be looped in many ways. You have already met the idea of having a unique terminator such as NUL at the end, so you test for this within the loop. Another common idea is to have the length recorded in a header field at the start of the table or field. As entries or deletions are made, you update the header. Let's revamp Program 6-16 to illustrate this and a few other tricks.

```
* Program 6-17  DBEQ: Find Last Zero Entry in Variable Length Table

* A2 points to the base of a table.  The first word in the table
* holds the number of signed words which follow.
* Scan the table and locate the last zero entry.
* Record its table position in D5.
* If no zeroes found set D5 to -1.
* If the table is empty, set D5 = 0 and D0 byte = $FF
* If table not empty set D0 byte = 0
```

```
         MOVE.W     (A2)+,D5        D5 = number of entries
                                    A2 now → first entry
         SEQ        D0              D0 byte set to "remember"
                                    if table empty or not
         BEQ        EMPTY           Table is bare! D5 = 0!
         MOVE.W     D5,D4           D4 = number entries also
         ASL.W      #1,D4           D4 x 2 = bytes in table
         ADDA.W     D4,A2           A2 now → beyond last
                                    entry
         SUBQ.W     #1,D5           Set DB counter = {D5 - 1}
SCAN     TST.W      -(A2)           Is (A2) word zero?
         DBEQ       D5,SCAN         SCAN until (A2) = 0
                                    or until 100 entries
                                    tested
         TST.W      D5              Is D5 negative (= -1)?
         BMI        NOFIND          If yes - NO entries = 0
                                    so branch to NOFIND with
                                    D5 = -1.
         ADDQ.W     #1,D5           D5 = D5 + 1
                                    D5 now = table position
NOFIND   <rest of program>
         *     *     *
EMPTY    <bypass - no entries in table>

* SEQ D0 tests the CCR after MOVE to D5.  If D5 = 0 (EQ is TRUE)
* we set D0 byte to 1's ($FF).  If D5 <> 0, SEQ clears D0.  Later
* in the program, long after A2, D5 and CCR may have changed, we
* can refer to D0 which "remembers" the SEQ result.
* Note the use of -(A2) to scan a table from the end.  We
* were careful to advance the pointer A2 to 1 word beyond the
* last entry before entering the SCAN loop.  We had to double the
* number of words in the table to get the correct byte offset to
* A2.  As in Program 6-16 we set the loop counter D5 to one less
* than the maximum number of iterations needed.
```

DBcc — GENERAL COMMENTS

We can only give you a brief glimpse at the rich possibilities of the DBcc family of instructions, so we conclude with a few general comments.

- The value remaining in the loop counter Dn when we exit the DBcc loop is useful, as shown in the last two programs. It tells us when and why the loop terminated.

- You can often use the loop counter Dn within the loop as an index register that is automatically decrementing for you.
- Sometimes you may want to branch directly to the DBcc line, rather than enter the loop from the top as we have done in our two examples. For example:

```
          MOVE.W    #<counter>,Dn  Set loop counter
          BRA       TEST           Branch to DBcc line
          *    *    *
LOOP      <loop program>
          *    *    *
TEST      DBcc  Dn,LOOP
```

This is perfectly valid, provided you watch the initial value for #<counter>. It is easy to get the wrong number of iterations. In fact, in the above example #<counter> needs to be set to the exact number of loops needed, rather than {loops – 1}.

- With care, you can modify Dn during a loop, thereby curtailing (decrease Dn) or prolonging (increase Dn) the loop.
- The MC68010 has a special loop mode for DBcc that alters the sequence of testing/decrementing without affecting the overall function. However, the execution speed of small loops is increased by holding the DBcc instruction and its displacement in a two-word pre-fetch queue, thus reducing the number of memory accesses.

MISCELLANEOUS MATH

We have seen the four basic M68000 mathematical operators, ADD, SUB, MULU/MULS, and DIVU/DIVS, and some of their simple variants (like ADDQ, ADDI, ADDA, etc.). We now look at the remaining instructions which perform various arithmetical functions.

NEG — NEGATE

We used NEG in an earlier example without too much explanation. In fact,

```
NEG.z     <adea>    Negate destination operand
```

simply replaces the destination <adea> with its 2's complement negative, namely {0 – <adea>}, using z = L, W, or B to stipulate which part of the operand is involved. The destination must be <alterable data effective address>, which, as you now must realize, excludes An, d(PC), d(PC,Xi) and Immediate.

If D0 contains $12345678, then

NEG.L D0 gives D0 = $EDCBA988 (32 bits negated)

NEG.W D0 gives D0 = $1234A988 (lower 16 bits negated, rest unchanged)

NEG.B D0 gives D0 = $12345688 (lower 8 bits negated, rest unchanged)

An excellent reason for keeping NEG in mind is that you cannot write

```
SUBI.z      Dn,#<data>          ILLEGAL
```

to calculate {#<data> – Dn}. But

```
SUBI.z      #<data>,Dn          Dn = Dn - #<data>
NEG.z       Dn                  Dn = -Dn
```

achieves the same end legally.

Note also, that you sometimes want {Dm – Dn} without altering the value of Dm. SUB.z Dn,Dm gets you {Dm – Dn} but you lose Dm. So why not do SUB.z Dm,Dn followed by NEG.z Dn?

Another use for NEG is after a Scc to convert TRUE = $FF to TRUE = 1, which is sometimes more convenient:

```
Scc         <adea>              Set byte <adea> to $FF if true
                                Set byte <adea> to $00 if false
NEG.B       <adea>              Set byte to 1 if true
                                Byte remains 0 if false
```

NEG changes the CCR, predictably, just like SUB — although the flags are less informative:

X Set equal to C
N Set if result is negative
Z Set if result is zero
V Set if overflow
C Set if a borrow generated (always the case unless operand is zero)

EXT — SIGN EXTEND

On many occasions we have observed that the M68000 automatically sign-bit extends a register or displacement from 16 to 32 bits, for example. The EXT instruction allows the programmer to perform this trick on a data register in two different ways:

```
EXT.W    Dn    Sign-bit extend from byte to word of Dn
               i.e. copy bit 7 of Dn into bits 8 through 15

EXT.L    Dn    Sign-bit extend from word to longword of Dn
               i.e. copy bit 15 of Dn into bits 16 through 31
```

If D0 = $12348765, then after

```
EXT.W    D0    D0 = $12340065
EXT.L    D0    D0 = $FFFF8765
```

since bit 7 = 0 and bit 15 = 1.

EXT is useful in preserving signs when you change data sizes during a program. It is sometimes easy to forget that if you have a negative number in, say, D0 byte, and then write:

```
MOVE.B   D0,D1
```

only the lower byte of D1 is "negative." Later in the program you might have one of the following:

```
ADD.W    D1,D3
ADD.L    D1,D3
```

which would give incorrect results. The use of EXT solves this:

```
MOVE.B   D0,D1
EXT.W    D1       D1 word now signed correctly
ADD.W    D1,D3
```

or

```
MOVE.B   D0,D1
EXT.W    D1       D1 word signed like D1 byte
```

```
        EXT.L       D1          D1 longword signed correctly
        ADD.L       D1,D3
```

EXT changes the CCR like a MOVE:

X Unchanged
N Set if result negative
Z Set if result zero
V Always cleared to 0
C Always cleared to 0

MULTI-PRECISION MATH

In this section we will be using the word *extend* in an entirely different sense — not as in sign-extend — but as a way of gaining an extra significant 9th, 17th, or 33rd bit to extend the accuracy of our sums.

THE ROLE OF THE X FLAG

So far, we have only hinted at what the X flag in the CCR is meant to do, and why it sometimes changes like the C flag, and sometimes remains unaltered. We have seen the X flag acting as an "extra" bit beyond the usual MSB (Most Significant Bit) of a register. In the ROXL (ROtate Left with eXtend), for example, we saw bytes rotating in a 9-bit field via the X flag, words rotating in a 17-bit field, and longwords rotating in a 33-bit field. We need some new instructions to explain the mysterious X flag.

EXTENDED ARITHMETIC INSTRUCTIONS

We now introduce three extended instructions, ADDX, SUBX, and NEGX, which use the X flag numerically, allowing carries and borrows from previous calculations to be incorporated in multiregister arithmetic.

```
ADDX.z   Dm,Dn          Add {Dm + Dn + X flag}. Put SUM in Dn
ADDX.z  -(Am),-(An)     Add {source + destination + X flag}
                            Put SUM in destination
```

```
SUBX.z  Dm,Dn          {Dn - Dm - X flag} replaces  Dn
SUBX.z  -(Am),-(An)    {destination - source - X flag}
                            replaces destination

NEGX    <adea>         {0 - <adea> - X flag} replaces <adea>
```

In the examples that follow it should be remembered that in all cases when we get carry or borrow during arithmetical operations, the X and C flags both get set to 1. The M68000 rules for CCR changes are carefully arranged so that certain instructions, such as MOVE, clear the C flag but keep the X flag unchanged. The X flag, as it were, "remembers" a carry or borrow until we are ready to use ADDX or SUBX, which may be several lines later. Let's add two 64-bit unsigned numbers together to illustrate these points. When we deal with numbers *over 32 bits* on the M68000, we are talking multi-precision math.

```
* Program 6-18  ADDX:  Adding 64-bit unsigned numbers

* Each 64-bit unsigned number takes 2 data registers.
* Number A = {D0}{D1} and Number B = {D2}{D3}
* D0 is most significant 32 bits of A, and so on.
* The sum A + B to be placed in {D4}{D5}
* CCR to reflect value of the 64-bit result e.g. C=X=1 if 64-bit
* carry; Z=1 if 64-bit result is 0 etc.
              MOVE.L    D1,D5
              MOVE.L    D0,D4
              ADD.L     D3,D5      D5 = D1 + D3; carry = X
              <any moves here: X unchanged, C cleared>
              ADDX.L    D2,D4      D4 = D0 + D2 + X
                                   where X is previous carry from D5
                                   ADDX will create a new X
* A + B now in {D4}{D5}.  CCR will reflect any carry from D4.
* But what will the Z flag represent?  What if D4=0 but D5<>0?
* The next section will answer this question.
```

EXTENDED ARITHMETIC AND THE CCR

In the following discussion, when we refer to ADDX we include SUBX and NEGX too — the CCR quirks are identical.

In the last program example, the final ADDX behaves very much like a normal ADD with the previous X (1 or 0) thrown in. An X carry of 1 actually represents 2^{32} (bit 33). The resulting sum in D4 happens to represent the "top" half of a 64-bit result, because we planned it that way. The processor is, of course, unaware of our interpretation and ADDX.L will change the CCR on the basis of the 32-bit addition {D0 + D2 + X}. If there is carry from this we will find it in both the C and X flags (the previous X is lost but we have no further use for it). The new X may be useful — its value is 2^{64} — and maybe we want to create an 80-bit, 96-bit, or even 128-bit sum from this and other 64-bit results. If so, we are free to engage in a variety of MOVEs and SWAPs knowing that X is safe. Again, this underlines the importance of knowing how the CCR flags change with each instruction.

So ADDX sets X = C like ADD. To cope with multi-precision signed numbers, ADDX also sets N and V like ADD.

THE Z FLAG QUIRK

But for the Z (Zero) flag we need a subtle twist. A nonzero result from ADDX will CLEAR Z, as normal, but a zero result from ADDX leaves Z unchanged, which is abnormal. Since there is always a reason for a Motorola quirk, let's look for it.

Going back to the last program example, suppose that the final ADDX.L D2,D4 gave a zero result — which is quite possible. (D0 and D2 can both be zero, and D1 + D3 need not produce a carry.) Under normal ADD conditions, D4 = 0 would set Z = 1, leading us to believe that our 64-bit sum, A + B, was zero. Clearly, we cannot decide whether A + B is zero simply by looking at the top 32 bits of our 64-bit answer. So, ADDX is designed to clear Z if the sum is nonzero, and leave Z alone if the sum is zero. In our example, then, if D4 were zero, the Z flag would reflect the sum formed in D5, the lower 32 bits. Z=1 would correctly imply that the entire 64-bit result was zero. Z=0 would mean that either D4 or D5 or both were nonzero.

Now you know why. One important consequence of this quirk is that you should make sure that Z = 1 (bit 2 of CCR) and X = 0 (bit 4 of CCR) before embarking on a multi-precision calculation involving successive ADDX's. Since 4 = 00000100, a neat way to do this is

```
MOVE.W  #4,CCR
```

We now show SUBX in action, subtracting 64-bit numbers.

```
* Program 6-19  SUBX: Subtracting 64-bit Unsigned Numbers

* Initial data as in Program 6-18
* Each 64-bit unsigned number takes 2 data registers.
* Number A = {D0}{D1} and Number B = {D2}{D3}.
* D0 is most-significant 32 bits of A, and so on.
```

```
* The difference A - B to be placed in {D4}{D5}.
* CCR to reflect value of the 64-bit result e.g. C=X=1 if 64-bit
* borrow; Z=1 if 64-bit result is 0 etc.
                MOVE.L    D1,D5
                MOVE.L    D0,D4
                SUB.L     D3,D5      D5 = D1 - D3; borrow = X
                <any moves here leave X unchanged>
                SUBX.L    D2,D4      D4 = D0 - D2 - X
                                     where X is previous borrow from D5

* A - B now in {D4}{D5}.  CCR will reflect any borrow from D4.
* Z flag reflects value of {D4}{D5} not just {D4}.
* Note that the borrowed X is subtracted.
```

MULTI-PRECISION MULTIPLICATION

Our normal MC68000 MULU/MULS allow us to multiply two 16-bit values to give a 32-bit answer. The MC68020 offers L versions, which provide 32-bit x 32-bit = 64-bit products with one instruction. (Division, too, has been extended.) The MC68881 math coprocessor takes us way beyond this with 80-bit floating-point operations. On the "lesser" M68000 models you have to program these extensions, but with ADDX and SUBX it is not too difficult. We will briefly outline the steps needed to multiply two longwords, A and B, to get a 64-bit product. Suppose A = (word1)(word2) and B = (word3)(word4). We first need four 16 x 16 = 32-bit products using MULU or MULS.

1. (word2) × (word4) = 32-bit (prod11) (prod12)
2. (word1) × (word4) = (prod21) (prod22)
3. (word2) × (word3) = (prod31) (prod32)
4. (word1) × (word3) = (prod41) (prod42)

where each (prod) is 16-bit. So far, we have no carries to worry about!

As in second grade, you can imagine these (prods) set out ready to be added column by column from right to left:

```
                    (prod11)  (prod12)
          (prod21)  (prod22)              +
          (prod31)  (prod32)              +
(prod41)  (prod42)                        +
------------------------------------------
(sum  4)  (sum  3)  (sum  2)  (sum  1)
```

where each sum is 16 bits:

sum 1 = prod12
sum 2 = prod11 + prod22 + prod32 with CARRY X1
sum 3 = prod21 + prod31 + prod42 + X1 with CARRY X2
sum 4 = prod41 + X2 with CARRY X3

With judicious use of ADDX, SWAP, and ASL, you finally get the product in two longwords.

EXTENDED MATH WITH MEMORY OPERANDS

So far, we have not used the

```
ADDX.z -(Am),-(An)
```

format, and you may have wondered why this strange option is offered. A glance at our multi-precision multiplication example above may offer a clue. If the various 16-bit or 32-bit components are stored suitably in memory, it turns out that a great deal of register shuffling can be avoided by ADDXing directly in memory while the pre-decrement automatically steps the address pointer through your list of operands.

BINARY CODED DECIMAL

The M68000 supports a data type known as BCD (Binary Coded Decimal). For certain jobs, especially financial calculations with large numbers, the vagaries of binary-decimal conversion inherent in the normal binary data types can be a problem, even with high-precision floating-point facilities. The BCD solution is at the expense of memory and speed, but it keeps and manipulates all numbers in exact decimal format, using a whole nibble (4 bits) to encode one decimal digit. Since 4 bits can encode unsigned numbers 0 through 15, and we need to encode only 0 through 9, you can already see the inherent inefficiency in BCD (see Chapter 1).

We handle BCDs with instructions rather similar in format to the ADDX, SUBX, and NEGX of the previous section.

```
ABCD.B   Dm,Dn         Add {Dm byte + Dn byte + X flag}. Put SUM in Dn
ABCD.B   -(Am),-(An)   Add {source byte + destination byte + X flag}
                           Put SUM in destination
```

```
SBCD.B   Dm,Dn          {Dn byte - Dm byte - X flag} replaces Dn
SBCD.B -(Am),-(An)      {destination - source - X flag}
                            replaces destination

NBCD.B   <adea>         {0 - <adea> - X flag} replaces <adea>
```

The first point to note is that all BCD operations are on bytes, which means we can add, subtract, or negate two decimal numbers with a single instruction. Most assemblers will default to a data size code B, but we will use it as a reminder. The BCD numbers we want to handle are usually packed 4 per word or 8 per longword. Longer sequences are best considered as strings of bytes, and this explains the –(Am),–(An) operand option, already seen with ADDX/SUBX. Suppose we want to store the decimal number 564728 in memory with pointer A0. This 3-byte (6-nibble) BCD string would look like this:

BCD String A = 564728

Byte Address	*Byte Stored*	*Decimal Equivalent*	
A0	(0101) (0110)	(5) (6)	Most significant
A0+1	(0100) (0111)	(4) (7)	
A0+2	(0010) (1000)	(2) (8)	Least significant

Note the sequence of nibble within byte and byte within string. The lesser significant digits are higher in memory, so if we set our pointer just beyond the end of this string (at A0+3), the pre-decrement format of ABCD will automatically sum with decimal carry in the correct arithmetical sequence, adding 28, then 47, then 56 to another designated destination BCD string.

BCD OPERATIONS AND THE CCR

Since the X carry is added as with ADDX, our previous discussion and caveats regarding the CCR apply — in particular the Z flag quirk (clear Z if result nonzero but leave Z unchanged if result is zero) is in force. The X carry is 1 or 0, but remember the 1 is a decimal carry representing 100 being carried over from the lower BCD byte (the range of which is 00 through 99). It is especially important to clear X and set Z=1 before any BCD work.

Some differences in CCR handling between ADDX and ABCD arise from the fact that BCD bytes are essentially unsigned, at least they are not 2's complement format, so the N and V flags are of no value and remain undefined during all BCD operations.

BCD CCR SUMMARY

X Set equal to C
N Undefined
Z Cleared if result is nonzero else unchanged
V Undefined
C Set if a decimal carry/borrow

ADDING BCD STRINGS IN MEMORY

Let's set up another BCD string called String B, and then write a program to add our earlier String A to B:

BCD String B = 390112

Byte Address	*Byte Stored*	*Decimal Equivalent*	
A1	(0011) (1001)	(3) (9)	Most significant
A1+1	(0000) (0001)	(0) (1)	
A1+2	(0001) (0010)	(1) (2)	Least significant

```
* Program 6-20  ABCD: Adding BCD Strings in Memory

* A0 and A1 point to top (MSD) of 3-byte BCD strings A and B
* Add A to B, place BCD sum in string B.  Signal any carry
* "error." i.e. if sum exceeds 999999.

     MOVE.W   #4,CCR          Set X=0 and Z=1 before all BCD ops
     MOVEQ.W  #2,D0           Set DBcc counter for 3 iterations
     ADDQ.W   #3,A0           Set A pointer beyond end of string
     ADDQ.W   #3,A1           Set B pointer beyond end of string
LOOP ABCD.B   -(A0),-(A1)     Add {A byte + X} to B byte
     DBF      D0,LOOP         Loop three times
     BCS      ERROR           Branch if carry
     <rest of program>
     *    *    *
ERROR <take appropriate action>
* String B would now contain 954840:

* A1                (1001) (0101)      (9) (5) Most significant
* A1+1              (0100) (1000)      (4) (8)
* A1+2              (0100) (0000)      (4) (0) Least significant
```

```
* The CCR would have X = C = 0, Z = 0.  A0 and A1 would be restored
* to their original values.
```

NEGATIVE BCD NUMBERS

The NBCD instruction simplifies the handling of negative BCD values, but since we have no N flag, the X and C flags must be watched with care to get your sums right. NBCD normally forms the 10's complement of the byte operand {0 – <adea>}, but if there is an X=1 from the previous operation, that X=1 is also subtracted, {0 – <adea> – 1} to give the 9's complement.

This allows a BCD string to be negated (sign-reversed) correctly, as the next example shows.

```
* Program 6-21 NBCD:  Negate a BCD String in Memory

* With the same data as Program 6-20, replace string A with its
* negative (10's complement).
* BCD string A = 564728:
* A0                  (0101)(0110)          (5)(6)  Most significant
* A0+1                (0100)(0111)          (4)(7)
* A0+2                (0010)(1000)          (2)(8)  Least significant

     MOVE.W   #4,CCR         Set X=0 and Z=1 before all BCD ops
     MOVEQ.W  #2,D0          Set DBcc counter for 3 iterations
     ADDQ.W   #3,A0          Set A pointer beyond end of string
LOOP NBCD.B   -(A0)          {0 - BCD byte - X} to -(A0)
     DBF      D0,LOOP        Loop three times
     *    *   *

* String A now contains 435272 the 10's complement of 564728
* A0                  (0100)(0011)          (4)(3) Most significant
* A0+1                (0101)(0010)          (5)(2)
* A0+2                (0111)(0010)          (7)(2) Least significant

* The CCR would have X = C = 1, Z = 0.  A0 would be restored
* to its original value.
```

X=0 before the lowest byte is negated, so we get {0 – 28} = 72 with borrow, then X is set to 1. Therefore the next negate gives {0 – 47 – 1} = 52 with X=1, and so on. If, later in the program, you look at string A, all you see is 435272. Is this plus or minus? Unless you have taken precautions, 435272 looks just as positive as the 564728 which we negated. Well, there are many solutions, but they have to be programmed — they are not built-in for you. One method is to append a sign byte to each BCD string, possibly using the ASCII plus and minus symbols, and always store the absolute value in the BCD string.

As a final example to underline the mechanics of BCD, lets subtract 2 BCD bytes that are assumed to be positive and are held in data registers.

```
* Program 6-22  SBCD: Subtracting BCD Numbers

* Given two +ve BCD bytes in D0 and D1, calculate D0 - D1.
* If positive set D1 = D0 - D1 with (A1) byte = ASCII "+"
* If negative set D1 = D1 - D0 with (A1) byte = ASCII "-"

     MOVE.W    #4,CCR          Set Z=1, X=0
     SBCD.B    D1,D0           Put BCD {D0 - D1} in D0
     BCS       NEG             If C=1 branch to NEG
     MOVE.B    #$2B,(A1)       Set ASCII "+" in (A1)
     BRA       REST
NEG  ANDI.B    #$EF,CCR        Set X=0 (rest of CCR unchanged)
     NBCD.B    D0              Negate BCD in D0 byte
     MOVE.B    #$2D,(A1)       Set ASCII "-" in (A1)
REST <rest of program>
     *    *    *
```

To get the absolute value of a negative BCD byte D0, we must clear X before the NBCD. For example, suppose D1 = (0000)(0010) and D0 = (0000)(0001), that is, D1=2, D0=1, and D0 – D1= – 1. Then BCD {D0 – D1} = (1001)(1001) with X=1. NBCD with X=1 would give D0 = {0 – 99 – 1} = 0 wrong. NBCD with X=0 would give D0 = {0 – 99} = 1 correct.

MISCELLANEOUS DATA HANDLING

There are five instructions under this heading, ranging from very simple to rather abstruse:

```
SWAP{.W}    Dn                     Swap register halves

EXG{.L}     Rm,Rn                  Exchange registers

MOVEP.Z     Dm,d(An)               Move peripheral data -- output
MOVEP.Z     d(An),Dm               Move peripheral data -- input

LINK        An,#< -block_size>     Link & allocate stack
UNLK        An                     Unlink & deallocate
```

In these instructions, Z = L or W.

SWAP REGISTER HALVES

SWAP Dn simply reverses the upper and lower words of any data register — so that bits 0 through 15 move to bits 16 through 31 and vice versa.

Example of SWAP

Suppose we have D0 = $ABCDEF12 and we need to MOVE just the upper word $ABCD to D6. We would first use:

```
SWAP      D0          D0 upper = $EF12. D0 lower = $ABCD
```

giving us D0 = $EF12ABCD. Now we can use:

```
MOVE.W    D6          D6 word = $ABCD
```

Finally, we may wish to restore D0 with another SWAP:

```
SWAP      D0          D0 upper = $ABCD. D0 lower = $EF12
```

In effect SWAP acts like a 16-bit rotate (left or right) — but SWAP is much faster. Also, SWAP and rotate (ROR/ROL) have slightly different CCR rules. The CCR changes for SWAP are exactly the same as for MOVE:

X Unchanged (hence useful during multi-precision jobs)
N Set to 1 if new bit 31 = 1, cleared to 0 otherwise
Z Set to 1 if new long word is zero, cleared otherwise (So, in truth, Z doesn't change. But you may still want to test for zero.)
V Always cleared to 0
C Always cleared to 0

ROR/ROL differ in setting the C flag as the bits are rotated.

EXG — EXCHANGE REGISTERS

EXG{.L} Rm,Rn works with any mix of data and address registers (any of the following, for example):

```
EXG{.L}  Dm,Dn    Contents of Dm moved to Dn and vice versa
EXG{.L}  Dm,An    Same as EXG An,Dm
EXG{.L}  Am,An
```

The L is optional, since EXG implies longword. (All 32 bits are always exchanged.)

All forms are useful, insofar as they are equivalent to the following three MOVEs:

```
MOVE.L Rm,Rx
MOVE.L Rn,Rm
MOVE.L Rx,Rn
```

without your having to use a third register Rx as a go-between.

MOVEP — MOVE PERIPHERAL DATA

MOVEP is a specialized version of MOVE introduced to simplify interfacing with the previous generation of 8-bit devices (which are still, of course, being used).

Although Motorola blazed many new trails with the M68000 family, they made the sensible decision to incorporate features that would maintain compatibility with peripherals and I/O support chips designed for 8-bit processors, especially their own M6800 family.

We have already mentioned the fact that the M68000 can interface with both high-speed 16-bit asynchronous devices as well as slower, usually 8-bit, synchronous peripherals.

The MOVEP instruction is aimed at easing the programming effort in transferring 8-bit bytes in "bursts" between data registers and I/O devices. The M68000 uses memory-mapped I/O which, for our present purposes, simply means that you can address peripheral ports as if they were memory addresses. In place of the special I/O instructions you find with some systems, the M68000 can perform I/O with MOVE and the appropriate memory operands (with, of course, a little help from the many friendly device controllers that interface disks, printers, terminals, and so on).

Because 8-bit peripherals are best attached either to the high eight lines or to the low eight lines of the M68000 16-bit system data bus, their control registers "occupy" alternate byte addresses in the M68000 memory address space, consecutive odd byte addresses or consecutive even byte addresses.

In sending data and control to such peripheral registers, therefore, the normal MOVE would require rather peculiar address changes. The (An)+ and –(An) modes, for instance, work fine for contiguous memory transfers, but a typical I/O transfer may require the following: D0 contains (byte4)(byte3)(byte2)(byte1). To output D0 to 8-bit port address A0 would need:

MOVE byte4 to address A0

MOVE byte3 to address A0+2

MOVE byte2 to address A0 + 4
MOVE byte1 to address A0 + 6

(Note the sequence — high bytes in low addresses.) Without MOVEP, this could be achieved in many ways, all quite tedious, for example:

```
MOVE.B    D0,6(A0)
ROR.L     #8,D0          Rotate byte2 to lower byte
                         position
MOVE.B    D0,4(A0)
ROR.L     #8,D0          Rotate byte3 to lower byte
                         position
MOVE.B    D0,2(A0)
ROR.L     #8,D0          Rotate byte4 to lower byte
                         position
MOVE.B    D0, (A0)
```

The MOVEP gives a one-line solution:

```
MOVEP.L   D0,0(A0)       Output D0 to (A0)...(A0+6)
```

MOVEP achieves this by applying its own built-in rules for post-incrementing addresses. MOVEP moves bytes starting from the top of D0, then post-incrementing by 2.

If we look at the MOVEP formats for output,

```
MOVEP.L   Dm,d(An)       Move 4 bytes from Dm to alternating I/O byte
                         addresses starting at d(An)

MOVEP.W   Dm,d(An)       As above but move 2 bytes
```

we see that L or W dictates the number of bytes, and that the destination must be address register indirect with offset, which is used to specify the starting address for the transfer.

Motorola had an excellent reason for choosing d(An) as the operand. Typically, an area of memory will be designated for I/O addressing. An address register would be set to point to the base of this area, and symbolic (mnemonic) offsets would be assigned in the assembly source to distinguish the peripheral register addresses within the I/O memory map. For example, you may find:

```
MOVEP.W   D3,PIAD(A5)
```

where A5 is pointing to the I/O memory base, and PIAD is the offset from A5 for the address assigned to a Motorola 6821 PIA (Peripheral Interface Adapter). In large systems, such mnemonic tags are indispensable.

Figure 6-15 shows the various possible sequences of data-byte to byte-addresses. The precise details are not as important as the general understanding that by choice of L or W with odd or even starting address d(An), the one MOVEP can quickly transfer bytes to load the correct upper or lower 8 bits of the data bus.

The reverse procedure provides input from peripherals to any data register:

```
MOVEP.Z     d(An),Dm      Load Dm with 2 or 4 bytes from
                          alternating I/O byte addresses starting d(An)
```

Input with MOVEP works exactly like output but in the opposite direction — from alternating I/O byte addresses to the chosen data register. This symmetry in the coding formats for input and output is yet another M68000 programmer-befriending feature.

Finally, note that MOVEP does not affect the CCR flags, which is quite sensible if you think about it. You are simply sending or receiving a series of bytes, and there are no reasonable criteria for changing the CCR.

MOVEP — SUMMARY

MOVEP simplifies the transfer of data to and from byte-oriented I/O devices by automatically incrementing the operand addresses by 2 for each byte transferred. This allows the 16-bit data bus to be assigned to two separate 8-bit I/O ports.

The final, and most complex, instructions in this group of miscellaneous data movement operations, LINK/UNLK (Link/Unlink), require a little preamble.

LINK/UNLK — PREAMBLE

LINK/UNLK requires a thorough understanding of the stack, so we will recap the salient features of the stack concept.

In Chapter 5 we saw how the stack could be used for saving data and contexts during programs and subroutine calls. In particular, we saw that the stack holds the return address needed to guide a subroutine back to the place it was called from. The success of the stack as a preserver of data lies in the LIFO (Last In First Out) mechanism — so that as you push data on, and pull

Longword MOVEP <u>even</u> address

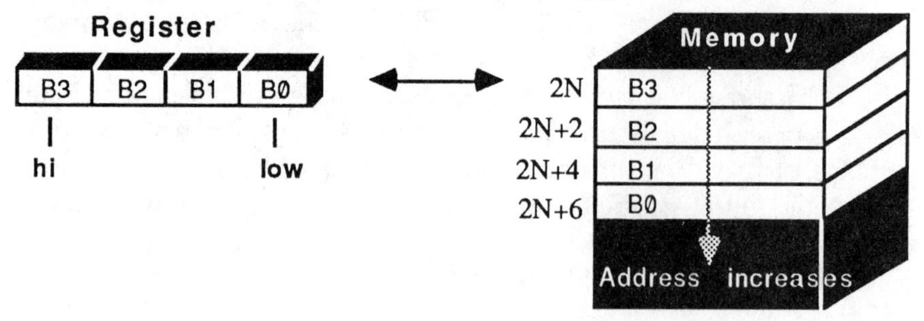

Longword MOVEP <u>odd</u> address

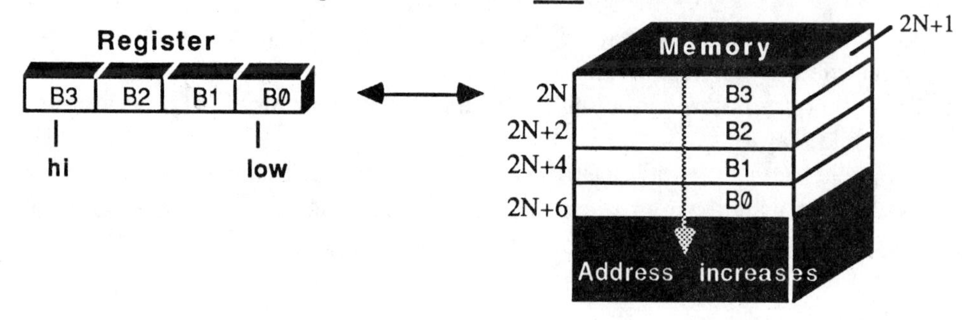

Word MOVEP <u>even</u> address

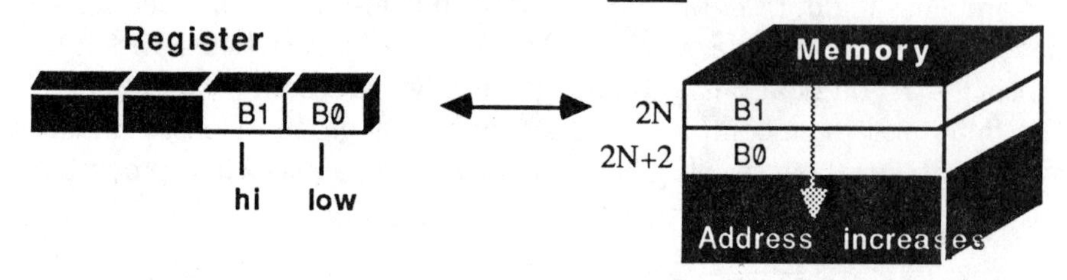

Word MOVEP <u>odd</u> address

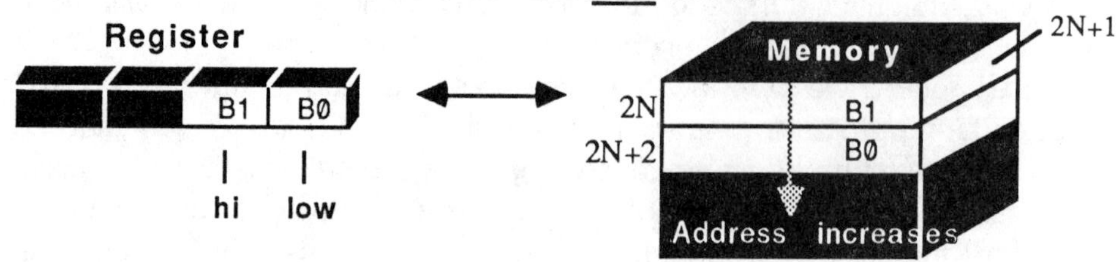

Fig. 6-15 MOVEP.Z Dm,d(An) and MOVEP.Z d(An),Dm

data from the stack, the stack is kept tidy without your having to worry unduly about memory addresses. The one address pointer, namely SP = A7, keeps track of where you are. SP always points to the last word saved on the stack.

There are many situations, however, where subroutines generate temporary or intermediate data, then call further sub-subroutines, and so on. When you get to several levels of what we call nested subroutines it can become a programmer's nightmare keeping track of each subroutine's temporary data locations. The natural place to hold each subroutine's data is on the stack itself, provided we can access and manipulate such areas without disturbing our normal stack processes. In particular, we must never lose a subroutine's return address.

So far, we have simply pushed and pulled items to and from the top of the stack with MOVE.z Dn,-(SP) and MOVE.z (SP)+,Dn but there is no law against your delving into other parts of the stack if you want to. You can treat the stack just like any other portion of memory using the stack pointer, SP (=A7), just as you would any other address pointer. You are completely free to use SP (= A7) with displacements and indexes in order to access and change stack data, as long as you observe two rules:

1. Never alter the subroutine's return address (which was pushed on the stack automatically by your BSR (Branch SubRoutine) or JSR (Jump SubRoutine).
2. Make sure that when the RTS (ReTurn from Subroutine) comes along, the value in SP is back to its correct value — because RTS will try to pull the return address from the top of the stack. If SP is not pointing at the right part of the stack, RTS will not recover the subroutine's return address, and chaos will reign.

The idea behind LINK/UNLK is to help the programmer in allocating data areas on the stack for any sequence of nested subroutines without violating these rules — well, at least, they reduce the risk.

We'll take you through the LINK/UNLK sequences. It will probably take several passes before all is clear.

THE STACK AS A DATA AREA — USING LINK AND UNLK

The LINK and UNLK instructions allow you to allocate and deallocate temporary data areas, known as **frames**, during nested subroutines without losing any earlier items saved on the stack, such as register values, CCR flags, and return addresses. The LINK/UNLK mechanism also helps you keep track of all previous frames set up by earlier subroutines.

WHAT IS A FRAME?

A frame is nothing more nor less than a portion of memory in a stack, assigned to any subroutine that needs working memory space. The maximum size of each frame is 32K bytes — but the total number of frames you assign is limited only by your pocketbook (how much RAM you have). Each subroutine that uses a LINK instruction will acquire its own unique frame. This frame remains on the stack until UNLK clears it. If, say, you have four nested subroutines, each using LINK, you would have four separate frames of data in your stack when the fourth subroutine is running. When a subroutine is completed it relinquishes or deallocates its frame before returning control to the previous subroutine.

LINK — Allocates a frame on the stack.

UNLK — Deallocates (removes) the frame from the stack.

The basic idea is that an address register (other than SP = A7) is assigned the job of FP (Frame Pointer). During a subroutine, you can manipulate the frame data using FP with any of the available address modes. The rest of the stack is undisturbed (as long as you keep within the frame). Look upon the FP as an address pointer to frame data located within a stack.

With this background, let's see how LINK is set up. The general format for LINK is:

```
LINK        An,#<-block_size>
```

where An, the designated FP (Frame Pointer), can be any address register except A7 (because A7 is your Stack Pointer). Once you designate an An as FP, you must use that chosen An for all subsequent LINK/UNLK operations. We will see that the address stored in An is changed as we move from one subroutine to another, so that it always gives us the correct FP for the active subroutine's frame.

The size of the frame in bytes is indicated by #<– block_size>. The negative sign in <– block_size> is needed because our stacks grow downwards in memory. Block_size is a 16-bit signed number (one extension word in the LINK instruction), so the maximum frame allowed is 32K bytes. Block_size must be an even number of bytes.

To achieve all that we have indicated, LINK performs the following three functions. We'll run them by you quickly, then elaborate the why's and wherefore's.

1. Save An on stack with a MOVE.L An,-(SP). The previous FP=An is now safe on the stack.

2. Save new value of SP in An with a MOVEA.L A7,An. Note A7 = SP. An is now our new, current FP.
3. Reset SP to {SP minus block_size}. This increases the stack size by <block_size> bytes. Our new frame of block_size bytes occupies memory addresses from An=FP to SP.

Let us go through LINK step by step, referring to Figures 6-16, 6-17, and 6-18.

Suppose we are executing subroutine A, and A5 holds the FP value for Subroutine A's frame. The contents of A's frame are not of immediate interest, except to note that the stack has grown (SP reducing) since A was first called.

Next, suppose that subroutine A reaches a BSR, which calls subroutine B. As you know, this immediately pushes B's return address on the stack.

B is now about to execute, and we may first want to save the CCR and some other registers on the stack. If so, we can push them on the stack in the usual way, and they will be safe there until B returns control back to A.

Assuming B needs 512 bytes of working memory (tables, buffers, etc), the next instruction in B would be:

```
        LINK      A5,#-512        Link via A5 with 512 bytes
```

This one line, in effect, performs these three operations:

```
MOVE.L    A5,-(SP)          Save subroutine A's FP on stack
```

(We push current FP = A5 on the stack because A5 changes during LINK and we will need to restore it later when we UNLK.)

```
MOVEA.L    {A7=SP},A5     A5 is now subroutine B's FP
```

(After step 1, SP is left pointing at A's FP on the stack. This part of the stack will become the start of B's frame, so we save SP in A5 as B's FP.)

```
ADDQ.L    #-512,SP
```

(Adding minus 512 to SP is the same as increasing the stack by 512 bytes. Between B's FP and the new SP we have allocated 512 bytes for use by B. Any subsequent pushes/pulls during subroutine B will take place on the enlarged stack beyond this allocated data area. We can use A5 = B's FP to reference any part of the 512-byte frame without altering SP; likewise we can push/pull the stack using SP without altering B's frame.)

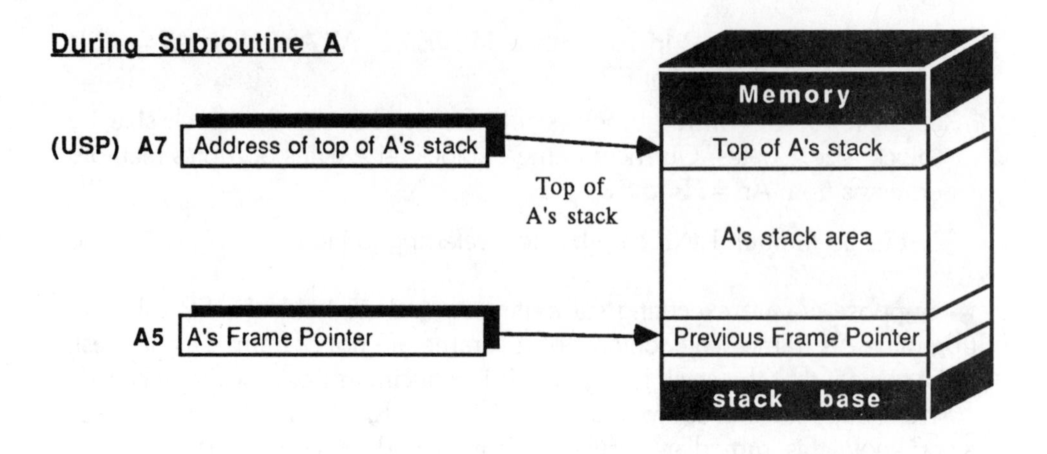

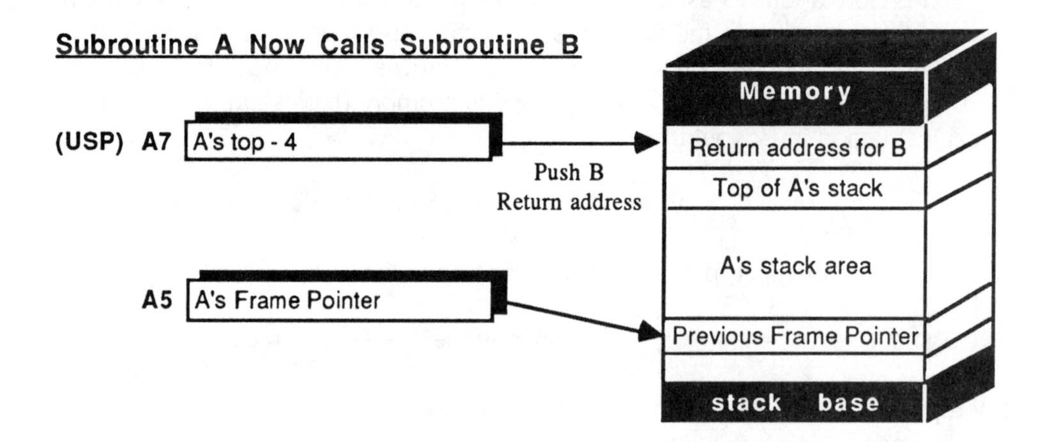

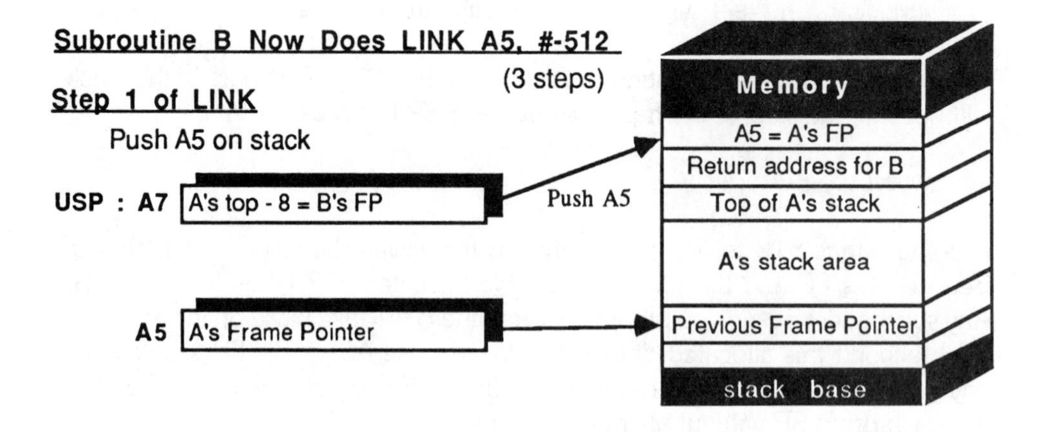

Fig. 6-16 LINK and UNLK (Part 1)

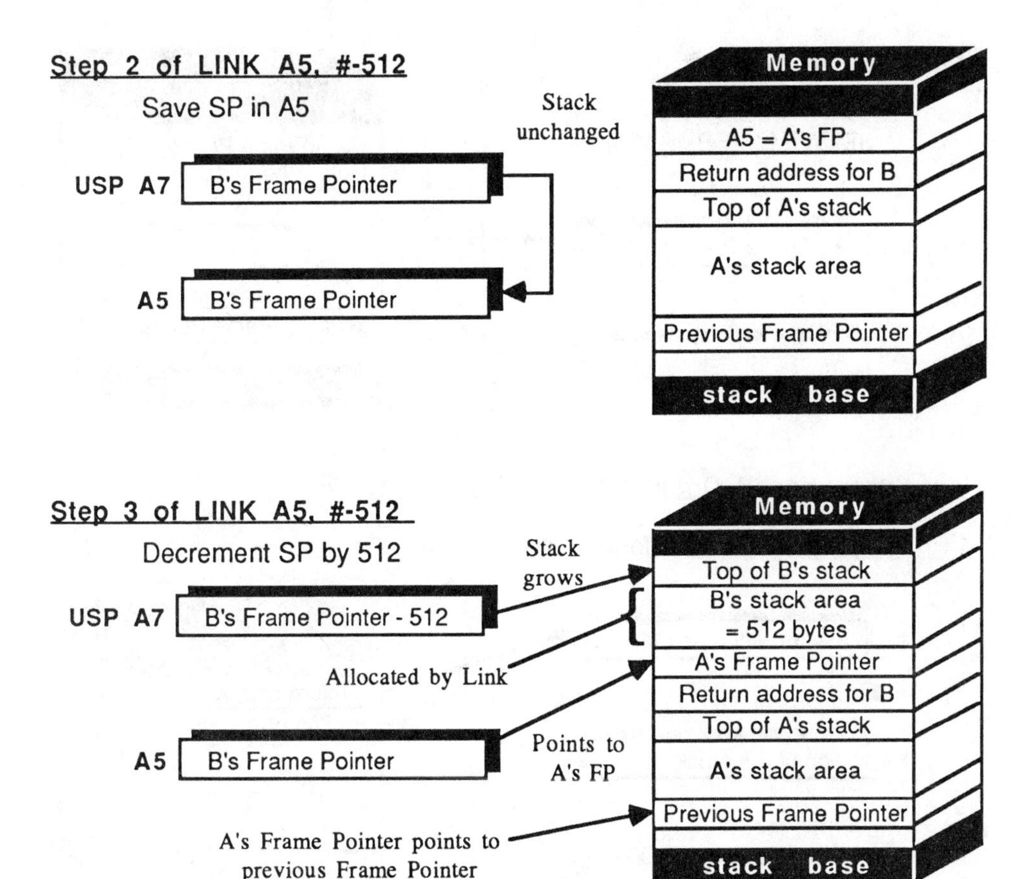

Subroutine B now proceeds using allocated stack area - SP changes (don't care)
Eventually Subroutine B does UNLK A5 (2 Steps)

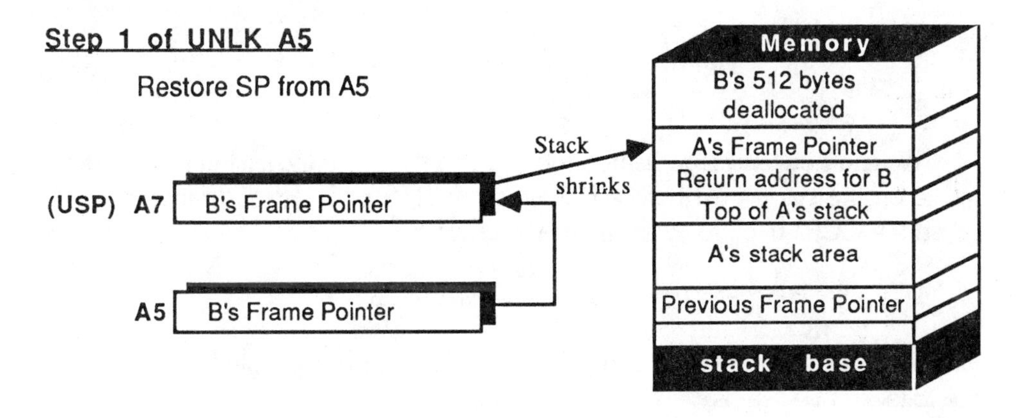

Fig. 6-17 LINK AND UNLK (Part 2)

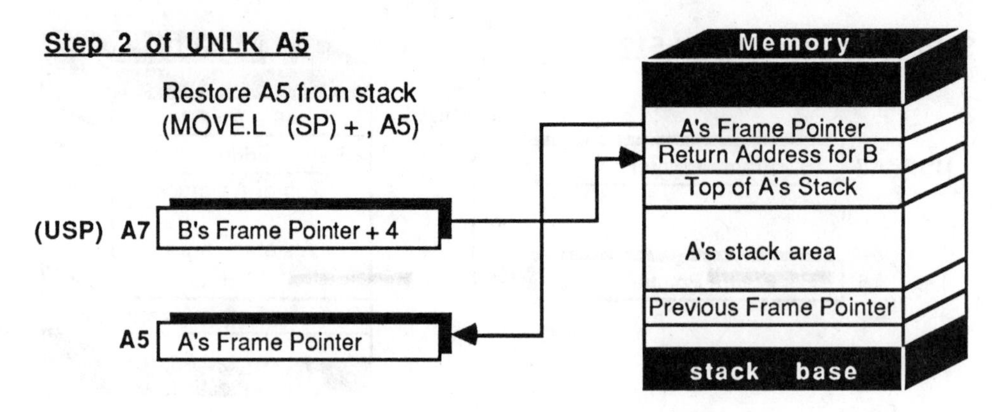

Now Subroutine B Does RTS Back to Subroutine A

Pull return address for B from stack → PC

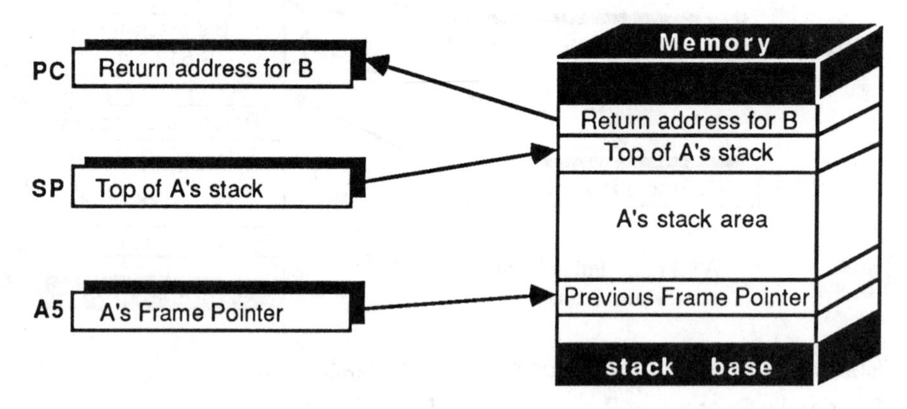

A Subroutine resumes with stack restored exactly.

Fig. 6-18 LINK and UNLK (Part 3)

We can now envisage subroutine B doing its own thing, using its 512-byte frame on the stack. Just before B is ready to RTS or RTR (assuming we had saved the CCR) back to subroutine A, we need:

```
UNLK      A5                  Unlink via A5
```

which deallocates B's frame and restores the stack automatically by performing the following two steps:

```
MOVEA.L   A5,{A7=SP}          Restore stack pointer
```

(This reverses step 2 of LINK by restoring B's FP into the stack pointer. SP now points to where we saved A's FP in Step 1 of LINK.)

```
MOVE.L     (SP)+,A5        Restore A's FP into A5
```

(Here we pull A's FP from the stack and put it back in A5. This reverses step 1 of LINK.)

If we had saved the CCR on the stack, an RTR now will restore the CCR and return us to subroutine A. If we had not saved the CCR, an RTS will return us to subroutine A.

In either case we are back into A with exactly the same stack disposition as when we left it for B. The stack and frame pointers are restored and B's data area has disappeared.

In turn A will unlink and return. The nested subroutines will eventually be completed to bring us back to the main program. By this time all our temporary frames will have been deallocated and A5 is now free of the FP chore.

LINK/UNLK — SUMMARY

We have spent some time explaining LINK/UNLK because it reveals several important aspects of contemporary software. The choice of the name LINK, for example, is worth pondering.

The first item in a frame is always a longword containing the address of the previous frame. So our frame pointer is actually pointing at another, earlier frame pointer. This idea of pointers pointing to pointers is not as difficult as it may sound. It is the basis of what we call **linked lists**, from which comes the name of the instruction LINK.

MORE ON PRIVILEGE

What is *privilege*? In the broadest sense, privilege can be established at any level in a computer system, ranging from padlocks on the terminals, to password-protected programs or files, and on to global privileges by which an operating system can guard against accidental or deliberate misuse by one user that can crash the system. The M68000 offers some unique hardware/software combinations that offer systems designers and programmers some assistance in this difficult area.

We conclude Chapter 6 with a roundup of the so-called privileged instructions, some of which we have already seen briefly.

Many of the privileged operations perform familiar tasks like MOVE and ANDI, and there is no mystery as to what they do, but because they change (or might change) vital system parameters or contexts, they are allowed only when the M68000 is in the supervisor state. Attempting to use a privileged instruction in the user state causes a TRAP, and we will see shortly how TRAPs are handled.

The state of the processor is indicated by the S flag (bit 13) in the status register. If S is set to 1, the M68000 is in supervisor state (also called system mode or privileged mode). If S is cleared to 0, the processor is in user state (or mode). In other words, the M68000 must be in one or the other state; there is no in-between. As the names imply, individual user programs normally run in user mode, while operating systems run in supervisor mode. Sitting at your terminal, you may be unaware of the fact, but the S flag is constantly switching between 0 and 1 as control passes to and from your job, other users' jobs, and the OS. A notable exception, by the way, is the Apple Macintosh, which operates in supervisor mode at all times.

The two states not only affect which instructions are legal, they also dictate whether certain registers can be accessed. Also, the M68000 indicates its state (S=0 or S=1) via signals on the FC (Function Control) pins, allowing other devices such as memory management chips, coprocessors, and so on, to detect and react to this state. A typical application here is to allow systems designers to control which segments of memory are assigned to user and system areas.

USER AND SUPERVISOR STACKS

One important consequence of the "either S=0 or S=1" situation is that the same register symbol, A7, can be used for two distinct physical registers without any ambiguity. *You* may be confused, but the chip knows! In supervisor mode, A7 = SSP (Supervisor Stack Pointer). In user mode, A7 = USP (User Stack Pointer).

The M68000 therefore maintains two distinct stack pointers and two distinct "A7-stacks", which are often called systems stacks (supervisor system stack and user system stack) to avoid confusion with the multitude of "private" user stacks that can be set up using A0 through A6 as stack pointers.

Now the user-programmer, in user mode, is free to access, manipulate, and even completely mutilate his or her user system stack using A7 (or the assembly mnemonic, SP) as an operand. The harm, if any, is confined to that user's job. But access to the supervisor stack is privileged, and this affords a certain measure of security, not absolute security, but protection against careless coding. As we'll see, the supervisor stack is constantly saving and restoring contexts for the entire system, so any unplanned interference with A7=SSP can be globally catastrophic.

On the other hand, the OS often needs to access A7=USP (for example, it will want to save your USP when switching jobs). If we are in supervisor mode we can't do this using A7, because A7 now means SSP. This catch-22 is avoided by the following privileged instructions.

```
MOVE.L    USP,An     Privileged: Move User Stack Pointer to An
MOVE.L    An,USP     Privileged: Move An to User Stack Pointer
```

In user mode, the above instructions would cause a trap. Having grabbed your stack pointer, the OS is at liberty to do what it likes to your stack data. The MOVE.L An,USP then allows the OS to restore your stack pointer if and when it feels the urge.

STACKS AND PRIVILEGE — SUMMARY

Summing up the privilege aspects of the two systems stacks: In user mode, there is unrestricted access using A7 or SP to the user stack, but the supervisor stack cannot be accessed. In supervisor mode, there is unrestricted access using MOVE with USP to the user stack, and unrestricted access using A7 or SSP to the supervisor stack.

PRIVILEGE AND THE SR (STATUS REGISTER)

The lower byte of the 16-bit SR is our much discussed CCR (Condition Code Register), which is freely accessible to all. You can test, move, and modify the CCR flags in both user and supervisor modes. The upper byte of the SR, the system byte, is an entirely different story. In user mode, the system byte is READ ONLY — with MOVE from SR. (However the MC68010/20 allow only MOVE from CCR — see Chapter 8.) In supervisor mode, the system byte is READ and WRITE — with MOVE from SR and MOVE to SR. We can also alter the SR with ANDI/ORI/EORI.

The system byte flags are:

Bits 8-10	Three-bit IM (Interrupt Mask)
Bit 13	S flag (Supervisor state = 1; User state = 0)
Bit 15	T flag (Trace mode on = 1; Trace mode off = 0)

so the user cannot directly alter these flags with a MOVE to. What you can do in either mode is MOVE from SR with

```
MOVE{.W}    SR,<adea>    Non-privileged -- read status word
```

allowing you to test any or all of the IM, S, T, or CCR flags. (Note the MC68010/20 exceptions referred to above.)

When the M68000 is initially switched on (or **reset**), it starts up in supervisor mode. This is quite natural and desirable since some kind of OS or booting firmware is going to initialize the system prior to user access.

Getting from supervisor to user mode presents no problem, since in supervisor mode the OS can clear the S flag at any time with

```
MOVE.W    #0,SR              Privileged Clear S flag
                             (and all other flags in SR)
```

or, if we do not want to clear all the SR, we can use one of the following.

```
EORI      #$2000,SR          Privileged Clear S flag
                             (other flags unchanged)


ANDI      #$DFFF,SR          Privileged Clear S flag
                             (other flags unchanged)
```

Similarly, you can use

```
ORI       #<mask>,SR         Privileged
```

to set selected SR flags.

You may wonder, then, how we ever pass from user mode to supervisor mode if the S flag cannot be "MOVEd to" in user mode. The answer lies in the M68000 concept of **exception processing**. An exception encountered while in user mode will switch the processor to supervisor mode, setting S = 1 and, depending on the exception, will save or attempt to save the processor context in a variety of ways.

EXCEPTIONS

In M68000 parlance, exceptions cover a wide variety of events, some of which are beyond the scope of this chapter. The following events met in user mode will initiate exception processing:

- TRAPs from detected errors
- Deliberate TRAP instructions
- Privilege violations
- Interrupts — internal or external
- Bus errors
- Reset

Each of these switch the processor to supervisor mode, where the exception is processed. Let's look at the first two exception types to get a feel for exception processing and how control is eventually returned to the user.

Error TRAPS

We saw in the DIVU/DIVS instruction that divide by zero was automatically detected, leading to a special TRAP. Very briefly, this is what happens in the trap on zero divide:

1. Switch to supervisor mode (S=1)
2. Save job context on system stack
3. Go to Vector #5 in exception vector table
4. Get address of exception handling program
5. Run this program which ends with RTE (ReTurn from Exception)
6. Restore job context and switch to user mode (S=0)
7. Resume user job

CHK — TRAP if Bound Exceeded

A similar type of error TRAP can be programmed to detect if values obtained during a calculation fall outside designated bounds:

```
CHK     <dea>,Dn        TRAP if Dn negative or greater than <dea>
```

If Dn is within stated limits, the next instruction is taken. If Dn is outside the limits, exception processing is triggered, just like TRAP on divide by zero, but this time we go to Vector #6 to pick up our handling program address.

TRAPV — TRAP on Overflow

TRAPV will generate a trap to Vector #7 if overflow is detected.

General TRAPs

```
TRAP    #<vector>       TRAP to #<vector>
```

This is a deliberate TRAP — so there is a way for the user-programmer to get into supervisor mode. In fact, TRAP #<vector> turns out to be a powerful systems programming tool for enlarging the instruction repertoire.

Table 6-5 shows the complete Exception Vector Assignment Table, from which you can see that there are 255 unique vectors available for exception

Table 6-5 Exception Vector Assignments

Vector Number(s)	*Dec*	*Address Hex*	*Space*	*Assignment*
0	0	0000	SP	Reset: Initial SSP[2]
1	4	004	SP	Reset: Initial PC[2]
2	8	008	SD	Bus Error
3	12	00C	SD	Address Error
4	16	010	SD	Illegal Instruction
5	20	014	SD	Zero Divide
6	24	018	SD	CHK Instruction
7	28	01C	SD	TRAPV Instruction
8	32	020	SD	Privilege Violation
9	36	024	SD	Trace
10	40	028	SD	Line 1010 Emulator
11	44	02C	SD	Line 1111 Emulator
12[1]	48	030	SD	(Unassigned, Reserved)
13[1]	52	034	SD	(Unassigned, Reserved)
14	56	038	SD	Format Error[5]
15	60	03C	SD	Uninitialized Interrupt Vector
16-23[1]	64	040	SD	(Unassigned, Reserved)
	95	05F		–
24	96	060	SD	Spurious interrupt[3]
25	100	064	SD	Level 1 Interrupt Autovector
26	104	068	SD	Level 2 Interrupt Autovector
27	108	06C	SD	Level 3 Interrupt Autovector
28	112	070	SD	Level 4 Interrupt Autovector
29	116	074	SD	Level 5 Interrupt Autovector
30	120	078	SD	Level 6 Interrupt Autovector
31	124	07C	SD	Level 7 Interrupt Autovector
32-47	128	080	SD	TRAP Instruction Vectors[4]
	191	0BF		
48-63[1]	192	0C0	SD	(Unassigned, Reserved)
	255	0FF		–
64-255	256	100	SD	User Interrupt Vectors
	1023	3FF		–

1. Vector numbers 12, 13, 16 through 23, and 48 through 63 are reserved for future enhancements by Motorola. No user peripheral devices should be assigned these numbers.
2. Reset vector (0) requires four words, unlike the other vectors which only require two words, and is located in the supervisor program space.
3. The spurious interrupt vector is taken when there is a bus error indication during interrupt processing. Refer to Paragraph 4.4.2.
4. TRAP #n uses vector number 32+n.

5. MC68010 only. See Return from Exception Section. This vector is unassigned, reserved on the MC68000, and MC68008.

routines. Some of these are fixed vectors, like CHK and TRAPV, others are reserved for present or future systems routines, like interrupt handling. The remaining vectors can be designated for TRAP #<vector> user applications.

As a simple example, an assembler might be written that converts, say, COSH into the machine language equivalent of TRAP #64. At address $100 (corresponding to vector #64) is the address of the COSH routine (whatever that may be). Such non-M68000 instructions are sometimes known as monitor, or service, calls. They are available to all users, and can be made to look just like M68000 instructions, complete with operands, which can be passed to the invoked routine via registers or the stack.

CONCLUSION

At this point you have seen all the *basic* M68000 instructions and address modes in action. Our examples were kept simple to isolate the "mechanics" of each group of instructions and operands. At the same time, we tried to reveal some of the underlying design motivations, the *why* that makes sense of the *how*. At least you now have the essential vocabulary of "the microchip of the 1980s", and we hope you are tempted and prepared to tackle the more cryptic texts which tend to accompany the commercially available M68000 assemblers. May the MOVE be with you! Before you rush away to raise havoc with your machines, we invite you to read our final two chapters on the MC68010 and MC68020.

7

The MC68010

The preceding chapters have focused specifically on the MC68000, the first chip in Motorola's 68000 family of micro-processors. This chapter discusses the next member of the 68000 family, the MC68010. Throughout this chapter, it is assumed that you are already familiar with the MC68000, that is, that you have read Chapters 1 through 6. Since the features added to the MC68010 are of a more advanced nature, the material in this chapter is more concentrated than the material in other chapters.

The keyword for the MC68010 is **emulation**, or "simulation of things that are not really there." Most of the features added to the MC68010 were for support of emulation. In typical emulations, nonexistent hardware is emulated by software. For example, some printers have been manufactured which have no formfeed capability. For these printers, it is common to emulate formfeeds in software by keeping track of the number of lines currently printed on a page, then printing enough additional linefeeds to make up a total of 66 lines. One of the most powerful applications of emulation is in virtual memory systems, wherein programs may directly access address locations far beyond the actual range of the available hardware memory. Virtual memory alone would have guaranteed the MC68010 a place in history. But the MC68010 does more.

The MC68010 is also capable of emulating whole operating systems and nonexistent (user-defined) 68000 instructions. These are commonly known as **virtual machine capabilities**. Such features simplify the development of new operating systems, which is by nature a very difficult but necessary task. The virtual machine also enables Motorola to check out (emulate) the behavior of future members of the 68000 processor family long before the chips are actually available, and even before the design of the new chip is finished on paper. This can be done in software on the MC68010 (or later 68000 processors). After the new 68000 processor is available, emulation performs yet another valuable function. MC68010 users who cannot upgrade their computers to a later 68000 processor can emulate in software many of the features of the later processor.

It is easy to see why Motorola implemented emulation capabilities early in the 68000 family history. From that point on, the MC68010 reduced the research costs of all further 68000 processors.

In this chapter we will talk about virtual memory and virtual machine capabilities, and the specific features that were added to the MC68010 to support them. Following that is a discussion of the different address spaces, and their role in the security features of virtual memory hardware. At the end of the chapter we will discuss loop mode, which speeds up the execution of certain small program loops; finally, we will discuss the MC68012 processor, a close relative to the MC68010.

VIRTUAL MEMORY

In any computer, there is a certain amount of real hardware memory available. In most computers, users are limited to using only this hardware memory. Previously, only mainframe computers and some minicomputers used software tricks to make it appear that there was, "virtually more memory available than there was hardware", hence the term **virtual memory**. In the friendliest type of virtual memory environment, the user accesses memory without any restrictions, and never knows (nor needs to be bothered by) how little hardware memory is actually available.

Does this not sound like a programmer's heaven? How is this possible, you ask, and what is the catch? Your suspicions are indeed well-founded; there are some important drawbacks.

At any given time, the hardware memory contains only part of the virtual memory being referenced. The remainder of the virtual memory is actually stored somewhere else, usually on a disk. For example, consider a simple virtual memory system which only has 192K of hardware memory, but allows programs to address up to 384K of virtual memory. In this system, memory is divided into segments (or "pages") of 64K each. Hence, no more than 3 pages of memory will be in hardware memory at any time, even though 6 pages appear to be available to any program. Page 1 is the operating system, and must always be in hardware memory. Pages 2 through 6 make up a large user program which is currently running, and which resides on the disk in its entirety. Figure 7-1 compares the arrangement of memory on disk, in hardware memory, and as it appears to the virtual memory user. The virtual memory configuration is a fantasy: it doesn't exist anywhere, except as a set of pointers to the disk and the

Disk Memory	Page 2	Page 3	Page 4	Page 5	Page 6	
Virtual Memory	Page 1 (OS)	Page 2	Page 3	Page 4	Page 5	Page 6
Hardware Memory	Page 1 (OS)	Page 2				

Beginning Memory Configuration

Disk Memory	Page 2	Page 3	Page 4	Page 5	Page 6	
Virtual Memory	Page 1 (OS)	Page 2	Page 3	Page 4	Page 5	Page 6
Hardware Memory	Page 1 (OS)	Page 2	Page 4			

Second Memory Configuration

Disk Memory	Page 2	Page 3	Page 4	Page 5	Page 6	
Virtual Memory	Page 1 (OS)	Page 2	Page 3	Page 4	Page 5	Page 6
Hardware Memory	Page 1 (OS)	Page 2	Page 5			

Third Memory Configuration

Fig. 7-1 68000 Virtual Memory Configurations

hardware memory. When the user program starts executing, memory is arranged as shown in the beginning configuration in Figure 7-1.

The virtual memory system has loaded in only the first page of the user program at this time (page 2). Now suppose that the user program asks for some data that is stored in page 4 of the program. As far as the user program is concerned, nothing is known about the virtual memory system; the program simply addresses a location within page 4, but the virtual memory system automatically detects that page 4 is not currently in hardware memory, and fetches it from the disk. Thus, memory is now arranged as in the second memory configuration in Figure 7-1.

Whenever the user program references data within page 4, the virtual memory system converts these address references into the corresponding true hardware addresses. Note that page 4 is actually residing in the third page of hardware memory; the user program will ask for addresses within page 4, but will end up getting addresses within the third page of hardware memory.

Now suppose that the program asks for some data within page 5. Since there is no unoccupied hardware memory left, either page 1, 2, or 4 must be dumped in order to make room for page 5. The best use of resources is to replace (or "swap") page 4 with page 5. If page 4 was changed while it was in hardware memory, it must first be written back to disk in its new form. In any case, page 5 then replaces page 4, and memory is now arranged as in the third memory configuration shown in Figure 7-1.

The decision about which page to swap out and the size of each page, is a function of many things. For now, let us just say that if you have some good ideas in this area your programming future will be a rosy one. Since disk accesses are at least 100 times slower than memory accesses, we see that the tradeoff in virtual memory is having more memory available, but at a slower execution speed. Furthermore, totally unrestricted and poorly planned use of virtual memory can result in situations where excessive disk/memory swapping goes on. For example, suppose that the program above went into a loop where page 4 and page 5 were accessed alternately 1000 times. This would cause 1000 disk swaps to read the same two pieces of data — a truly wasteful situation. So remember, virtual memory should be used with caution.

In order to efficiently implement virtual memory, it is necessary to detect or "trap" illegal memory references and do translation of addresses from virtual address into hardware address, all via external hardware, usually a memory management unit. Without this capability, the CPU would be hopelessly bogged down checking every memory reference in every single instruction.

When an illegal memory reference is made in a system without virtual memory, it is not initially detected by the 68000. With no loss of time, the 68000 passes on the request to the bus, which dutifully passes it on to the memory ("call for Mr Hex FFFFFFF0!"), which is not a real hardware memory location. The bus detects this, and notifies the 68000. The 68000 generates a bus error exception in the middle of the current instruction within the user program, saves (on the system stack) information about the instruction in progress when the bus error occurred, and then goes to the OS's standard bus error processing routine. Usually, the bus error is reported, and the user program is aborted.

How is virtual memory implemented? Imagine that some instruction such as MOVE asks for a memory location (the virtual memory location) that is well beyond the real hardware memory limit. How is it possible for this fact to be quickly detected and remedied? In a system with virtual memory, a hardware memory management unit is generally present between the 68000 and the bus. This unit intercepts each memory request, translates the virtual address into a possibly different hardware memory address, then fetches data from this location and returns it to the 68000. It appears to the programmer and the 68000 processor that the data was actually fetched from the virtual memory location. The memory management unit maintains a table of what virtual memory pages are currently in hardware memory, and where they are located in hardware memory. If the virtual address is currently not available in hardware memory, the memory management unit generates a bus error, which suspends the current instruction in the middle of its execution. The instruction in progress is suspended, information is stored on the system stack, and the operating system's bus error routine is activated. The bus error routine examines the information that was saved on the system stack. If it was due to a virtual memory access, then the appropriate disk/memory swap is done. Afterward, an RTE instruction returns to the user program, and finishes the user instruction that was in progress.

Why is virtual memory possible on the MC68010 but not on the MC68000? Unlike the MC68010, the information pushed on the system stack by the MC68000 during the middle of the instruction that generated the bus error exception is not sufficient for the RTE instruction to finish that instruction. It is only sufficient to enable software diagnosis of what happened, so that an informative error message can be sent to the user when his or her program is aborted.

VIRTUAL MACHINE

The MC68010 not only supports virtual memory, but the more general concept of a virtual machine. In virtual memory, actual disk room emulates imaginary hardware memory. Other software and hardware emulations can be effected in similiar ways.

For example, the concept of disk buffer caching is the exact opposite of virtual memory; the user appears to be writing to disk, but is actually writing to memory. In a caching system, everything read and written to the disk is also redundantly stored in hardware memory for future use. Later on, if the same disk data is again requested, it is fetched from the memory cache rather than from the disk. Since memory fetches are several orders of magnitude faster than disk accesses, the benefits should be obvious.

Another classic example of hardware emulation is a printer spooler. In some spooling systems, the user is convinced that his program is sending data directly to the printer, when actually it is going to a temporary file on disk, or to mag tape. The disk file may actually be printed immediately, hours later, or never. This is of particular importance on machines with one printer and many users, since only one user can be allowed on the printer at a time, but it would be unreasonable to make everyone else wait for the current user to finish his printing.

Even more sophisticated is the ability of an Operating System (OS) to emulate another OS. What is an OS? It is the most important program run on any given computer. It is there when the computer is turned on, remains there until the computer is powered down, and controls the execution of every other program run on the computer. It is sometimes refered to as the **monitor**. In many personal computers, the OS is stored in Read Only Memory (ROM), to protect it from accidental destruction.

How is the OS program originally created? It can be done from scratch, but only with a great degree of difficulty. A more feasible method is to use a pre-existing OS (call it OS-1) to oversee the development and execution of the new OS (call it OS-2), until OS-2 has been debugged to a point where it can survive on its own. During this development phase, OS-1 is actually in control of the computer, and subexecutes (emulates) OS-2. When any special circumstances arise, control passes back to OS-1, which decides what to do, and decides afterwards whether or not to return to OS-2. This emulation requires a bit of trickery. The typical OS is, by profession, an omnipotent creature. It is the constant and sole controller of an entire computer system. In order to properly emulate an OS that will eventually be on its own, OS-1 must trick OS-2 into thinking that it too is omnipotent. On the MC68010, this is achieved by running the emulated OS-2 in user mode, at a lower privilege than the controlling OS-1, which is in system, or supervisor, mode. As long as the emulated OS-2 executes simple instructions, it is doing nothing more than is allowed to the average user, and life is simple. As soon as OS-2 encounters any special conditions (for example, if hardware interrupts are received from external hardware, or if errors occur due to bugs in OS-2), a 68000 exception is generated, the controlling OS-1 emulates the request (often via a software routine), and returns control to OS-2. One virtual resource that the emulated OS-2 must have access to is the system bit. OS-2 must be able to set it, test it, and execute all of the privileged 68000 instructions that require it be set. OS-2 must be able to do all of these successfully, and do them while actually remaining in user mode. The trick is no different than the other virtual methods described above. Any of these actions generates a 68000 exception, the controlling OS-1 carries out the request, and returns control to OS-2.

On the MC68000, the OS-2 can determine that it is not the controlling OS by doing a MOVE SR,Dn and then testing the system bit. This works because MOVE from SR is not a privileged instruction on the MC68000. Because of this and other loopholes, the MC68000 cannot fully support emulation.

On the MC68010, this loophole is closed by making MOVE from SR privileged. When executed from user mode, MOVE from SR generates an exception, the controlling OS-1 takes over, and then has the option to copy a counterfeit SR (with the system bit off) into Dn, and return. The emulated OS-2 has no way of detecting that this is actually what happened. The (unprivileged)

MOVE from CCR instruction was added to the MC68010 so that the condition codes could still be accessed without generating an exception.

Another loophole preventing the MC68000 from fully supporting emulation is the fact that the information pushed on the stack during an exception is not sufficient to complete the instruction, but only to diagnose what happened. This was mentioned in the preceding section on virtual memory.

What is to prevent the emulated OS-2, omnipotent as it (thinks it) is, from doing its own emulation of a third OS-3 while it is still in the emulated environment? The answer is nothing at all. If this were not so, the original emulation would not be a true emulation. Furthermore, there could be a long chain of emulated OS-n's, each thinking it is on top, and totally incapable of determining whether or not it really is.

The most sophisticated emulation is the emulation of a CPU by another CPU. This allows software for a new CPU (for example, the MC68020) to be developed and debugged on a pre-existing CPU (for example, the MC68010), while the new CPU is still under hardware development. This CPU emulation is possible within the 68000 processor family because its instructions sets have been designed to be upward compatible. Thus, any instruction from any 68000 processor will execute the same on all later 68000 processors; on earlier 68000 processors, the instruction either executes the same, or is an illegal instruction and generates an illegal instruction exception. Thus, to emulate an MC68020 instruction in an MC68010 operating system, it is only necessary to modify the illegal instruction routine in the OS to check for this particular instruction, and, if detected, emulate the instruction in software before returning.

If emulation is so versatile, why aren't more CPUs and OSs emulated in day-to-day use? The simple answer is efficiency. The emulated (software) CPU may run many times slower than the true (hardware) CPU, due to the overhead of exception processing and the use of whole routines to emulate single instructions.

This finishes our discussion of the major emulation features of the MC68010. The next three sections examine the new registers and instructions that are used to support emulation and virtual memory hardware.

VECTOR BASE REGISTER

The MC68010 has a Vector Base Register (VBR), used during emulation. It is not present on the MC68000. It is used to support transitions between a normal operating system environment and an emulation environment. In order to appreciate its significance, we will need a little background.

When an exception is generated on the MC68000, several events take place. Depending on the kind of exception, certain special registers are modified, certain information is pushed onto one or more stacks, and, last of all, a branch is made to one of 255 possible exception routines. All we are concerned with here is that final branch. For example, division by zero causes a branch to exception routine number 5. The addresses of these 255 routines are found in the first 256 longwords in memory (the first of the 256 longwords is not an address, but is the stack pointer at power-up time). Rigorously, the address of exception routine number n is found in the longword at memory location 4n. For example, the address of the divide-by-zero routine is at hex memory location $14 (= 4 x 5). In conventional 68000 terminology, n is called the **exception vector number**, 4n is called the **exception vector offset**, the address at longword 4n is called the **exception vector**, and the table of 255 longword addresses is called the **exception vector table**.

Now imagine that the normal OS is overseeing the emulation of another OS. Based on discussions earlier in this chapter, it is easy to see that, during emulation, exceptions will be treated radically different than during normal operation, since they will be heavily concerned with making sure that the emulated OS is kept in the dark about what is really happening. An alternate set of exception routines will be active, having different addresses from the normal set of routines. There are various ways to switch between two sets of exception routines, some of which do not require any new registers, but the simplest is to use the vector base register.

In the MC68010, exceptions end with a branch to the address contained at memory location 4n + VBR, where VBR represents the number currently stored in the vector base register. Note that, if VBR is zero, this is the same as the MC68000 exception branch. Indeed, during power-up, VBR is set to zero. Thus, an OS for the MC68000 will run exactly the same on the MC68010.

When an OS sets up an emulation environment, it loads a set of alternate exception routines and sets up an alternate vector table (not located at memory location zero). Thereafter, to enable the alternate exception routines, it is only necessary to move the location of the alternate vector table into VBR. This is done with a single MOVEC instruction. To go back to normal operation, it is only necessary to set VBR back to zero. The overhead for switching between sets of exception routines is thus reduced to its bare minimum, namely, one MOVEC instruction. This quick switch not only saves time and program steps, but also avoids a potential problem; if an interrupt occurred in the middle of a lengthy vector table changeover, how could we guarantee that the correct interrupt routine is used?

The following sample program changes the value of VBR to hex $00100000.

```
MOVE.L     #$100000,D0      Set up new VBR value
MOVEC      D0,VBR           Change vector base register
```

The MOVEC command is discussed in the following section.

Figure 7-2 shows typical memory allocations for a regular operating system and an emulated operating system. Steps 1 to 3 follow what happens during a

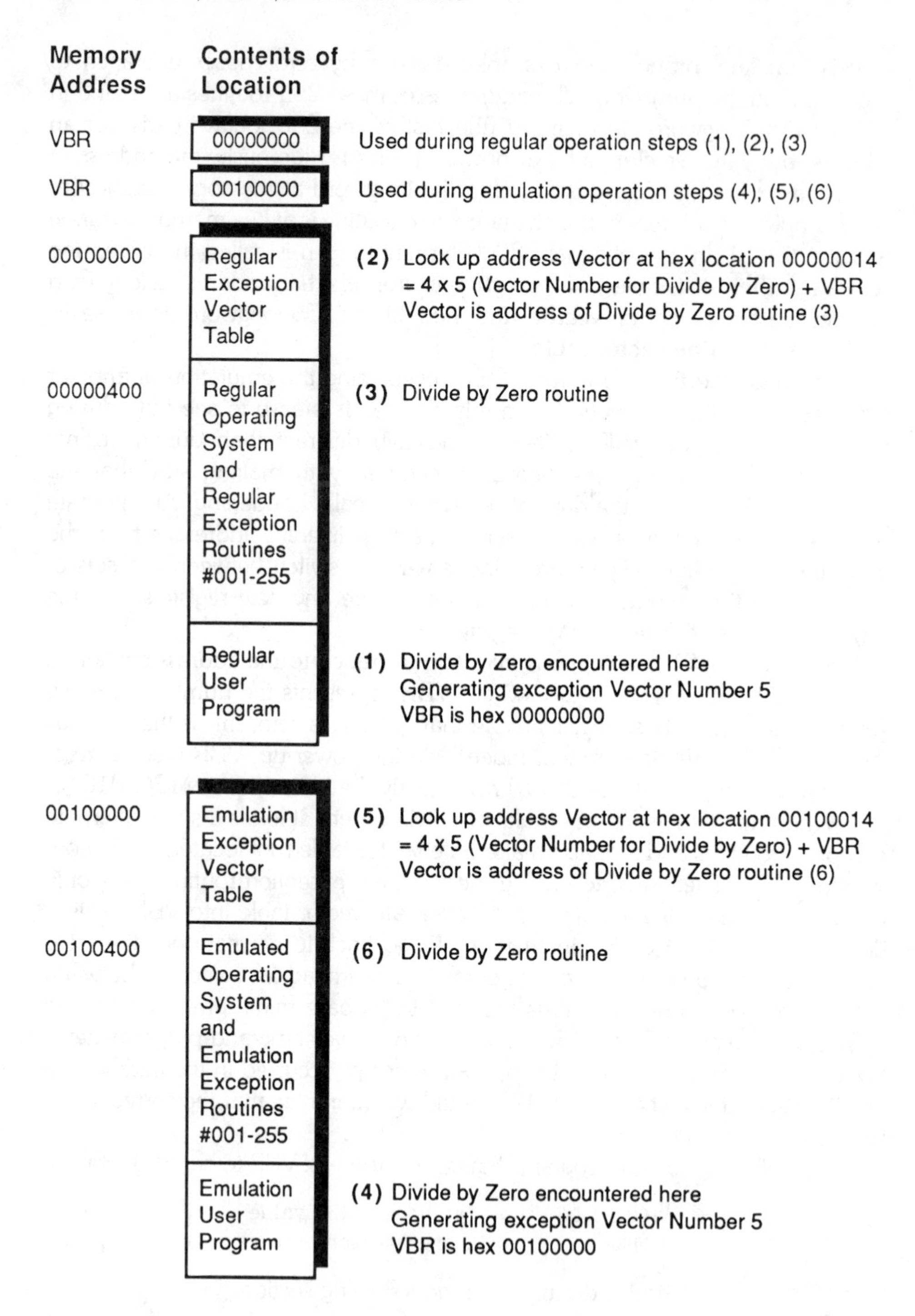
Memory Address
Contents of Location
VBR
00000000
Used during regular operation steps (1), (2), (3)
VBR
00100000
Used during emulation operation steps (4), (5), (6)
00000000
Regular Exception Vector Table
(2) Look up address Vector at hex location 00000014
= 4 x 5 (Vector Number for Divide by Zero) + VBR
Vector is address of Divide by Zero routine (3)
00000400
Regular Operating System and Regular Exception Routines #001-255
(3) Divide by Zero routine
Regular User Program
(1) Divide by Zero encountered here
Generating exception Vector Number 5
VBR is hex 00000000
00100000
Emulation Exception Vector Table
(5) Look up address Vector at hex location 00100014
= 4 x 5 (Vector Number for Divide by Zero) + VBR
Vector is address of Divide by Zero routine (6)
00100400
Emulated Operating System and Emulation Exception Routines #001-255
(6) Divide by Zero routine
Emulation User Program
(4) Divide by Zero encountered here
Generating exception Vector Number 5
VBR is hex 00100000

Fig. 7-2 Use of the VBR During an Emulation

Table 7-1 Control Register Move Commands

Control Register	Hex Code	MOVEC Instruction	MOVE Instruction	Privilege Status
To SR			68000	Privileged
From SR			68000	Not privileged
From SR			68010	Privileged
To CCR			68000	Not privileged
From CCR			68010	Not privileged
USP	800	68010	68000	Privileged
VBR	801	68010		Privileged
SFC	000	68010		Privileged
DFC	001	68010		Privileged
MSP	803	68020		Privileged
ISP	804	68020		Privileged
CACR	002	68020		Privileged
CAAR	802	68020		Privileged

divide-by-zero exception under a regular operating situation. Steps 4 to 6 follow what happens during a divide-by-zero exception under an operating system emulation environment. Switching back and forth between the two sets of exceptions is accomplished by simply changing the vector base register.

THE MOVEC AND MOVES INSTRUCTIONS

MOVEC is a privileged instruction on the MC68010 which moves data to and from "control registers". An easy rule of thumb is that MOVEC performs all the moves that MOVE doesn't perform. The only exception to this rule is register USP, which can be moved using either MOVE or MOVEC. If Motorola had it to do all over again, it would probably have MOVEC also perform the functions of the other special MOVE instructions, namely, MOVE USP, MOVE SR, and MOVE CCR. This would have made for a more homogeneous instruction set.

The chief uses of MOVEC on the MC68010 are to change the values of the vector base register (discussed above) and the function code registers, SFC and DFC (discussed below).

Table 7-1 summarizes all of the 68000 instructions that move control registers. For each type of control register, the table indicates whether the register can be moved using MOVE or MOVEC, and the first processor on which each instruction is implemented. A blank entry indicates that the instruction is not available on any existing 68000 processor. The hex code column gives the 3-digit hex code used to represent each control register in the MOVEC instruction. MC68020 instructions have been included in the table for completeness.

THE SFC AND DFC REGISTERS AND ADDRESS SPACES

The Source and Destination Function Code (SFC and DFC) registers are 3-bit registers which designate different "address spaces". Only 68000 programmers involved in the deepest system work will probably ever have to deal with these registers. They are involved in the support of memory management and system security. In a system that protects certain parts of memory, the SFC and DFC are used within supervisor mode to access memory that is normally inaccessible. In order to fully explain how the function code registers operate, it is necessary to look at the actual 68000 hardware.

Up to 32 of the pins coming out of a 68000 processor are address lines. When data is read from or written to memory, these lines carry the 32-bit address of the affected memory location. Three more pins are used as function code lines. The function code tells what kind of memory is being accessed, for example, whether it is program memory or data memory, or whether it is user memory or system memory. At the same time, the function code indicates a memory bank or "address space" to look in. Technically speaking, it is possible to specify up to 8 different address spaces, each having a 32-bit address range, and each conceivably corresponding to different hardware memory. Initially, this sounds equivalent to a 35-bit address range. In actuality, however, only 4 full 32-bit address spaces are used by the 68000 and, in typical hardware implementations, these 4 address spaces are made to address the same 32-bit address range of hardware memory. Hence, expectant programmers dreaming of more than 32 bits of addressing should beware.

Table 7-2 lists the 8 function codes and their currently assigned address spaces.

If the 68000 is currently in user mode (that is, the system, or supervisor, bit is 0), and an instruction is being fetched from memory, then a function code of 001 goes out the function code lines. When an instruction fetches data from memory during user mode, a 010 goes out the function code lines. When the same two operations occur in supervisor mode, a 101 or 110 goes out the function code lines.

The fifth and last function code is the **CPU space function code**. This special code appears during four types of communications with external hardware devices, namely, during interrupts, breakpoints (BKPT instruction), access

Table 7-2 Address Space Function Codes

Function Code Bits	*Address Space*
000	Unavailable — reserved for future Motorola use
001	User Data Space
010	User Program Space
011	Reserved for user definition
100	Reserved for future Motorola use
101	Supervisor Data Space [includes Exception Vectors 2 to 255]
110	Supervisor Program Space [includes Exception Vectors 0 and 1]
111	CPU Space [in MC68000, only used for Interrupt Acknowledge]

level control (the MC68020 instructions CALLM and RTM), and coprocessor communications (the MC68020 coprocessor instructions). The CPU space is special in that it does not address memory. Instead, the 32 address lines are used to pass various parameters.

When the 68000 reads or writes to memory, a 32-bit address is sent out, along with one of the first four function codes. Hardware outside of the 68000 decides what to do about the request. In the simplest situation, the external hardware simply ignores the function code, uses the 32-bit address, and looks up the location in hardware memory. In a more sophisticated situation, four different sets of hardware memory can exist, one for each of the first four function codes. In such a case, it is possible for an operating system, an OS data table, a user program, and a user data table to all reside at the same numerical address. Each can be accessed with the same address, but with a different function code.

The function code can also be used to implement system security. This can be done via an external memory management device, whose duty is to make sure that users are not allowed to access certain parts of memory. For instance, an OS might wish to allow users to run programs that are in the supervisor space (function code 110), but not allow them to look at the programs themselves (function code 101). If the address spaces for these two function codes actually correspond to different hardware memory, then the user can never actually access the program as data. The program is thus invisible and secure from examination. If these two address spaces actually correspond to the same hardware memory, then the user can access the program as data, and it is necessary to enlist the aid of the external memory management device in order to prevent the user from examining the program.

Say that you are on one of those wonderful systems where there are indeed four different sets of memory. Assume that you wish to access the contents of address 123456 in all four memory address spaces. The data memory address spaces are easy to get to, but the program memory address spaces are inaccessible. Inaccessible, that is, unless you use MOVEC and MOVES. The following example shows how to access one of the four memories, the user program space.

```
MOVE.L      #2,D0        User program space function code = 2
MOVEC       D0,SFC       Move into source function code
MOVES.L     123456,D1    Get word 123456 from user program
                         space
```

Note: Changing SFC or DFC only affects the execution of the MOVES instruction. It does not have any effect on the execution of other instructions.

The ability to distinguish different address spaces enables the MC68010 to indicate to external hardware when it is accessing system programs, system data, user programs, and user data. It is thus possible to selectively protect one or more of these address spaces from user access via external memory management hardware, without bogging down the 68000 CPU with time-consuming checks. With proper hardware, each address space can be made to correspond to different hardware memory. Typical implementations, however, use only one set of hardware memory. Using the SFC and DFC registers, the MOVEC instruction, and the MOVES instruction within (privileged) supervisor mode, it is possible for the OS to access all four of these address spaces.

LOOP MODE

The MC68010 automatically detects when certain 3-word instruction loops have repeated more than one time, and then goes into loop mode. In this mode, the instructions are not repeatedly fetched from memory, as would occur during normal operation, but are locked into the CPU pre-fetch queue and decode register, and not fetched again. If the loop is interrupted by any exceptions, loop mode will resume after returning and going through two more loop repetitions. Thus, simple loops such as the movement of a block of bytes, the summation of a list of numbers, and the shifting of a group of numbers, can be executed at speeds comparable to the speed of a single (for example, block move) instruction.

The allowable loops consist of certain 1-word instructions followed by a DBcc instruction. The 1-word instructions allowed are summarized in Table 7-3 where lea represents loop effective address modes (An), –(An), or (An)+ and rea represents Dn or An.

Table 7-3 MC68010 Loopable Instructions

Instructions	*Operands*		
MOVE	lea,lea	or	rea,lea
ADD SUB	lea,rea	or	Dn,lea
CMP	lea,rea	or	(Ax)+,(Ay)+
AND OR	lea,Dn	or	Dn,lea
EOR	Dn,lea		
ABCD ADDX SBCD SUBX	−(Ax),−(Ay)		
CLR NEG NEGX NOT	lea		
TST NBCD	lea		
ASL ASR LSL LSR	lea		
ROL ROR ROXL ROXR	lea		

THE MC68012

The only difference between the MC68010 and the MC68012 is that the MC68012 can address up to either 1024MB or 2048MB of RAM (a 30-bit or 31-bit address), compared to 16MB on the MC68010 (a 24-bit address). For all practical purposes, the programmer may consider them identical.

Why did Motorola make the MC68012? If an application requires more than 24 bits of addressing, it might seem appropriate to simply use an MC68020, which allows a full 32-bit address. However, there are two good reasons why an MC68012 can be preferable: money and materials. The MC68020 will be priced significantly higher for a while, due to the development cost of its many new features. Also, the MC68020 has a different pin configuration, and will not fit into the sockets that fit all of the preceding members of the 68000 family. Thus, it is possible to produce hardware using the MC68010, and later upgrade them to a 30-bit address by simply replacing the MC68010 with an MC68012. Upgrading to an MC68020 would require a new socket.

CONCLUSION

Starting with the MC68010, any 68000 processor can emulate all of the instructions of any other 68000 processor. Except for the loop mode feature, all of the features that were added to the MC68010 were solely to support these emulation capabilities. Fully supported emulation can also be used to carry out other very powerful emulation functions, such as virtual memory and virtual machines.

8

The MC68020

In this chapter we discuss the additional features of the MC68020, as compared with the MC68010. This chapter assumes that you are familiar with the 68000 family in general, and that you have read Chapter 7 on the MC68010.

The new features of the MC68020 cover much territory. Additional features include a full 32-bit addressing path, an instruction cache to speed up 68000 instruction execution, 7 instructions to support coprocessors such as Motorola's MC68881 floating point coprocessor, 6 new addressing modes to support more versatile addressing, and a master system bit to support environments with multiple operating systems.

In addition, a variety of miscellaneous instructions have been either extended or added, including 8 instructions to manipulate bit fields, several new divide-and-multiply formats, and extended displacements on branch instructions.

Finally, the MC68020 has a dynamic bus sizing interface, which enables the processor to communicate with 8-, 16-, or 32-bit devices, making 8-, 16-, or 32-bit data transfers, and to do them in any combination at any time. Thus, all data alignment restrictions have been eliminated, except that instructions must still lie on even-byte boundaries.

The processor has 120 pins, which are arranged in a square pattern on the bottom, rather than the edges, of the chip. Hence, upgrading a system from an older 68000 processor to a MC68020 requires a new socket.

INSTRUCTION CACHE

The **instruction caching** system of the MC68020 is a mechanism that speeds up the execution time of programs with small loops. It is an MC68020 feature that will benefit all of its users. It can be easily enabled or disabled, requires no change in how programs are written, and introduces no overhead in the normal processing of the MC68020 in exchange for its advantages.

CACHING IN THE 68000 FAMILY

Motorola has used analysis of past programming experiences to guide the design of the 68000 family. The MC68020 on-chip cache is another application of this philosophy. Studies of assembly programs show that most of their overall execution time is spent inside of fairly small-sized loops. Without any kind of instruction cache system, each time a loop executes, its instructions must be fetched from memory. If a small loop executes more than once, the same instructions are repeatedly fetched. This is how the MC68000 and most other processors function.

The MC68010 introduced a medium-scale version of caching, called loop mode. Loop mode only caches 3 instruction words, and only occurs when the last 2 words are a DBcc instruction. See Chapter 7 for further details on loop mode.

The MC68020 introduced a full-scale version of caching. Previously executed instructions are stored within the MC68020 processor, in a 64-longword cache (a 256-byte internal memory area). The first time a program loop executes, no benefits are realized from the cache; each instruction is fetched from memory, just as in the MC68010. Starting with the second time through the loop, however, the cache system detects that the instructions are already within the cache, and does not tie up the external bus fetching them again. The net result is faster execution time.

HOW CACHE WORKS

We now detail how the cache functions. First, however, some preparation is necessary. You should review the discussion about the function codes in Chapter 7. In that discussion, you saw how 68000 memory references involve a total of 35 bits. A 3-bit function code tells which "address space" to look in, and a 32-bit address gives the hardware memory address within that address space. The 5 address spaces used by the 68000 and their use in the cache system are outlined in Table 8-1.

Note that instruction fetches only occur with binary function codes 010 or 110. We can represent either of these binary function codes in general by f10. Accesses made to the other three address spaces are not instruction fetches, and are thus not cached. Whenever an instruction word is fetched on the

Table 8-1 Caching of Address Spaces

Function Code	*Address Space*	*Cache Capability*
001	User Data Space	Not cached
010	User Program Space	Cachable
101	Supervisor Data Space	Not cached
110	Supervisor Program Space	Cachable
111	CPU Address Space	Does not access memory

MC68020, the entire even-word-boundary longword containing that word is fetched. Hence, the last two bits in the address of the longword fetched are always zero. Thus, we may figuratively view the 35 bits in the memory fetch parameters as:

Function Code (3 bits)	*Hardware Memory Address (32 bits)*
`f 1 0`	`tttttttt tttttttt tttttttt iiiiii00`

The 24 t-bits are called the **cache tag**, and the 6 i-bits are called the **cache index**. It is the 6-bit cache index that determines which of 64 positions the instruction longword will occupy in the cache. If two instruction longwords have the same cache index, then only one of them can be in the cache at any given time. Thus, any two longwords located exactly 256 (or 256n) bytes apart in memory will not be able to coexist within the cache. Note that this allocation method satisfies two basic criteria: it is simple (that is, fast) to carry out by the processor, and it guarantees that any contiguous segment of up to 64 longwords in memory will fit into the cache at the same time.

In the instruction cache, 5 quantities are maintained for each instruction longword, as follows:

Cache index	= Address[7:2]	= 6 bits of the longword address
Cache tag	= Address[31:8]	= The upper 24 bits of the longword address
Cache FC2	= The leftmost bit of the function code (1 for supervisor program space, 0 for user program space)	
Valid bit	= 1 if cache data is valid, 0 if not valid	
Cache data	= The contents of memory location address if valid bit is 1 (undefined if the valid bit is 0)	

Table 8-2a Initial Program Instructions

Address	Hex
001000F4	aaaa
001000F6	bbbb
001000F8	cccc
001000FA	dddd
001000FC	eeee
001000FE	ffff
00100100	gggg
00100102	hhhh

Table 8-2b Contents of Instruction Cache at Start of Program

Index	Valid	FC2	Tag	Data
00	0			
04-F4	0			
F4	0			
F8	0			
FC	0			

The cache index is a number from 0 to 63, and defines which of the 64 cache positions to look up. The other four quantities are stored at that position in the cache.

CACHE EXAMPLE

When the MC68020 first powers up, all of the valid bits are cleared to zero. Table 8-2a shows a sample program at startup, and Table 8-2b shows the initial state of the instruction cache. Note that the actual instructions stored at the locations shown in Table 8-2a are represented figuratively by the hex numbers "aaaa" through "hhhh".

Table 8-3a Program Instructions After Six Instructions Have Been Executed

Address	Hex
001000F4	aaaa
001000F6	**bbbb**
001000F8	**cccc**
001000FA	**dddd**
001000FC	**eeee**
001000FE	**ffff**
00100100	**gggg**
00100102	hhhh

Table 8-3b Contents of Instruction Cache After Six Program Instructions Have Been Executed

Index	Valid	FC2	Tag	Data
00	1	0	001001	gggghhhh
04-F4	0			
F4	1	0	001000	aaaabbbb
F8	1	0	001000	ccccdddd
FC	1	0	001000	eeeeffff

The first instructions executed by the MC68020 are all cache "misses", that is, they are not in the cache, and have to be fetched from external memory. For each cache miss, the appropriate cache tag, cache FC2, and cache data are stored in the cache, and the valid bit is set to 1 to indicate that valid data is now present at that cache position.

In Table 8-3a the instructions at hex locations 001000F6 through 00100100 have been executed, as indicated by boldface type. Table 8-3b shows that the instruction cache has also been suitably updated, that is, the valid bits for all affected cache positions have been set to 1, and the appropriate cache FC2, cache tag, and cache data values have been stored. Note that the cache picked up the entire longword at hex location 001000F4, even though only the lower order word was needed. This is because the cache only reads longwords on longword boundaries. Similiarly, the cache picked up the entire longword at hex location 00100100, even though only the higher order word was needed. Note also that when the last two hex digits of the program address went from FE to 00, the cache index wrapped around from the end of the cache to the beginning.

If a cached instruction is executed again while it is still in the cache, a hit is made. When a hit occurs, the instruction is fetched directly from the cache, and no external bus cycles are required. For example, in Figure 8-2, if the instruction represented by hex digits "gggg" happens to be a branch to instruction "aaaa" at hex location 001000F4, then a hit will occur because instruction "aaaa" is already stored in the cache. Note that instruction "aaaa" was never actually executed, but was previously fetched along with instruction "bbbb" because these two instructions are part of the same longword. Rigorously speaking, a cache hit occurs whenever the cache index, cache tag, and cache FC2 for an instruction fetch matches a cache entry from a previous "miss".

CACHE REGISTERS

In support of the cache system, two new control registers have been added to the MC68020, namely, the CAche Control Register (CACR) and the CAche Address Register (CAAR). Both are 32-bit registers, although only 4 bits of the CACR and 6 bits of the CAAR are currently used. In addition, the MOVEC instruction has been revised to allow access to these registers.

The CACR contains four bits that allow the user some control over the cache. Except for these four operations, the cache is automatic and inaccessible. The four bits are:

1 bit — Enable cache (E)
2 bit — Freeze cache (F)
4 bit — Clear Cache Entry (CE); uses CAAR
8 bit — Clear cache (C)

If the E bit is 0, no caching occurs; all instructions will be fetched from external memory. If the E bit is 1, caching occurs. On power-up, the E bit is 0, so it must be set before caching can begin. This can be done via the following instructions:

```
MOVE.L  #1,D0           Set up an E bit
MOVEC   D0,CACR         Move into CACR
```

If the F bit is 0, caching goes on as described above. If it is 1, then the cache becomes read only; hits are processed as before, but misses do not create new cache entries. This could be of use during emulations when the programmer wishes the emulation routine not to change the cache. It can also be used in certain cases to get better cache results. One such case is discussed below under "Cache Limitations". The F bit can be set as follows:

```
MOVE.L  #3,D0         Set up an F bit and an E bit
MOVEC   D0,CACR       Move into CACR
```

Or, alternately,

```
MOVEC  CACR,D0        Read current CACR
ORI    #2,D0          Set F bit, don't change other bits
MOVEC  D0,CACR        Write new CACR
```

If the C bit is read, it will always be found to be zero. If the C bit is set, however, it causes the entire cache to be cleared. The C bit can be set as follows:

```
MOVE.L  #5,D0         Set up a C bit and an E bit
MOVEC   D0,CACR       Move into CACR
```

The CE bit is similiar to the C bit, except that it only clears one cache entry. If the CE bit is read, it will always be zero. If the CE bit is set, the cache entry designated by CAAR is cleared. This entry is given by the cache index (bits [7:2]) of CAAR.

CACHE LIMITATIONS

The cache system is simple in execution, and is modestly sized. Hence, there are situations where the programmer should be aware of the limitations of the cache. Keep in mind that in all the situations described below an active cache is always as fast or faster than an inactive cache. Thus, enabling the cache can only improve execution speed.

First, the instruction cache may fail to improve the execution of large program loops. The cache is limited to 256 bytes. If a loop is greater than 256 bytes and is executed many times, the cache will not have enough room to store all of the instructions. Some instructions will have to be repeatedly refetched to replace others.

Second, routines used in both user and supervisor modes may be refetched, even if they are already in the instruction cache. The cache considers user and supervisor memory accesses to be distinct. In a typical hardware situation (as explained in Chapter 7) all four address spaces actually end up referencing the same hardware memory. In another environment, there could be four entirely separate address banks. Because this is all determined outside of the MC68020 chip, the MC68020 itself has no way of knowing what is actually happening. Therefore, it has to assume the worst case, namely, that supervisor and user instruction (program) references are accessing distinct memory banks.

If an instruction is accessed while in supervisor mode (function code 110), then immediately accessed again while in user mode (function code 010) the MC68020 has no way of knowing if supervisor instruction addresses and user instruction addresses are actually in separate hardware memory, and the MC68020 is forced to refetch the instruction.

Third, data accesses are not cached. For example, say that the following instructions are executed:

```
MOVE.L #3, (A0)
MOVE.L (A1), (A2)
```

Both MOVE instructions, including the immediate field, are cached. The memory data areas, however, are not cached. Thus, if these instructions are executed again, the data area (A0) will be refetched. There are good reasons for not caching data areas. One reason is that to do so would require the cache to allow for four address spaces, versus two. Another reason is that since data areas are subject to be changed, proper caching of data areas would require caching of both inputs and outputs.

Fourth, the cache may have to be cleared at certain critical times. For example, if a program is loaded into memory, and if the previous contents of that area of memory are still in the cache, then the cache has to be cleared (or at least disabled). Otherwise, false hits will occur, leading to disastrous results.

Fifth, two or more very short program loops may be unimproved by caching. Consider an uncommon but possible situation where part A of a program resides at hex memory locations xxxxxx00 through xxxxxx7F, and part B of it resides at yyyyyy00 through yyyyyy7F. Note that each segment occupies 32 longwords, that is, half of the cache, but both will unfortunately be stored in the same half of the cache, due to the way that the cache stores and addresses its data. If it turns out that A and B alternate back and forth, then the cache will never make a single hit because each segment keeps replacing the previous segment in the cache. At this point, the freeze bit comes to the rescue. If the F bit in the CACR is set to 1 after one execution of A, then part B will not make any hits, but part A always will. Is not half a cache better than none?

Sixth, if a self-modifying program is cached, wrong results may occur. Self-modifying programs are totally at odds with the 68000 design philosophy, so this particular problem should come as no surprise. If a 68000 instruction is cached, then modified, it is left unchanged in cache memory. In the event of a subsequent hit, the old version of the instruction (in cache memory) will be used in place of the new one (in external memory). The problem here is that the user is treating his or her program as data output, and the cache is not designed to cache data or output.

For example, the following program finds the first condition code that tests positive in the comparison of D0 and D1. It modifies itself, and then loops through the modified instruction.

```
LOOP    CMP.L   D0,D1          These two registers stay the
                                same
TEST    BHI     FINISH         This is changed to LS,CC,CS,etc
        LEA     TEST,A0        Pick up address of test
                                instruction
        ADD.W   #$100,(A0)     Change the 4-bit condition code
                                above
        BR      LOOP           Do another compare & test
FINISH  MOVE.W  (A0),D2        Pick up the Bcc instruction
        ASR     #$8,D2         Isolate the condition code
        AND     #$F,D2         Mask off all but the last 4
                                bits
```

If caching is active, the Bcc instructions will all execute as BHI. If caching is not active, all is okay. The best solution is to avoid self-modifying programs. The wisest solution to the above problem is to substitute code that checks each of the 16 condition codes in 16 separate instructions. A few extra words of program will avoid a very sticky problem. The next best solution is to disable caching and lock out all other users during the self-modifying routine. After the routine is done, the code should be returned to its original state, the cache enabled, and the other users unlocked.

NEW ADDRESSING MODES

The MC68020 introduces several additional addressing modes that allow for more displacements, larger displacements, a scaling factor, and an additional level of indirection. The beginning programmer will probably encounter few (if any) situations where these new addressing modes are useful. He may conclude that they simply save an extra instruction here and there. As more complex programming situations arise, however, the programmer will find increasing usefulness in these new (and more complex) addressing modes. It is hoped that the examples described in this section will help this process along.

The new MC68020 addressing modes consist of six variants to two of the 12 basic 68000 addressing modes. Three variants are variants of mode 110, whose original form is called *address register indirect with index and 8-bit displacement*; the other three variants are variants to mode 110 011, whose original form is called *program counter indirect with index and 8-bit displacement*. These two sets of variants are implemented in a parallel fashion. Because of this parallelism, we need only to discuss one of the two sets in detail; the other set follows by simple analogy.

Because of the complexity of these addressing modes, two points should be clarified before proceeding.

First, the new addressing modes add together several numbers, including signed, unsigned, 32-bit, 16-bit, and 8-bit numbers. Throughout this section it is assumed that whenever numbers are added together in address calculations all 8-bit and 16-bit numbers are first sign-extended to 32-bits, then added. This applies to all fields: immediate fields, shortened register values, and memory references.

Second, assemblers on various computers may use slightly different syntaxes to represent the 68000 addressing modes. This is especially true of the variants discussed below, since so many parameters and operations are involved. These syntactical differences, however, should be obvious and easily translatable.

In the next five sections, we describe the original form of one addressing mode on the MC68000, the "address register indirect with index and 8-bit displacement" mode, and its three variants available on the MC68020. For the original addressing form and its variants, we give sample effective addresses, all built around the use of an ASCII-to-EBCDIC conversion table. As the variants become more complex, so do the examples.

ADDRESS REGISTER AND MEMORY INDIRECT WITH INDEX

This addressing mode has bit pattern 110 rrr, where rrr is the 3-bit number of an address register (A0 to A7). The title *address register and memory indirect with index* applies to all five forms of this addressing mode available on the MC68020, including the original MC68000 form and three MC68020 variants.

As previously mentioned, the original form of this addressing mode, available on all 68000 processors, is called *address register indirect with index and 8-bit displacement*. It is represented by (d8,An,Rn.SIZE), where:

> d8 is any 8-bit signed displacement (values from –128 to +127)
>
> An is any address register
>
> Rn is any address or data register
>
> SIZE is either W (for word) or L (for longword)

The effective address is equal to the sum of d8, An, and Rn.SIZE. Note that d8 and Rn.SIZE are both sign-extended before being added to An.

A useful example of this original form is given by (0,A0,D0.W). If A0 contains the base of an ASCII-to-EBCDIC conversion table, and if D0 contains an ASCII byte, then (0,A0,D0.W) is the effective address of the corresponding EBCDIC byte.

SCALE FACTOR

The MC68020 allows the inclusion of a scale factor in the effective address, represented by (d8,An,Rn.SIZE*SCALE), where SCALE has the value 1, 2, 4, or 8.

Evaluation is similiar to the evaluation of the original form. The effective address is equal to the sum of d8, An, and Rn.SIZE*SCALE. Note that d8 and Rn.SIZE*SCALE are both sign extended before being added to An.

An example using the scale factor is given by (0,A0,D0.W*2). As in the example given above for the original form, A0 contains the base of an ASCII-to-EBCDIC conversion table. This time, however, the conversion table contains two bytes per entry; the first byte indicates if the ASCII byte can be converted to EBCDIC, and the second byte gives the actual EBCDIC byte. Thus, if D0 contains an ASCII byte, then (0,A0,D0.W*2) is the effective address of the conversion indicator, and (1,A0,D0.W*2) is the effective address of the EBCDIC byte.

In the original MC68000 form and in this MC68020 scaled form, d8 can have a zero value, but d8, An, and Rn must all be present. This is in contrast to the three variants described below, where all registers and displacements are optional.

ADDRESSING MODE VARIANT #1

This variant is called *address register indirect with index and base displacement*, and is represented by (bd,An,Rn.SIZE*SCALE), where bd is a base displacement of 0, 16, or 32 bits.

All three of the parameters bd,An,Rn are optional. This optional usage is convenient whenever any of these registers is not needed, and a dummy (zero-value) register is not immediately available for calculating the effective address.

Evaluation of variant #1 is similar to the evaluation of the original form. If any of the three parameters are not present, they are evaluated as zero. The effective address is evaluated as the sum of bd, An, and Rn.SIZE*SCALE. Rn.SIZE*SCALE is sign-extended.

An example using this form is given by (displace1,A0,D0.W*2). This time, let A0 be the base of a general data area, which contains several tables, one of which is our familiar ASCII-to-EBCDIC conversion table. If displace1 is the displacement of our conversion table from the base of the general data area, and D0 contains an ASCII byte, then (displace1,A0,D0.W*2) and (displace1 + 1,A0,D0.W*2) are the effective addresses of the conversion indicator and the EBCDIC byte (explained above in the example for the scale factor).

Note that a data indirect addressing mode, represented by (Dn), can be generated using variant #1. This is accomplished by opting not to use bd and An, and using a data register for Rn.

ADDRESSING MODE VARIANT #2

This variant is called *memory indirect post-indexed*, and is represented by ([bd,An],Rn.SIZE*SCALE,od), where od is an outer displacement of 0, 16, or 32 bits.

Evaluation of variant #2 is similiar to the evaluation of variant #1, except that one extra level of indirection occurs midway in the effective address calculation. All four of the parameters bd,An,Rn,od are optional. Any parameters not present are evaluated as zero. The effective address is evaluated by first taking the sum of bd and An, then fetching the contents of the longword at this memory address, and finally taking the sum of this memory longword, Rn.SIZE*SCALE, and od.

An example using this form is given by ([displace1,A0],D0.W*2). This time, suppose that the data tables are not in one place, but are scattered all over. The starting address of each table is known, however, and all these addresses are gathered together into a master address table, whose base is given by A0. The quantity displace1 is now a displacement in this master address table, pointing to a number which in turn points to our conversion table. The expression [displace1,A0] itself represents the base of our conversion table, and ([displace1,A0],D0.W*2) is the effective address of the two-byte entry for the conversion of an ASCII byte in D0 to EBCDIC.

ADDRESSING MODE VARIANT #3

This variant is called *memory indirect pre-indexed*, and is represented by ([bd,An,Rn.SIZE*SCALE],od).

Evaluation of variant #3 is similiar to the evaluation of variant #2, except that the extra level of indirection occurs at a different point in the effective address calculation. All four of the parameters bd,An,Rn,od are optional. Any parameters not present are evaluated as zero. The effective address is evaluated by first taking the sum of bd, An, and Rn.SIZE*SCALE, then fetching the contents of the longword at this memory address, and finally taking the sum of this memory longword and od.

Note that variant #2 and variant #3 differ only in whether the index is added before (variant #3) or after (variant #2) the memory reference is made.

PROGRAM COUNTER AND MEMORY INDIRECT WITH INDEX

This addressing mode has bit pattern 111 011. The title *program counter and memory indirect with index* applies to all five forms of this addressing mode available on the MC68020, including the original MC68000 form and three MC68020 variants.

The entire preceding discussion regarding the address and memory indirect with index addressing mode and its three MC68020 variants, applies analogously to the program-counter-and-memory-indirect-with-index addressing mode. The only difference between these two sets of addressing modes is that the program counter (PC) is used in place of an address register (An). Thus, wherever "address register" appears in the preceding discussions, substitute the words "program counter", wherever "An" appears, substitute "PC", and wherever "memory indirect" appears, substitute "PC memory indirect".

Note that in each of the effective address examples presented earlier, the ASCII-to-EBCDIC conversion table can be located anywhere in memory. If the table is located within the program itself, however, then the "program counter and memory indirect with index" addressing modes should be used, because they do not require the use of an address register (An).

For example, consider the effective address example presented above for variant #1. In the original example, the ASCII-to-EBCDIC conversion table could be located anywhere in memory. If the table is actually located within the program itself, then it is better to use the PC-relative addressing mode (label,PC,D0.W*2), rather than addressing mode (displace1,A0,D0.W*2). Using the latter mode, A0 is unnecessarily tied up, and has to be pre-loaded with data area base address via an "LEA label,A0" instruction.

Tables 8-4 and 8-5 summarize the new addressing modes, and their effective address syntaxes.

TRACE BITS T0 AND T1

The trace bits allow the monitoring of one program by another program. For example, it is possible for a master program P-1 to monitor a slave program P-2 on an instruction-by-instruction basis. This is done using the trace bit T1,

Table 8-4 Address Register and Memory Indirect with Index: Mode 110 rrr

Format	*CPU*	*Effective Address Syntax*	*Parameters*
Original	68000	(d8,An,Rn.SIZE)	Required
Original	68020	(d8,An,Rn.SIZE*SCALE)	Required
Variant #1	68020	(bd,An,Rn.SIZE*SCALE)	Optional
Variant #2	68020	([bd,An],Rn.SIZE*SCALE,od)	Optional
Variant #3	68020	([bd,An,Rn.SIZE*SCALE],od)	Optional

Table 8-5 Program Counter and Memory Indirect with Index: Mode 111 011

Format	*CPU*	*Effective Address Syntax*	*Parameters*
Original	68000	(d8,PC,Rn.SIZE)	Required
Original	68020	(d8,PC,Rn.SIZE*SCALE)	Required
Variant #1	68020	(bd,PC,Rn.SIZE*SCALE)	Optional
Variant #2	68020	([bd,PC],Rn.SIZE*SCALE,od)	Optional
Variant #3	68020	([bd,PC,Rn.SIZE*SCALE],od)	Optional

which is bit 15 in the status register. When this bit is set to 1, a trace exception occurs at the end of each instruction. Thus, P-1 must set the T1 bit using the privileged instruction and begin executing the P-2 program. After each instruction of the P-2 program, a trace exception is generated by the 68000. Control is returned to P-1, P-1 analyzes what happened, then does an RTE. The whole process repeats until P-1 decides to stop.

Tracing allows for the creation of programs which must be able to monitor the results of individual instructions. Such programs include assembler debugging utilities, and programs to analyze how often each instruction gets executed.

When the other trace bit T0 (bit 14 in the status register) is set to 1, a trace exception occurs only when a change in program flow occurs, such as after a BRA or JMP instruction.

In the MC68000, trace bit T0 is not used, and is always zero; furthermore, trace bit T1 is the only trace bit, and is called the T bit. The function of the trace bits is thus upward compatible, that is, MC68000 programs using the trace function will run correctly on the MC68020. The exception is: if some adven-

Table 8-6 Trace Bits

T1	*T0*	*Trace Function*
0	0	No trace
0	1	Trace on Flow Change (Bcc,JMP,DBcc)
1	0	Trace on each instruction
1	1	[Reserved by Motorola]

turous programmer has been fiddling with the T0 bit on the MC68000, then such programs may fail to execute correctly on the MC68020.

COPROCESSOR SUPPORT

The MC68020 has 7 additional instructions which support communications between the MC68020 and coprocessors. Coprocessors are processors that satisfy certain hardware interface requirements established by Motorola. One of the main requirements is that the coprocessor must have certain interface registers that are necessary for communications with the host processor.

A complete discussion of coprocessors would include details of the functions of each 68000 coprocessor instruction, a description of Motorola's hardware interface requirements, and the specific functions of each available coprocessor. In this section we will limit our discussion to an overview of the 68000 coprocessor instructions, and how the 68000 actually communicates with the coprocessor hardware. The goal of this section is to clarify, from the 68000 programmer's point of view at least, how instructions and data get from the 68000 to the coprocessor. We will also consider what happens when a coprocessor is not yet physically present in a computer system, and is being emulated in software until some future installation date.

If the immediately following paragraphs are confusing, you should review the section on function codes in Chapter 7.

COPROCESSOR HARDWARE COMMUNICATION

First, we look at what is happening on the hardware level. In order to properly communicate with the MC68020 coprocessor instructions, a coprocessor is required to have a standard set of 13 interface registers (control register, command register, condition register, etc.) totaling 32 bytes in all. We will be using one of these registers, the coprocessor command register, in succeeding examples. It is always located at address position 10 (decimal) within the 32 bytes. When the 68000 chip actually communicates with a coprocessor, it either reads from or writes to one or more of the coprocessor registers. In order to do this, the 3 function code lines of the 68000 send out bits 111, indicating a special CPU space access; the 32 address lines of the 68000 send out 32 bits in the following format:

xxxx xxxx xxxx 0010 cccx xxxx xxxr rrrr

and the 32 data lines of the 68000 may send out 32 bits of data.

When the function code is 111, the 32 bits on the address line are not interpreted as a full 32-bit address (as with the other four function codes), but are broken down into smaller bit fields of information used to determine the final location of the special CPU space I/O. Thus, the 0010 bits above indicate that this is a coprocessor communication (as opposed to some other kind of CPU space transfer), ccc is the coprocessor code (0 to 7) that indicates which coprocessor is being accessed, and rrrrr is the coprocessor register address (0 to 31 decimal). The bit fields represented by x are not currently used.

The coprocessor codes are currently allocated as follows:

000	MC68851 paged memory management unit
001	MC68881 floating point coprocessor
010-101	[Reserved for Motorola]
110-111	[Reserved for users]

As part of the coprocessor interface, it is necessary for either the coprocessor or some intermediary hardware to detect when the above signals have been sent out from the 68000, to recognize them as coprocessor communications, and to respond accordingly.

If the 68000 is trying to write to the coprocessor, then the proper response for the coprocessor is to take the data being sent to it (via the 32 data lines from the 68000), and store it in coprocessor ccc at register location rrrrr. If the 68000 is trying to read from the coprocessor, then coprocessor ccc should send the contents of register location rrrrr to the 68000 over the data lines.

That covers the hardware end of the coprocessor interface. Next we will see how the programmer actually sends out the function codes and address bits which access the desired coprocessor.

COPROCESSOR SOFTWARE COMMUNICATION

How does the average programmer communicate with the coprocessor? In general, you will use an assembler that supports your coprocessor. You will include various coprocessor instructions in your programs to communicate with the coprocessor, as explained in the documentation for your coprocessor. And finally, the assembler will create object code with the correct parameters for that coprocessor. Note that the same kind of communication with different coprocessors will result in different object code, due to different coprocessor ID codes, and different coprocessor command languages.

For example, suppose that a hypothetical coprocessor exists, called the MC99999, which monitors power consumption by polling hundreds of meters. The MC68020 communicates once to the MC99999 to get it started, and the coprocessor then spends several seconds or minutes doing the actual polling, thus relieving the 68000 of this burdensome task. The MC99999 leaves the numerical results of the polling in memory, and informs the MC68020 when it is done.

One of the MC68020 coprocessor instructions, the cpGEN instruction, sends a GENeral 16-bit command to the command register of a coprocessor. Suppose that the MC99999 has a coprocessor code of 2, that the receipt of a single 16-bit POLL instruction in its command register causes the MC99999 to begin its poll cycle, and that, in MC99999 language, a POLL instruction is hex $1234. A hypothetical assembler which supports the MC99999 would accept this instruction:

```
        cpGEN    METER,POLL
```

Our hypothetical assembler would associate the symbol "METER" with the MC99999's coprocessor code (namely, 2), and would assemble the POLL command into its proper MC99999 bit pattern (hex $1234). A cpGEN instruction assembles into two words that are generally represented as follows:

```
1  1  1  1  C  c  c  0  0  0  X  x  x  x  x  x
I  i  i  i  i  i  i  i  i  i  i  i  i  i  i  i
```

where Ccc is the coprocessor code, Xxxxxx is an optional effective address (not used by the MC99999), and the second word is the actual instruction sent to the coprocessor. Thus, our particular cpGEN instruction assembles as:

```
1  1  1  1  0  1  0  0  0  0  0  0  0  0  0  0
0  0  0  1  0  0  1  0  0  0  1  1  0  1  0  0
```

Now that we have looked at how the coprocessor interface functions, both in hardware and in software, let's look at what happens when one or more parts of that interface are missing.

EMULATION OF THE MC68020 COPROCESSOR INSTRUCTIONS

Is the MC68020 itself indispensable for coprocessor communications? No. It is simply easier, faster, and uses fewer registers than the MC68010.

The MC99999 cpGEN instruction discussed in the previous section is equivalent to the following MC68010 instructions:

```
MOVE.L    #7,D0            CPU space function code
MOVEC     D0,DFC           Move to destination function code
                            register
MOVE.L    #$0002400A,A0    Set up bits for ccc=2, rrrrr=10
                            (decimal)
MOVE.L    #$1234,D1        Set up data to move
MOVES     D1,(A0)          Move D1 to coprocessor 2 register
                            10 (dec)
```

Note that the MC68020 accomplishes all this in only one instruction, and without using registers D0,D1,A0.

Since all of the above instructions exist on the MC68010, the coprocessor software instructions can be emulated on the MC68010. Since the MOVES and MOVEC instructions do not exist on the MC68000, however, the coprocessor software instructions can not be emulated on the MC68000. We will now discuss the coprocessor capabilities available to the MC68000 and MC68010.

COPROCESSORS ON THE MC68010

If an MC99999 is connected to an MC68010, it is necessary to emulate the MC68020 software coprocessor instructions using MC68010 instructions.

A more elegant solution, however, would be as follows. Include the coprocessor instructions (for example, cpGEN) in the MC68010 program, even though these instructions are not part of the MC68010 instruction set. Change the MC68010 assembler so that it assembles the coprocessor instructions into the same bit patterns as the MC68020 assembler, or use an MC68020 assembler. Finally, change the unimplemented 1111 instruction exception routine to check for these bit patterns and emulate them in software.

Later on, if the computer is upgraded to an MC68020, the coprocessor interface will function fully, without any changes in the software.

COPROCESSORS ON THE MC68000

Unfortunately, the MC68000 is not capable of communicating with coprocessors at all, because it lacks not only the MC68020 coprocessor instructions, but also the MC68010 instructions, MOVEC and MOVES. The best the MC68000 can do is emulate the MC99999 hardware in software.

Software emulation of coprocessor hardware is not always possible. For a coprocessor with specialized hardware functions like the MC99999, emulation may be impossible. For some coprocessors, emulation can be accomplished using another piece of hardware. And for some coprocessors, such as the MC68881 floating point coprocessor, software emulation is completely possible. Indeed, there are probably many 68000 systems right now that are running MC68881 software emulations.

The advantages of emulating hardware features in software are manifold. First, it allows the MC99999 manufacturer to model the chip's behavior in software, before having to invest in actual hardware development. Second, it allows the manufacturer to implement the MC99999 in software at customer sites before the MC99999 is actually available. The emulation will probably be several times slower than the actual MC99999, but in the computer world, a slow routine is better than no routine at all.

Third, when the MC99999 or MC68881 is finally available, it only has to be plugged in, along with an MC68010 or MC68020, and the coprocessor interface will function with no software changes necessary.

MISSING COPROCESSORS ON THE MC68020

If there is no actual MC99999 present, and the MC68020 attempts to communicate with it, the MC68020 will be notified of this fact after one bus cycle, and will execute an unimplemented 1111 instruction exception. All this occurs automatically.

The unimplemented 1111 instruction exception routine is free to either report that the MC99999 is missing, or to emulate the MC99999 hardware in software and then return. As discussed in the previous section, if the MC99999 is emulated in software, and the MC99999 is later plugged into the computer, then no software changes are necessary.

NONSTANDARD COPROCESSOR HARDWARE

What happens in the situation where an MC68020 is connected to a coprocessor having a nonstandard coprocessor interface? The MC68020 coprocessor instructions will not be able to communicate correctly with the coprocessor, and hence cannot be used. They must be replaced by routines which explicitly use MOVEC, MOVES, and MOVE to communicate to the proper addresses within the coprocessor. These routines will be similar, but not identical to the MC68010 routines which emulate the MC68020 coprocessor instructions.

Table 8-7 Summary of Coprocessor Commands

Mnemonic	*Description of Operation*
cpGEN	Sends a general instruction to the coprocessor
cpScc	Like Scc, but uses coprocessor condition codes
cpDBcc	Like DBcc, but uses coprocessor condition codes
cpTRAPcc	Like TRAPcc, but uses coprocessor condition codes
cpBcc	Like Bcc, but uses coprocessor condition codes
cpSAVE	Saves status of coprocessor [privileged]
cpRESTORE	Restore status of coprocessor [privileged]

SUMMARY OF MC68020 COPROCESSOR COMMANDS

The seven coprocessor instructions on the MC68020 all have the following bit patterns for the primary instruction word:

1 1 1 1 C c c I n s X x x x x x

where Ccc is the 3-bit coprocessor code, Ins indicates the instruction, and Xxxxxx is dependent upon the instruction. Note that the first four bits of each instruction are 1111. As with other 68000 instructions, some of the coprocessor instructions are followed by additional words which are displacements, data, or condition codes.

THE MASTER BIT

The Master (M) bit is used to support environments where multiple operating systems (privileged jobs) are running concurrently. The M bit distinguishes the master operating system from all the others. It should be noted that, except for deep operating systems programming, the average 68000 programmer will probably never have to be concerned with the M bit.

USER AND SUPERVISOR MODES

The M bit is an extension of the S bit, and the S bit is the basic mechanism used by the 68000 to control privileged operations. In order to clarify the function of the S bit and M bit, we first explain the primary motivation for having both of them.

Certain processor functions are considered so important that they are accessible only to privileged users, or privileged programs (for example, an operating system). In the 68000, these functions include

- An irrevocable abort of all current processing (RESET,STOP)
- Errors of all kinds (bus error, address error, instruction error, zero divisor, coprocessor error)
- User traps
- External hardware interrupts

The 68000 simplifies the concept of privilege to the simplest possible mechanism, namely, at any given time the 68000 is either in a privileged (supervisor) mode, or in an unprivileged (user) mode. Whenever any of the conditions listed above occurs, control is yanked away from the current program (whether supervisor or user), the privileged (Supervisor) mode is entered, and one of several special routine decides what to do about what just happened. In some of these routines, the decision of how to proceed will critically depend on whether the original program was in the supervisor or user mode.

Once the privilege mechanism has been set up in this way, two more privileged functions suddenly surface, namely:

- Changing between supervisor and user mode
- Querying the current mode (MC68010)

Requesting the supervisor mode is a privileged function, and requires a privileged routine to decide whether or not to grant it. Even querying the current mode ("Am I now in supervisor mode?") is a privileged function. This privilege is necessary in order to allow for situations where the main operating system emulates another operating system. The emulated operating system actually runs in user mode, but thinks it is in supervisor mode. It must be kept in user mode so that the main operating system can intercept any queries that the emulated system may make regarding his mode and set up a counterfeit response to keep him fooled.

There are only two privilege levels inherent in the 68000 privilege system, but more can be artificially implemented in software. Simply keep everyone at user mode (that is, with no actual privileges), and assign each one a privilege level (for example, 0 to 255). Anytime someone executes a privileged function, control will be taken away and the controlling routine will check the assigned privilege level and will emulate what should actually be allowed.

IMPLEMENTATION OF USER, SUPERVISOR, AND MASTER MODES

In the MC68000, bit 13 in the status register is called the S bit, or supervisor bit. It is used to indicate whether the processor is currently in user mode (S bit 0) or supervisor mode (S bit 1). Certain instructions are considered privileged, and are only allowed when the processor is in supervisor mode. These instructions are: instructions that change the S bit, instructions that read the S bit (MC68010), and the MOVE USP, MOVEC, MOVES, RESET, STOP, and RTE instructions.

If a privileged operation is attempted in user mode, a privilege violation exception is generated. All other exceptions occur in the same way, whether they occurred while in user mode or supervisor mode.

There are two stacks, each having their own stack pointer. The User Stack Pointer (USP) is in effect during user mode, and the Supervisor Stack Pointer (SSP) is in effect during supervisor mode. The stack pointer currently in use is always referenced by A7, whether it is USP or SSP. When any exception occurs, a block of information (called a **stack frame**) is pushed onto the supervisor stack, the supervisor mode is set, and the exception routine is entered. When the routine is done, the stack frame is cleared from the supervisor stack, and control usually returns to the place where the exception occurred (unless it is irrecoverable).

In the MC68020, a second bit is assigned for use, in conjunction with the S bit. It is bit 12 in the status register, and is called the M bit, or master bit. In user mode (S=0), things run just like on the MC68000. In supervisor mode (S=1), however, two possible submodes are possible. When the master bit is clear (M=0), the interrupt mode is in effect, and A7 references the Interrupt Stack Pointer (ISP), which points to the interrupt stack. When the master bit is set (M=1), the master mode is in effect, and A7 references the Master Stack Pointer (MSP), which points to the master stack. The stack pointer currently in use is always referenced by A7, whether it is USP, ISP, or MSP.

When the M bit is cleared to 0, all of the mode and stack changes happen just like on the MC68000, with the understanding that the supervisor stack being used is always the interrupt stack. When M is set to 1, however, the treatment of exceptions changes in two ways. First, exceptions now create stack frames on the master stack, instead of the interrupt stack. Second, during an external hardware interrupt exception, the usual stack frame is created on the master stack, but then the same stack frame is also created on the interrupt stack, and the master bit is cleared, causing a change to the interrupt mode.

Thus, a user who is normally in master mode operates off of the master stack, but during the processing of external hardware interrupt exceptions, the user operates off of the interrupt stack, just as with other jobs.

Each exception processing usually ends with an RTE instruction, which returns to the previous mode and stack. In the case of the double stack frame situation described above, RTE clears both stack frames, and returns through both modes.

NEW INSTRUCTIONS ON THE MC68020

Several categories of changes were made to the MC68020 instruction set. Many old instructions were extended in their operations, and many new instructions were added. The final section in this chapter covers all instructions that are either new or extended on the MC68020.

BRANCH INSTRUCTIONS SUPPORT 32-BIT DISPLACEMENTS

The Bcc, BRA, and BSR instructions now support 32-bit displacements. The original single-word instruction formats contain an 8-bit op code and an 8-bit displacement. If the 8-bit displacement is zero, then the following word is used as a 16-bit displacement.

In the MC68020, if the 8-bit displacement is 255 (decimal), then the following two words are used as a 32-bit displacement. The assembly programmer generally does not need to know these particulars. The assembler automatically decides the best format to use.

LINK INSTRUCTION SUPPORTS 32-BIT DISPLACEMENTS

The LINK instruction originally allowed only a 16-bit displacement, but now supports both 16-bit and 32-bit displacements.

EXTEND BYTE TO LONGWORD

The EXTB.L instruction sign extends a byte to a longword in a data register. The original MC68000 instructions are EXT.W, which sign-extends a byte to a word, and EXT.L, which sign-extends a word to a longword. On older 68000 processors, it is necessary to do both an EXT.W and EXT.L in order to get the equivalent of one EXTB.L instruction.

CHK SUPPORTS LONGWORD UPPER BOUNDS

The MC68000 CHK instruction checks a data register against a word upper bound. The MC68020 CHK instruction checks a data register against either a word or longword upper bound. There is no apparent change in the instruction syntax, but the assembler will allow bounds greater than 16 bits, and will automatically decide which format is best to assemble.

CHK2 (NEW INSTRUCTION)

This is a further generalization of the CHK instruction. A new CHK2 (check two bounds) instruction allows either a data or address register to be checked against a lower and upper bound, both of which are byte, word, or longword. All combinations of the above are allowed. The syntax is CHK2 ea,Rn where ea is the location of the lower bound, and the upper bound must immediately follow the lower bound in memory, either 1, 2, or 4 bytes away, depending on the operand length.

CMP2 (NEW INSTRUCTION)

A new CMP2 (compare two bounds) instruction operates just like the CHK2 instruction, except that, instead of a trap occurring on an out-of-bounds condition, the condition codes are set, leaving the user to subsequently branch as desired. The syntax is CMP2 ea,Rn and the condition codes are set as follows:

N Undefined
Z Set if Rn is equal to either bound, cleared otherwise
V Undefined
C Set if Rn is out of bounds, cleared otherwise
X Not affected

CAS AND CAS2 (NEW INSTRUCTIONS)

CAS and CAS2 are compare and swap instructions, and both guard against multiuser accesses to the same areas. They can be viewed as extensions of the original MC68000 TAS instruction. In a multiuser environment the simplest method of guarding against the problem of simultaneous updates to the same data is to set up a flag somewhere that (by mutual agreement) can only be set (or "owned") by one user at a time. The TAS instruction allows the user to test if a flag is set and if it isn't, sets it. Most important, TAS guarantees that no one else will have access to this flag during the entire read-modify-write process.

Thus, TAS satisfies the minimum requirements for implementing multiuser safeguards. The user is then free to execute the update routine, because he or she knows that no one else will gain access until he or she clears the flag. The other jobs must cooperate by not executing the update routine until they have possession of this flag. In addition the lucky possessor of the flag should cooperate by keeping the flag set for as short a time as possible. If this is done, then whenever a program fails to get ownership of the flag via a TAS, it can safely loop forever until it finally gets the flag, because the understanding is that this will not take very long.

Even in a single-user environment, TAS is needed because there are still multiusers in the form of external interrupts, all of which can occur at any time and at varying frequencies. The ability to temporarily lock out certain resources becomes critical in order to process these requests.

CAS goes one step further than TAS, and CAS2 goes two steps further. They have the following instruction formats:

```
CAS    Dc,Du,ea
CAS2   Dc1:Dc2,Du1:Du2,(Rn1):(Rn2)
```

CAS compares Dc and ea; if they are the same, then Du replaces ea. In the simplest application, ea is a counter that is subject to be incremented by more than one user. The procedure is to read ea into Dc (the old or compare value), create the new value in Du (the new or update value), then execute the CAS instruction. If it fails, simply try again. Caution: If the Dc counter undergoes constant and rapid updating, then it is probably safer to use TAS; otherwise, several users may get hopelessly locked up retrying their updates.

CAS2 is similiar to CAS, except that it does two comparisons. If either compare fails, the update is not made. Note that whereas CAS allows any alterable memory-effective address mode, CAS2 only allows (address or data) register indirect modes. The caution above regarding the use of CAS also applies here.

DIV AND MUL SUPPORT NEW FORMATS

Several additional multiply and divide formats have been added to the MC68020. All formats use one or two data registers and one data-effective address as source operands, and leave the results in one or more data registers. Following are all of the formats available on the MC68020, including the previous formats.

Table 8-8 Divide and Multiply Formats

Instruction		*Operation of Instruction*			*Processor*
DIVU.W	dea,Dn	Dn(32)	/ dea(16)	= Dn(16r:16q)	68000
DIVU.L	dea,Dq	Dq(32)	/ dea(32)	= Dq(32)	68020
DIVU.L	dea,Dr:Dq	Dr:Dq(64)	/ dea(32)	= Dr(32) , Dq(32)	68020
DIVUL.L	dea,Dr:Dq	Dq(32)	/ dea(32)	= Dr(32) , Dq(32)	68020
DIVS.W	dea,Dn	Dn(32)	/ dea(16)	= Dn(16r:16q)	68000
DIVS.L	dea,Dq	Dq(32)	/ dea(32)	= Dq(32)	68020
DIVS.L	dea,Dr:Dq	Dr:Dq(64)	/ dea(32)	= Dr(32) , Dq(32)	68020
DIVSL.L	dea,Dr:Dq	Dq(32)	/ dea(32)	= Dr(32) , Dq(32)	68020
MULU.W	dea,Dn	dea(16)	x Dn(16)	= Dn(32)	68000
MULU.L	dea,Dl	dea(32)	x Dl(32)	= Dl(32)	68020
MULU.L	dea,Dh:Dl	dea(32)	x Dl(32)	= Dh:Dl(64)	68020
MULS.W	dea,Dn	dea(16)	x Dn(16)	= Dn(32)	68000
MULS.L	dea,Dl	dea(32)	x Dl(32)	= Dl(32)	68020
MULS.L	dea,Dh:Dl	dea(32)	x Dl (32)	= Dh:Dl(64)	68020

The various subscripts used with the data registers are n for any register, r for a remainder, q for a quotient, h for a high order longword, and l for a low order longword. The numbers 16, 32, and 64 indicate word, longword, and quadword respectively.

PACK AND UNPK (NEW INSTRUCTIONS)

PACK simplifies the conversion of ASCII and EBCDIC numbers to BCD, and UNPK simplifies the conversion from BCD back to ASCII and EBCDIC. In a likely situation, a sequence of ASCII or EBCDIC digits is obtained from an input device (for example, a terminal, tape, or disk file); they are converted to internal BCD format using the PACK instruction; and BCD computations are done on them using the ABCD, SBCD, and NBCD instructions. Afterwards, they are converted back to ASCII or EBCDIC using the UNPK instruction; finally, they are sent to an output device. The formats available are:

PACK –(Ax),–(Ay),#adjustment

PACK Dx,Dy,#adjustment

UNPK –(Ax),–(Ay),#adjustment

UNPK Dx,Dy,#adjustment

PACK takes a word from the source operand, adds the adjustment word to it, then writes the second and fourth hex digits (bits [11:8] and [3:0]) of the result to the destination byte. For ASCII conversions, the adjustment is –3030 (hex) = CFD0 (hex). For EBCDIC conversions, the adjustment is –F0F0 (hex) = 0F10 (hex). A string of digits of any length can be converted using a two-instruction loop consisting of a pre-decrement PACK command and a DBcc command. Thus, a string of digits of any length can be converted as follows:

```
        MOVE.L      #<size-1>,D0          set up digit count
        MOVEA.L     #<packend>,A0         ending of packed digits
        MOVEA.L     #<unpackend>,A1       ending of unpacked
                                          digits
LOOP    PACK        -(A0),-(A1),#$CFD0    convert to ASCII
        DBF         D0,LOOP               stop when count is -1
```

UNPK takes a byte from the source operand, creates a word from it whose second and fourth hex digits are the two hex digits from the source byte and whose first and third hex digits are zero, adds the adjustment to it, then writes the word to the destination address. For ASCII conversions, the adjustment is +3030 (hex). For EBCDIC conversions, the adjustment is +F0F0 (hex).

TST AND CMPI SUPPORT ALL ADDRESSING MODES

On the MC68000, TST (TeST) and CMPI (CoMPare Immediate) only allow alterable data effective addresses (adea). On the MC68020, TST.B and CMPI.B remain restricted to adea, but TST.W, CMPI.W, TST.L, and CMPI.L may operate on any effective address. The net effect of this change is to include the PC addressing modes, and the address register direct mode.

TRAPcc (NEW INSTRUCTION)

TRAPcc is a new instruction on the MC68020 which generates a trap if a given condition code is true. All 16 conditions are allowed, including the "always trap" (TRAPT) and "never trap" (TRAPF) cases. Optionally, a word or longword may follow the TRAPcc instruction; it is not used by the processor, but is available to the user's trap routine. Forms available are as follows:

```
TRAPcc
TRAPcc.W     #d16
TRAPcc.L     #d32
```

Table 8-9 Summary of Bit Field Instructions

Mnemonic	*Operands*	*Description of Operation*
BFEXTS	ea[offset:width],Dn	Extract signed bit field (extend)
BFEXTU	ea[offset:width],Dn	Extract unsigned bit field (zero fill)
BFFFO	ea[offset:width],Dn	Find first one bit in bit field
BFFINS	Dn,ea[offset:width]	Insert (low order) bits into field
BFCLR	ea[offset:width]	Clear all bits to zeros
BFSET	ea[offset:width]	Set all bits to ones
BFCHG	ea[offset:width]	Test bit field, then complement
BFTST	ea[offset:width]	Test bit field

COPROCESSOR INSTRUCTIONS (NEW)

See the section on coprocessors, elsewhere in this chapter.

MOVEC SUPPORTS NEW CONTROL REGISTERS

MOVEC now reads and writes to the cache registers CAAR and CACR. See Chapter 7 for details on the MOVEC instruction.

BIT FIELD INSTRUCTIONS (NEW)

There are eight bit-manipulation instructions on the MC68020. In each, the main operand is a bit field of 1 to 32 bits. This bit field is referenced off of either a data register or a byte in memory, either of whose leftmost (highest order) bits is considered bit number zero. The actual bit field is designated by a bit offset from bit number zero, and the bit width (1 to 32). If a second operand is present, it is a data register.

In Table 8-9:

- ea is an effective address.
- Offset is the bit offset, either an immediate value of 0 to 31 or a data register value from –2,147,483,647 to +2,147,483,648.
- Width is the bit field width, either an immediate value of 0 to 31, or a data register value from 0 to 31 (taken modulo 32). Zero represents a value of 32.
- Dn is a data register.

Below are examples of bit field instructions:

```
BFEXTU D0[8:15],D1          move 2nd byte of D0 to D1
BFCLR  (A0)[2:5]            clear middle 4 bits of memory
                             byte (A0)
BFFFO  (A0)[D0:32],D1       find first 1 bit starting at
                             D0-th bit of memory byte (A0);
                             search 32 bits.
```

CONCLUSION

Whereas the MC68010 concentrated on one critical function (emulation), the MC68020 introduced a variety of new features. Compared to the MC68010, the MC68020 has 256 times as much address range, faster execution due to the on-board cache, and faster communication with co-processors. Six additional addressing modes, enhanced instructions, and new instructions save programming time, program room, and execution time. Branch instructions were revised to allow for full 32-bit branches. Multiply and divide now fully support 64-bit products and dividends. Finally, the new bit field operations significantly increase the speed and power of instructions that change individual bits; this aids in the updating of disk directory bitmaps, and is critically important in the handling of real-time graphics displays.

A

M68000 Instructions—Number of Operands

No Operand:

NOP
ILLEGAL
RESET*
RTE*/RTR/RTS
TRAPV

Single Operand:

ASL/ASR~
Bcc/BRA/BSR
CLR
EXT
JMP/JSR
NBCD
NEG/NEGX
NOT
PEA
RTD
Scc
STOP*
SWAP
TAS
TRAP
TST
UNLK

Two Operands:

ABCD
ADD/ADDA/ADDI/ADDQ/ADDX
AND/ANDI/ANDI-CCR/ANDI-SR*
ASL/ASR~
BCHG/BCLR/BSET/BTST
CHK
CMP/CMPA/CMPI/CMPM
DBcc
DIVS/DIVU
EOR/EORI/EORI-CCR/EORI-SR*
EXG
LEA
LINK
LSL/LSR~

MOVE/MOVE-from-CCR/MOVE-to-CCR/MOVE-to-SR*/MOVE-from-SR**
MOVE-USP*/MOVEA/MOVEC**/MOVEM/MOVEP/MOVEQ/MOVES**

MULS/MULU
OR/ORI/ORI-CCR/ORI-SR*
ROL/ROR/ROXL/ROXR~
SBCD
SUB/SUBA/SUBI/SUBQ/SUBX

Legend: ~ = can have one or two operands
* = privileged MC68000
** = privileged MC68010

B

M68000 Addressing Mode Types

<ea>	= Any Effective Address
<rea>	= Register Effective Address
<dea>	= Data Effective Address
<mea>	= Memory Effective Address
<cea>	= Control Effective Address
<aea>	= Alterable Effective Address (data or memory)
<adea>	= Alterable Data Effective Address
<amea>	= Alterable Memory Effective Address
<acea>	= Alterable Control Effective Address

Mode	*ea*	*rea*	*dea*	*mea*	*cea*	*aea*	*adea*	*amea*	*acea*
Dn	*	*	*			*	*		
An	*	*				*			
(An)	*		*	*	*	*	*	*	*
(An)+	*		*	*		*	*	*	
−(An)	*		*	*		*	*	*	
d(An)	*		*	*	*	*	*	*	*
d(An,Xi)	*		*	*	*	*	*	*	*
Abs.W	*		*	*	*	*	*	*	*
Abs.L	*		*	*	*	*	*	*	*
d(PC)	*		*	*	*				
d(PC,Xi)	*		*	*	*				

Mode	*ea*	*rea*	*dea*	*mea*	*cea*	*aea*	*adea*	*amea*	*acea*	
Immed	*		*	*						
bd(An,Xi)	*		*	*	*	*	*	*	*	68020
bd(PC,Xi)	*		*	*	*					68020
[bd,An],Xi,od	*		*	*	*	*	*	*	*	68020
[bd,An,Xi],od	*		*	*	*	*	*	*	*	68020
[bd,PC],Xi,od	*		*	*	*					68020
[bd,PC,Xi],od	*		*	*	*					68020

Addressing Mode Description

Common to All M68000 Family:

Dn	Data register direct } Jointly called register direct
An	Address register direct }
(An)	Address register indirect
(An)+	Address register indirect with postincrement
−(An)	Address register indirect with predecrement
d16(An)	Address register indirect with offset—also written as d(An) or <label>(An)
d8(An,Xi.Z)	Address register indirect with offset and index—also written as d(An,Xi) or <label>(An,Xi)
Abs.W	Absolute short address—also written as xxx.W or <label>
Abs.L	Absolute long address—also written as xxx.L or <label>
d16(PC)	Program counter with offset (relative mode)— also written as d(PC) or <label>(PC) or <label>
d8(PC,Xi.Z)	Program counter with offset and index (relative mode)—also written as d(PC,Xi) or <label>(PC,Xi) or <label>(Xi)
Immed	Immediate data operand—also written as #<data>

MC68020 Variations and Additions:

bd(An,Xi.Z*s)	Address register indirect with base displacement and index [similar to d(An,Xi) but bd can be d16 or d32]
bd(PC,Xi.Z*s)	Program counter with base displacement and index [similar to d(PC,Xi) but bd can be d16 or d32]
[bd,An],Xi.Z*s,od	Memory indirect post-indexed
[bd,An,Xi.Z*s],od	Memory indirect pre-indexed

[bd,PC],Xi.Z*s,od	PC memory indirect post-indexed
[bd,PC,Xi.Z*s],od	PC memory indirect pre-indexed

(NOTE: Some books use "displacement" in place of "offset.")

<label>	Is a user-supplied symbol indicating the location of an instruction or data field. Some instructions treat <label> as a d8 or d16 relative offset; others, depending on assembler directives available to the programmer, are treated as Abs.L, Abs.W or d(PC) modes.

Abbreviations:

Dn	Any data register, D0 - D7
An	Any address register, A0 - A7
Xi	Any Dn or An used as an index register
z	Data size code (L, W or B)
Z	Data size code (L or W)
s	Scale factor (1, 2, 4 or 8)
PC	Program counter (20, 24 or 32 bits)
d	A 2's complement or sign-extended offset, or displacement (d16, d8, d3 etc indicates the number of bits)
bd	A 2's complement base displacement (16 or 32 bits)
od	A 2's complement outer displacement (16 or 32 bits)
xxx	Any valid absolute address

C

M68000 Instructions/Legal Modes

(See Appendix B for register and mode definitions.)

Mnemonic	*Function*	*Legal Modes*	*Data Size(s) or Attribute*
ABCD	Add Decimal	Dm,Dn or -(Am),-(An)	B
ADD	Add Binary	<ea>,Dn or Dn,<amea>	L,W,B
ADDA	Add Address	<ea>,An	L,W
ADDI	Add Immediate	#<data>,<adea>	L,W,B
ADDQ	Add Quick	#<d3>,<aea>	L,W,{B}
ADDX	Add Extended	Dm,Dn or -(Am),-(An)	L,W.B
AND	AND Logical	<dea>,Dn or Dn,<amea>	L,W,B
ANDI	AND Immediate	#<data>,<adea>	L,W,B
ANDI->CCR	AND Immediate CCR	#<d8>,CCR	B
ANDI->SR*	AND Immediate SR	#<d16>,SR	W
ASL/ASR	Arithmetic Shift	Dm,Dn or #<d3>,Dn	L,W,B (Dm mod 64)
ASL/ASR	Arithmetic Shift	<amea>	W (shift count=1)
Bcc	Branch Condition	<label>	16 bit disp.
Bcc.S	Branch Cond. Short	<label>	8 bit disp.
BCHG	Bit Test/Change	Dm,Dn or #<d5>,Dn	L (Dm mod 32)
BCHG		Dm,<amea> or #<d3>,<amea>	B (Dm mod 8)

Mnemonic	*Function*	*Legal Modes*	*Data Size(s) or Attribute*
BCLR	Bit Test/Clear	same as BCHG	
BRA	Branch Always	<label>	8 or 16 bit disp.
BSET	Bit Test/Set	same as BCHG	
BSR	Branch Subroutine	same as BRA	
BTST	Bit Test	Dm,Dn or #<d5>,Dn	L (Dm mod 32)
BTST		Dm,<mea> or #<d3>,<mea>	B (Dm mod 8)
CHK	Check Reg Bounds	<dea>,Dn	W
CLR	Clear Operand	<adea>	L,W,B
CMP	Compare	<ea>,Dn	L,W,{B}
CMPA	Compare Address	<ea>,An	L,W
CMPI	Compare Immediate	#<data>,<adea>	L,W,B
CMPM	Compare Memory	(Am)+,(An)+	L,W,B
DBcc	Dec. Branch Cond.	Dm,<label>	16 bit disp.
DIVS/DIVU	Divide Sign/Unsign.	<dea>,Dn	W
EOR	Exclusive OR	Dn,<adea>	L,W,B
EORI	Exclusive OR Immed.	#<data>,<adea>	L,W,B
EORI->CCR	EORI Cond. Codes	#<d8>,CCR	B
EORI->SR*	EORI Status Reg.	#<d16>,SR	W
EXG	Exchange Registers	Rm,Rn	L
EXT	Extend sign	Dn	L,W
ILLEGAL	Illegal	no operand	
JMP/JSR	Jump/JMP Subroutine	<cea>	unsized
LEA	Load Effective Add	<cea>,An	L
LINK	Link/Allocate	An,#<d16>	unsized
LSL/LSR	Logical Shift	same as ASL/ASR	
MOVE	Move data	<ea>,<adea>	L,W,{B}
MOVE<-CCR	Move from CCR	CCR,<adea>	W (lower B only)
MOVE->CCR	Move to CCR	<dea>,CCR	W (lower B only)
MOVE<-SR	Move from SR	SR,<adea>	W
MOVE<-SR^^*		SR,<adea>	W (* for 68010 only)
MOVE->SR*	Move to SR	<dea>,SR	W (* all models)
MOVE-USP*	Move USP	USP,An or An,USP	L
MOVEA	Move Address	<ea>,An	L,W
MOVEC^^*	Move Contrl. Reg	Rc,Rn or Rn,Rc	L
MOVEM	Move Multi Reg.	<reg.list>,<acea>+	L,W (+ plus -(An))
		<cea>+,<reg.list>	L,W (+ plus +(An))
MOVEP	Move Periph. Data	Dn,d(An) or d(An),Dn	L,W
MOVEQ	Move Quick	#<d8>,Dn	L (sign ext 32)
MOVES^^*	Move Address Space	Rn,DFC<amea> or SFC<amea>,Rn	L,W,B
MULS/MULU	Multiply Sign/Unsign	<dea>,Dn	W
NBCD	Negate Decimal	<adea>	B
NEG/NEGX	Negate/Negate Ext.	<adea>	L,W.B
NOP	No operation	no operand	unsized

Mnemonic	*Function*	*Legal Modes*	*Data Size(s) or Attribute*
NOT	Logical Complement	<adea>	L,W,B
OR	Inclusive OR Logical	same as AND	
ORI	Inclusive OR Immed.	same as ANDI	
ORI->CCR	ORI Cond. Codes	same as ANDI->CCR	
ORI->SR*	ORI Status Reg.	same as ANDI->SR	
PEA	Push Effective Addr.	<cea>	L
RESET*	Reset External Dev.	no operand	unsized
ROL/ROR	Rotate Left/Right	same as ASL/ASR	
ROXL/ROXR	Rotate with Extend	same as ASL/ASR	
RTD^ ^	Return/Deallocate	#<d16>	unsized (sign ext 32)
RTE*	Return from Exception	no operand	unsized
RTE^ ^ *		no operand	unsized
RTR	Return Restore CCR	no operand	unsized
RTS	Return from Subroutine	no operand	unsized
SBCD	Subtract Decimal	same as ABCD	
Scc	Set Conditionally	<adea>	B
STOP*	Load SR/Stop	#<d16>	unsized
SUB	Subtract Binary	same as ADD	
SUBA	Subtract Address	same as ADDA	
SUBI	Subtract Immediate	same as ADDI	
SUBQ	Subtract Quick	same as ADDQ	
SUBX	Subtract with Extend	same as ADDX	
SWAP	Swap Register Halves	Dn	W
TAS	Test and Set operand	<adea>	B
TRAP	Trap	#<d4>	unsized
TRAPV	Trap on Overflow	no operand	unsized
TST	Test operand	<adea>	L,W,B
UNLK	Unlink	An	unsized

{B} reminds you that Byte data size not allowed for An operands.

#<data> = up to 32 bits of immediate data.
#<dn> = n bits of immediate data.
* = M68000 privileged instruction.
** = MC68010 privileged instruction.
^ ^ = MC68010 only.
Rc = control register (SFC,DFC,USP or VBR).

D

M68000 Instruction Summary

This appendix is a reference for all of the instructions implemented thus far in the 68000 processor family, that is, all of the instructions on the MC68000, the MC68010, and the MC68020. Included are the instruction bit patterns, addressing mode bit patterns, and allowable addressing modes for each instruction. This appendix does not describe the actual execution of these instructions; that material constitutes the first 8 chapters of this primer. We will be looking at the 68000 instruction set in very general terms, and will hopefully impart to you some tips that will help you to memorize the complete instruction set.

68000 ADDRESSING MODES

The 68000 processor family uses a rich set of addressing modes. There are 12 basic addressing modes, and some additional implied addressing modes for certain instructions. The MC68020 further enlarges the functions of two of the basic addressing modes, giving it a total of 18 variations on the basic 12 addressing modes. See Chapter 8 for further details on these addressing mode variations.

Table D-1 contains information on these 18 addressing modes. The first column contains the full name/description of each addressing mode. Note that some of these descriptions are somewhat long.

The "CPU" column indicates which members of the 68000 family have this addressing mode available; a blank refers to all 68000 processors, a "20" refers to the MC68020 only.

The "Mod Reg" column contains the actual 6-bit codes for each address mode. Actual binary register numbers are represented by "rrr", which can be "000" to "111".

The next four columns define four categories of addressing modes. These categories are very helpful for summarizing the legal addressing modes of each 68000 instruction.

Register (REA) — These addressing modes refer to registers. This includes address register direct and data register direct.

Data (DEA) — These addressing modes refer to data operands. This includes all modes except address register direct. Many 68000 instructions that operate on data are prevented from altering the address registers. This is part of the 68000 philosophy that the benefits obtained from preventing erroneous operations to the address registers (which can waste lots of development time), far outweigh the extra programming steps necessary to do legitimate operations to the address registers.

Memory (MEA) — These addressing modes refer to memory operands. This includes all modes except the two register direct modes. Two instructions are restricted to MEA because they are truly memory based operations, namely, TAS and MOVES. OR, AND, ADD, and the 4 shift instructions also impose the MEA restriction on some of their instruction formats, in order to avoid duplication of functions. For example, ADD D0,D1 is allowed in the format ADD ea,D1, but not allowed in the format ADD D0,ea (to avoid duplication). Thus, the format ADD D0,ea only allows MEA as destination, whereas the format ADD ea,D1 allows any EA as source.

Control (CEA) — These addressing modes refer to memory locations, without specifying if they are byte, word, or longword in size. This applies to the destinations of jump commands (Jxx), and to indefinite-sized destinations (LEA,PEA,MOVEM,BFxxxx).

Alterable (AxEA) — These refer to operands which may be changed. This excludes the PC relative and immediate modes. Motorola is inferring that programs may not alter themselves. In actuality, 68000 programs can change themselves, but an extra instruction (usually an LEA) must be used to do this. This is part of the 68000 philosophy that the benefits obtained from preventing erroneous program self-changes (which can waste lots of development time), far outweigh the extra programming steps necessary to

Table D-1 Effective Addressing Modes

Address Mode Name	*CPU*	*Mod*	*Reg*	*Register (R)*	*Data (D)*	*Memory (M)*	*Control (C)*	*Alterable (A)*	*Assembler Syntax*	*Extension Words*
Data register direct		000	rrr	X	X	–	–	X	Dn	0
Address register direct		001	rrr	X	–	–	–	X	An	0
Address register indirect		010	rrr	–	X	X	X	X	(An)	0
Address register indirect with postincrement		011	rrr	–	X	X	–	X	(An)+	0
Address register indirect with predecrement		100	rrr	–	X	X	–	X	–(An)	0
Address register indirect with displacement		101	rrr	–	X	X	X	X	(d16,An)	1
Address register indirect with index and 8-bit displacement		110	rrr	–	X	X	X	X	(d8,An,Rn)	1
Address register indirect with index and base displacement	20	110	rrr	–	X	X	X	X	(bd,An,Rn)	1-3
Memory indirect post-indexed	20	110	rrr	–	X	X	X	X	([bd,An],Rn,od)	1-5
Memory indirect pre-indexed	20	110	rrr	–	X	X	X	X	([bd,An,Rn],od)	1-5
Absolute short		111	000	–	X	X	X	X	addr .W	1
Absolute long		111	001	–	X	X	X	X	addr .L	2
Program counter indirect with displacement		111	010	–	X	X	X	–	(d16,PC)	1

Address Mode Name	CPU	Mod	Reg	Register (R)	Data (D)	Memory (M)	Control (C)	Alterable (A)	Assembler Syntax	Extension Words
Program counter indirect with index and 8-bit displacement		111	011	–	X	X	X	–	(d8,PC,Rn)	1
Program counter indirect with index and base displacement	20	111	011	–	X	X	X	–	(bd,PC,Rn)	1-3
PC memory indirect post-indexed	20	111	011	–	X	X	X	–	([bd,PC],Rn,od)	1-5
PC memory indirect pre-indexed	20	111	011	–	X	X	X	–	([bd,PC,Rn],od)	1-5
Immediate		111	100	–	X	X	–	–	#n	1-2
[Reserved by Motorola]	?	111	101							
[Reserved by Motorola]	?	111	110							
[Reserved by Motorola]	?	111	111							

do legitimate changes. If you plan to make many self-references within a program, simply do a "LEA label1,An" at the very beginning, then do all self-references using "label2-label1(An)".

By combining the above categories, other categories can be created, namely, the alterable data, alterable memory, and alterable control categories. For example, alterable data addresses are those addresses which are both alterable addresses and data addresses.

The "Assembler Syntax" column contains a figurative representation of the actual characters used to code each address mode in a 68000 program. The actual assembler you use on a particular computer may have slightly different syntax. The symbol An represents any register from A0 to A7, Dn represents D0 through D7, Rn represents An or Dn. d8 represents any unsigned number 0 to 255 or any signed number –128 to +127, d16 represents unsigned 0 to 65536 or signed –32768 to +32767, d32 represents unsigned 0 to 4294967295 or signed –2147483648 to +2147483647. #n represents d8, d16, or d32 in byte, word, or longword instructions respectively.

ADDRESSING MODE ORTHOGONALITY AND LEGALITY

An important design feature of the 68000 instruction set is the orthogonality between its instructions and addressing modes. Complete addressing orthogonality would mean that every instruction is able to use every addressing mode in all of its operands (source, destination, counter, etc.), thereby promoting convenience and flexibility in assembly programming. Few processors, however, have been designed with complete orthogonality because there are disadvantages. High orthogonality often comes at the expense of instruction set power; typically, many unimportant instruction/addressing combinations occupy bit patterns that could be better used by more powerful instructions. The 68000 instruction set is a state of the art optimization, both highly orthogonal and very powerful.

Each 68000 instruction consists of an operator and 0 or more operands. For example, some instructions with various numbers of operands are

```
RTN                                         0 operands
BR         LABEL                            1 operand
OR.W       D0,4(A0)                         2 operands
CAS2.W     D0:D1,D2:D3,4(A0)                5 operands
```

In most instructions, each operand is either allowed to be only one of the 12 addressing modes, or is allowed to be any of the 12 addressing modes which is "legal". An important goal for all 68000 programmers is to fully understand Motorola's criteria for "legal" addressing modes. These criteria are consistently applied throughout the 68000 instruction set. Without an understanding of these criteria, the 68000 instruction set will appear to lack much of its actual orthogonality. Armed with such understanding, complete memorization of the 68000 instruction set is possible.

An example should clarify all of this. The OR instruction given above is one of a group of OR instructions, all having the general form

```
OR.size   Dn,<destination>
```

and the 16-bit patterns represented by

1 0 0 0 S d r 1 S z D e s t i n

Explanations of the abbreviations Sdr, Sz, and Destin are not necessary for this discussion, but may be found below. There are two operands in this instruction. The second operand must always be data register direct mode, but the first may be any "legal" addressing mode. In this group of OR instructions, fully 5 of the 12 addressing modes are illegal. Furthermore, the 5 illegal modes violate three general rules of legality. The illegal modes, with their associated rule violations are:

1. PC relative or immediate: These may never be altered.
2. An: Data operations are not usually allowed to An.
3. Dn: This duplicates the function of another group of instructions.

Rule 1 is rigorously true for all 68000 instructions which alter the destination operand. Rule 2 is mostly true, but a few necessary operations are allowed to An, namely, MOVE, ADD, SUB, ADDQ, and SUBQ. Some assemblers allow you to use these "loophole" instructions without complaint. Some, however, require you to substitute MOVEA, ADDA, and SUBA for MOVE, ADD, and SUB when the destination is an address register. The net result is the same, but inadvertent program errors are reduced. To understand Rule 3, we need to know that there is a second group of OR instructions, all having the form:

```
OR.size   <source>,Dn
```

and the 16-bit patterns represented by

1 0 0 0 D d r 0 S z S o u r c e

If both of these OR groups allowed for the case

```
OR.size  Dn1,Dn2
```

then there would be more orthogonality in the instruction set, but less power, because fewer bit patterns would be available for other instructions. Indeed, some of the bit patterns made available by Rule 3, above, are used to code the NBCD instruction. As a programmer, you need not worry about Rule 3, because any 68000 assembler will automatically assemble an OR.size Dn1,Dn2 instruction as the correct bit pattern. If you are coding an assembler (or dis-assembler), however, Rule 3 is of critical importance.

The above example will hopefully make more palatable the following rigorous list of rules (and their exceptions) governing 68000 illegal addressing modes:

1. PC relative modes or immediate mode are illegal destinations if altered. This is the reason for the "alterable" address modes category (AEA). Note that "test" instructions do not alter their destinations, even though they "simulate" a subtraction from the destination. Exceptions: TST and CMPI with these address modes are illegal, even though they do not alter their destinations. On the MC68020, TST.W, TST.L, CMPI.W, and CMPI.L are legal in all modes, but TST.B and CMPI.B are not.
2. Duplicate functions are handled by only one of the instructions. For example, in all shift instructions, "op #1,Dn" is legal while "op Dn" isn't. Exceptions: CMP #c,Dn and CMPI #c,Dn are equivalent in function, but are assembled as different instructions (both with 2 words). The same is true for the corresponding cases involving ADD/ADDI, SUB/SUBI, AND/ANDI, and OR/ORI. Note: if 1 <= c <= 8, then ADDQ #c,Dn and SUBQ #c,Dn are also possible, and are a third equivalent to the ADD/ADDI and SUB/SUBI cases considered above, but take one less word. Hence, ADDQ and SUBQ are not considered to be duplicated (or triplicated) functions.
3. Many data operations are not allowed with An (address registers). This is the reason for the "data" address categories. The following sub-rules cover all cases, and are in cumulative order, that is, later rules override earlier rules in the sequence.

a. An never participates in any byte operations.
b. An does not interact with special data registers. Exception: the MOVES command may move any special register to or from any data or address register.
c. An may participate in straight moves. Thus, EXG, and MOVE are OK. MOVE.B is excluded by Rule 3a. Note that An may be moved from/to special address registers (USP, for example) but not from/to special data registers (CCR,SR), by Rule 3b.
d. An may be tested (not permanently changed). Thus, CMP (except CMP.B), CMPA, and TST (except TST.B) are OK.
e. An is allowed a few addition and subtraction calculations, namely ADD An1,Dn2 and SUB An1,Dn2 (except byte size); ADDA, SUBA, ADDQ, SUBQ (except byte size). The following are not allowed: ADD Dn1,An2 and SUB Dn1,An2. Note that ADDI #c,An and SUBI #c,An are excluded by Rule 2.

4. LEA, PEA, MOVEM, Jxx, and BFxxxx use only control address operands. Exceptions: MOVEM also allows (An)+ as source and –(An) as destination; BFxxxx also allows Dn as a bit field operand.
5. Completely pointless calculations are illegal. Exception: BTST #a,#b should be replaced by ANDI or ORI to CCR.

THE 68000 INSTRUCTION SUMMARY TABLE — PRELIMINARIES

Table D-2 summarizes the instruction sets of all five CPU processors in the 68000 family, namely, the MC68008, MC68000, MC68010, MC68012, and MC68020. The MC68008 and MC68000 instruction sets are identical, as are the MC68010 and MC68012 instruction sets. Hence, in the table, we only need to distinguish MC68000, MC68010, and MC68020 instructions. In addition, strict upward compatibility has been designed into the 68000 CPU family. That is, any instruction that is legal on any CPU in the 68000 family is also a legal instruction on all later CPUs. Thus, MC68000 instructions execute the same on all five processors, MC68010 instructions execute the same on the MC68010, MC68012, and the MC68020, and MC68020 instructions execute only on the MC68020.

By design, Table D-2 is compact, uses lots of abbreviations, and does not include exhaustive details of how each instruction functions. For details and examples of each instruction, see Chapter 4. The following sections explain the symbols used in each column of Table D-2.

INSTRUCTION COLUMN

The first column in Table D-2 gives the standard Motorola mnemonic for each instruction. Other assemblers may use minor variants of these mnemonics. The following abbreviations are used:

Code	*Represents*
.s	.B, .W, .L for byte, word, and longword instructions, respectively
.s2	.W and .L for word and longword instructions, respectively
.s3	[blank], .W, and .L for none, word, and longword operands (TRAPcc and cpTRAPcc only)
cc	A condition code (CC,CS,EQ,GE,GT,HI,LE,LS,LT,MI, NE,PL,VC,VS)

CPU COLUMN

This column indicates whether an instruction is a MC68000 instruction (blank), MC68010 instruction ("10"), or MC68020 instruction ("20"). See the notes above about upward compatibility in the 68000 family.

SYNTAX COLUMN

This column gives the general syntax of the instruction as it appears in actual programs. In cases where a source and destination operand appear, the source operand is first. Thus, if ever in doubt, remember that 68000 instructions "ADD first operand to second operand", "SUBtract first from second", "MULtiply first into second", "DIVide first into second".

For a few instructions, two syntaxes are given. In these instructions, there is always a D bit or a Q bit in the instruction code map (explained below). The first syntax corresponds to a D or Q bit of 0, and the second corresponds to a D or Q bit of 1.

Abbreviations used in the syntax column are:

Code	*Represents*
Dn,Dn1,Dn2	Any data register (D0 to D7)
An,An1,An2	Any address register (A0 to A7)
Rn,Rn1,Rn2	Any An or Dn
PC	Program counter (longword)
SR	Status register (word)
CCR	Condition code register (byte)

SSP	Supervisor stack pointer (longword)
USP	User stack pointer (longword)
SP	Active stack pointer (longword, synonymous with A7)
Rc	Any control register (USP,MSP,ISP,VBR,SFC,DFC,CACR,CAAR)
d3	An unsigned 3-bit number from 0 to 7 (except for the BKPT instruction, 0 represents a value of 8)
d4	An unsigned 4-bit number from 0 to 15 (a trap vector)
d5	An unsigned 5-bit number from 0 to 31 (a bit position number)
d8	An unsigned 8-bit number 0 to 255, or signed 8-bit number −128 to +127
d16	An unsigned 16-bit number 0 to 65536, or 16-bit signed number −32768 to +32767
d32	An unsigned 32-bit number 0 to 4294967295, or 32-bit signed number −2147483648 to +2147483647
#n	#d8 for byte instructions, #d16 for word instructions, and #d32 for longword instructions ea,ea1,ea2 an effective address (see Table D-1 for the 12 modes). In most instructions, not all of the 12 modes are legal; the SRC and DAT columns in Table D-2 indicate which modes are legal (see explanation of SRC and DAT columns below).
Dc,Dc1,Dc2	Any Dn, used for comparisons.
Du,Du1,Du2	Any Dn, used for updates.
reglist	A list of 0 to 16 registers (all An or Dn), separated by commas.
label	Source code: a label found elsewhere in the program. Object code: a d8, d16, or d32 offset from the current position.

Any expression contained within braces (eg, {#n}) is optional; it may either be present or omitted (left blank). Any commas, parentheses, colons, or hyphens correspond to actual program code.

INSTRUCTION CODE MAP COLUMN

This column contains bit-by-bit descriptions of the assembled instructions. Each bit is given as a 0 bit, a 1 bit, or as part of a bit "field". Each bit field begins with a capital letter, and may be 1 to 32 bits in length. The bit fields used are described below.

Sz	A 2-bit size indicator (00 = byte, 01 = word, 10 = longword).
S	A 1-bit size indicator (0 = word, 1 = longword). Exception: CHK reverses the bit (see note *a* to Table D-2).

Siz	A 3-bit operand size indicator (010=word, 011=longword, 100=none).
Q	A 1-bit size indicator for MULx and DIVx (0=longword, 1=quadword).
Source	A full 6-bit source effective address. 12 possible address modes can be encoded in these 6 bits. See Table D-1 for a summary of all 12 modes.
Destin	A 6-bit destination effective address (see Table D-1).
Tindes	Same as Destin, except the first and last 3 bits are swapped. Occurs only in the MOVE instruction.
Sar	A 3-bit source address register.
Dar	A 3-bit destination address register.
Sdr,Ddr	3-bit data registers (source, destination).
Sdar,Ddar	4-bit data or address registers (source, destination). An address register is indicated by a 0 bit, followed by the 3-bit address register number. A data register is indicated by a 1 bit, followed by the 3-bit data register number.
D	A 1-bit direction indicator, which determines whether various fields are source or destination. In general, when an instruction contains a D bit all "from" fields are source, and "to" fields are destination. When the D bit is 1, all "from" fields are destinations, and all "to" fields are sources. All fields affected by the D bit are included in the next eight entries.
Fefadr	A 6-bit "from" effective address. It is source when D bit is 0, destination when D bit is 1.
Tefadr	A 6-bit "to" effective address. It is destination if D bit is 0, source if D bit is 1.
Fdr	A 3-bit "from" data register. It is source when D bit is 0, destination when D bit is 1.
Tdr	A 3-bit "to" data register. It is destination when D bit is 0, source when D bit is 1.
Far	A 3-bit "from" address register. It is source when D bit is 0, destination when D bit is 1.
Tar	A 3-bit "to" address register. It is destination when D bit is 0, source when D bit is 1.
Fdar	A 4-bit "from" data or address register. It is source when D bit is 0, destination when D bit is 1.
Tdar	A 4-bit "to" data or address register. It is destination when D bit is 0, source when D bit is 1.
Udr	A 3-bit update data register (for CAS,CAS2).
Cdr	A 3-bit compare data register (for CAS,CAS2).

Hdr	A 3-bit high order word data register (for MULx and DIVx).
Imm	Immediate data field (3-bit).
Immediat	Immediate data field (8-bit, 16-bit, 32- bit).
Displace	Immediate address displacement field (8- bit, 16-bit, 32-bit).
Cnt	A 3-bit shift count.
Argcount	8-bit argument byte count (for CALLM).
Bitno	A 5-bit or 3-bit bit position number (for BTST,BCHG,BCLR,BSET).
Vec	A 3-bit vector (for BKPT).
Vect	A 4-bit vector (for TRAP).
Registerlistmask	A 16-bit field selecting 0 to 16 registers (for MOVEM). The order is D0 at bit 0 through A7 at bit 15, except for pre-decrement address mode, when it is reversed.
T	A 1-bit sign indicator for MULx and DIVx (0 = unsigned, 1 = signed).
R	A 1-bit rotation direction indicator (0 = right, 0 = left).
Bitoff	A 6-bit field specifying a bit offset, either 0 n n n n n, indicating a 5-bit immediate value, or 1 0 0 n n n, indicating data register Dn.
Bitwid	A 6-bit field specifying a bit width (same format as Bitoff).
Coprocessorcommd	A 16-bit co-processor instruction.
Cpi	A 3-bit co-processor id code.
Cpcond	A 6-bit co-processor condition code.
Controlregis	A 12-bit control register code. Codes defined are:

0000 0000 0000 = SFC (68010)
0000 0000 0001 = DFC (68010)
0000 0000 0010 = CACR (68020)
1000 0000 0000 = USP (68010)
1000 0000 0001 = VBR (68010)
1000 0000 0010 = CAAR (68020)
1000 0000 0011 = MSP (68020)
1000 0000 0100 = ISP (68020)

Cond — A 4-bit condition code. Codes defined are:

0000 = True	0001 = False
0010 = High	0011 = Low/Same
0100 = Carry Clear	0101 = Carry Set
0110 = Not Equal	0111 = Equal

1000 =	Overflow Clear	1001 =	Overflow Set
1010 =	Plus	1011 =	Minus
1100 =	Greater/Equal	1101 =	Less Than
1110 =	Greater Than	1111 =	Less/Equal

Each 68000 instruction is 1 to 11 words in length, and consists of 1 to 3 words for the basic instruction followed by 0 to 10 address extension words. Table D-1 lists only the basic instruction words. Any 16-bit word patterns surrounded by parentheses are optional, e.g., whenever an immediate field can have 16 or 32 bits, the second 16 bits will always be shown surrounded by parentheses. For each of the 12 addressing modes, the address extension word(s) always have the same format. Table D-1 lists the number of address extension words possible for each addressing mode. Because of their regularity, address extension words are not included in Table D-2.

SRC AND DST COLUMNS

The SRC and DST columns summarize the legal addressing modes for source and destination operands in a few symbols. The symbols are consistent, concise, and conducive to memorization.

If only one of the 12 basic addressing modes is legal in an operand, it is represented by one of the following symbols: Dn, An, (An), (An)+, –(An), d(An), SP, (SP)+, –(SP), I, where all of the symbols should be self-explanatory, except for I, which represents an immediate field.

A "Q" code indicates that the operand is a 3-bit immediate value.

If several addressing modes are legal in an operand, then they are represented by one of the following category codes: EA, REA, DEA, MEA, CEA, AEA, ADEA, AMEA, ACEA. These categories are explained earlier in this appendix. EA represents all addressing modes.

Special registers are represented by the symbols CCR, SR, PC, USP, which should also be self-explanatory. A "cr" symbol represents any of the control registers USP, MSP, ISP, VBR, SFC, DFC, CACR, CAAR.

A few cases require additional notation:

(Dn)	Represents data indirect addressing
&	Used to join groups, for example "CEA&Dn" means "any control address or Data Direct addressing"
~	Used to subtract parts of one group from another, for example, "DEA~I" means any DEA except immediate mode addresses
,	Used to indicate two operands: "Dn,An" means one Dn operand and one An operand; "Dn,Dn" means two Dn operands

Observant assembler programmers may notice that in operands where only one addresssing mode is allowed, that addressing mode's code often matches the last 6 bits in the instruction. For example, the SWAP command implicitly uses only data register direct addressing, which corresponds to a 6-bit code of 000rrr. The last 6 bits of SWAP are, indeed, these same 6 bits. But, beware, this agreement occurs only about half of the time.

CONDITION CODES COLUMN

This column indicates which condition codes are affected by each instruction. Symbols used are

–	Code is unchanged by instruction
0	Code is set to 0
1	Code is set to 1
*	Code is changed
U	Code is left with undefined value

PRIV COLUMN

This column indicates which instructions are privileged. Privileged instructions may only be executed when the system bit is set to 1. Otherwise, an exception is generated.

NOTES COLUMN

Letters in this column refer to footnotes at the end of the table.

Table D-2 68000 Instruction Summary

Instruction	CPU	Syntax	Instruction Code Map	SRC	DST	Condition Codes	Priv	Notes
			F E D C B A 9 8 7 6 5 4 3 2 1 0			XNZVC		
ORI.s		#n,ea	0 0 0 0 0 0 0 0 S z D e s t i n I m m e d i a t x x x x x x x x (x x x x x x x x x x x x x x x x)	I	ADEA	-**00		
ORI.B (to CCR)		#n,CCR	0 0 0 0 0 0 0 0 0 0 1 1 1 1 0 0 0 0 0 0 0 0 0 0 I m m e d i a t	I	CCR	*****		
ORI.W (to SR)		#n,SR	0 0 0 0 0 0 0 0 0 1 1 1 1 1 0 0 I m m e d i a t x x x x x x x x	I	SR	*****	X	
CMP2.s	20	ea,Rn	0 0 0 0 0 S z 0 1 1 S o u r c e D d a r 0 0 0 0 0 0 0 0 0 0 0 0	CEA	REA	-U*U*		
CHK2.s	20	ea,Rn	0 0 0 0 0 S z 0 1 1 S o u r c e D d a r 1 0 0 0 0 0 0 0 0 0 0 0	CEA	REA	-U*U*		
BTST		Dn,ea	0 0 0 0 S d r 1 0 0 D e s t i n	Dn	DEA	--*--		
BCHG		Dn,ea	0 0 0 0 S d r 1 0 1 D e s t i n	Dn	ADEA	--*--		
BCLR		Dn,ea	0 0 0 0 S d r 1 1 0 D e s t i n	Dn	ADEA	--*--		
BSET		Dn,ea	0 0 0 0 S d r 1 1 1 D e s t i n	Dn	ADEA	--*--		
MOVEP.s2		d16(An1),Dn2 Dn1,d16(An2)	0 0 0 0 T d r 1 D S 0 0 1 F a r D i s p l a c e x x x x x x x x	d(An) Dn	Dn d(An)	-----		

Instruction	*CPU*	*Syntax*	*Instruction Code Map*	*SRC*	*DST*	*Condition Codes*	*Priv*	*Notes*
ANDI.s		#n,ea	0 0 0 0 0 0 1 0 S z D e s t i n I m m e d i a t x x x x x x x x (x x x x x x x x x x x x x x x x)	I	ADEA	-**00		
ANDI.B (to CCR)		#d8,CCR	0 0 0 0 0 0 1 0 0 0 1 1 1 1 0 0 0 0 0 0 0 0 0 0 I m m e d i a t	I	CCR	*****		
ANDI.W (to SR)		#d16,SR	0 0 0 0 0 0 1 0 0 1 1 1 1 1 0 0 I m m e d i a t x x x x x x x x	I	SR	*****	X	
SUBI.s		#n,ea	0 0 0 0 0 1 0 0 S z D e s t i n I m m e d i a t x x x x x x x x (x x x x x x x x x x x x x x x x)	I	ADEA	*****		
ADDI.s		#n,ea	0 0 0 0 0 1 1 0 S z D e s t i n I m m e d i a t x x x x x x x x (x x x x x x x x x x x x x x x x)	I	ADEA	*****		
RTM	20	Rn	0 0 0 0 0 1 1 0 1 1 0 0 S d a r	REA		*****		
CALLM	20	#d8,ea	0 0 0 0 0 1 1 0 1 1 S o u r c e 0 0 0 0 0 0 0 0 A r g c o u n t	CEA		-----		
CAS.s	20	Dc,Du,ea	0 0 0 0 1 S z 0 1 1 D e s t i n 0 0 0 0 0 0 0 U d r 0 0 0 C d r	Dn	AMEA	-****		
CAS2.s	20	Dc1:Dc2,Du1:Du2,(Rn1:Rn2)	0 0 0 0 1 S z 0 1 1 1 1 1 1 0 0 D d a r 0 0 0 U d r 0 0 0 C d r D d a r 0 0 0 U d r 0 0 0 C d r	Dn	(An) & (Dn)	-****		[m]

Instruction		Operands	Encoding	Source	Destination	Flags	
BTST		#d5,ea	0 0 0 0 1 0 0 0 0 0 D e s t i n 0 0 0 0 0 0 0 0 0 0 0 B i t n o	I	DEA~I	--*--	
BCHG		#d5,ea	0 0 0 0 1 0 0 0 0 1 D e s t i n 0 0 0 0 0 0 0 0 0 0 0 B i t n o	I	ADEA	--*--	
BCLR		#d5,ea	0 0 0 0 1 0 0 0 1 0 D e s t i n 0 0 0 0 0 0 0 0 0 0 0 B i t n o	I	ADEA	--*--	
BSET		#d5,ea	0 0 0 0 1 0 0 0 1 1 D e s t i n 0 0 0 0 0 0 0 0 0 0 0 B i t n o	I	ADEA	--*--	
EORI.s		#n,ea	0 0 0 0 1 0 1 0 S z D e s t i n I m m e d i a t x x x x x x x x (x x x x x x x x x x x x x x x x)	I	ADEA	-**00	
EORI.B (to CCR)		#d8,CCR	0 0 0 0 1 0 1 0 0 0 1 1 1 1 0 0 0 0 0 0 0 0 0 0 I m m e d i a t	I	CCR	*****	
EORI.W (to SR)		#d16,SR	0 0 0 0 1 0 1 0 0 1 1 1 1 1 0 0 I m m e d i a t x x x x x x x x	I	SR	*****	X
CMPI.s	[e]	#n,ea	0 0 0 0 1 1 0 0 S z D e s t i n I m m e d i a t x x x x x x x x (x x x x x x x x x x x x x x x x)	I	ADEA	-****	
MOVES.s	10	ea,Rn Rn,ea	0 0 0 0 1 1 1 0 S z F e f a d r T d a r D 0 0 0 0 0 0 0 0 0 0 0	AMEA [q] REA	REA AMEA [q]	-----	X
MOVE.B		ea1,ea2	0 0 0 1 T i n d e s S o u r c e	DEA	ADEA	-**00	
MOVEA.L		ea,An	0 0 1 0 D a r 0 0 1 S o u r c e	EA	An	-----	
MOVE.L		ea1,ea2	0 0 1 0 T i n d e s S o u r c e	EA	ADEA	-**00	
MOVEA.W		ea,An	0 0 1 1 D a r 0 0 1 S o u r c e	EA	An	-----	

Instruction	CPU	Syntax	Instruction Code Map	SRC	DST	Condition Codes	Priv	Notes
MOVE.W		ea1,ea2	0 0 1 1 T i n d e s S o u r c e	EA	ADEA	-**00		
NEGX.s		ea	0 1 0 0 0 0 0 0 S z D e s t i n		ADEA	*****		
MOVE.W (from SR)		SR,ea	0 1 0 0 0 0 0 0 1 1 D e s t i n	CCR	ADEA	-----	[p]	
CHK.s2	[e]	ea,Dn	0 1 0 0 D d r 1 S 0 S o u r c e	DEA	Dn	-*UUU		[a]
LEA		ea,An	0 1 0 0 D a r 1 1 1 S o u r c e	CEA	An	-----		
CLR.s		ea	0 1 0 0 0 0 1 0 S z D e s t i n		ADEA	-0100		
MOVE.W (from CCR)	10	CCR,ea	0 1 0 0 0 0 1 0 1 1 D e s t i n	CCR	ADEA	-----		[i]
NEG.s		ea	0 1 0 0 0 1 0 0 S z D e s t i n		ADEA	*****		
MOVE.W (to CCR)		ea,CCR	0 1 0 0 0 1 0 0 1 1 S o u r c e	DEA	CCR	-----		[i]
NOT.s		ea	0 1 0 0 0 1 1 0 S z D e s t i n		ADEA	-**00		
MOVE.W (to SR)		ea,CR	0 1 0 0 0 1 1 0 1 1 S o u r c e	DEA	CCR	-----	X	
NBCD		ea	0 1 0 0 1 0 0 0 0 0 D e s t i n		ADEA	*U*U*		
LINK.L	20	An,#d32	0 0 1 0 1 0 0 0 0 0 0 1 D a r D i s p l a c e x x x x x x x x x x x x x x x x x x x x x x x x	I	An,Pc	-----		

SWAP		Dn	0 1 0 0 1 0 0 0 0 1 0 0 0 D d r		Dn	-**00		
BKPT	10	#d3	0 1 0 0 1 0 0 0 0 1 0 0 1 V e c			-----		[g]
PEA		ea	0 1 0 0 1 0 0 0 0 1 S o u r c e	CEA	–(SP)	-----		
EXT.s2		Dn	0 1 0 0 1 0 0 0 1 S 0 0 0 D d r		Dn	-**00		
EXTB.L	20	Dn	0 1 0 0 1 0 0 1 1 1 0 0 0 D d r		Dn	-**00		
MOVEM.s2		reglist,ea	0 1 0 0 1 D 0 0 1 S T e f a d r	all REA	ACEA & –(An)	-----		
		ea,reglist	R e g i s t e r l i s t m a s k	CEA & (An)+	all REA			
TST.s		ea	0 1 0 0 1 0 1 0 S z D e s t i n		ADEA	-**00		[e]
TST.W/TST.L	20	ea			EA			
TAS		ea	0 1 0 0 1 0 1 0 1 1 D e s t i n		ADEA	-**00		
ILLEGAL			0 1 0 0 1 0 1 0 1 1 1 1 1 1 0 0			-----		[b]
MULS.L/MULU.L	20	ea,Dn	0 1 0 0 1 1 0 0 0 0 S o u r c e	DEA	Dn,Dn	-***0		
	20	ea,Dn1:Dn2	0 D d r T Q 0 0 0 0 0 0 0 H d r					
DIVS.L/DIVU.L	20	ea,Dn	0 1 0 0 1 1 0 0 0 1 S o u r c e	DEA	Dn,Dn	-***0		[v]
	20	ea,Dn1:Dn2	0 D d r T Q 0 0 0 0 0 0 0 H d r					
DIVSL.L/DIVUL.L	20	ea,Dn1:Dn2						
TRAP		#d4	0 1 0 0 1 1 1 0 0 1 0 0 V e c t	[t]	[t]	-----		
LINK.W		An,#d16	0 1 0 0 1 1 1 0 0 1 0 1 0 D a r	I	An,Pc	-----		
UNLK		An	0 1 0 0 1 1 1 0 0 1 0 1 1 D a r	An,(SP)+	SP,An	-----		
MOVE		An,USP	0 1 0 0 1 1 1 0 0 1 1 0 D S a r	An	USP	-----	X	
(USP)		USP,An		USP	An		X	
RESET			0 1 0 0 1 1 1 0 0 1 1 1 0 0 0 0			-----	X	

Instruction	CPU	Syntax	Instruction Code Map	SRC	DST	Condition Codes	Priv	Notes
NOP			0 1 0 0 1 1 1 0 0 1 1 1 0 0 0 1			-----		
STOP			0 1 0 0 1 1 1 0 0 1 1 1 0 0 1 0		SR	*****	X	
RTE			0 1 0 0 1 1 1 0 0 1 1 1 0 0 1 1	(SP)+	SR,PC	*****	X	[s]
RTD	10		0 1 0 0 1 1 1 0 0 1 1 1 0 1 0 0	(SP)+ [r]	PC	-----		
RTS			0 1 0 0 1 1 1 0 0 1 1 1 0 1 0 1	(SP)+	PC	-----		
TRAPV			0 1 0 0 1 1 1 0 0 1 1 1 0 1 1 0	[t]	[t]	-----		
RTR			0 1 0 0 1 1 1 0 0 1 1 1 0 1 1 1	(SP)+	CCR,PC	*****		
MOVEC	10	Rc,Rn Rn,Rc	0 1 0 0 1 1 1 0 0 1 1 1 1 0 1 D T d a r C o n t r o l r e g i s	cr	REA	-----	X	[h]
JSR		ea	0 1 0 0 1 1 1 0 1 0 D e s t i n	CEA	PC	-----		
JMP		ea	0 1 0 0 1 1 1 0 1 1 D e s t i n	CEA	PC	-----		
ADDQ.s		#d3,ea	0 1 0 1 I m m 0 S z D e s t i n	Q	AEA [k]	*****		[c]
Scc		ea	0 1 0 1 C o n d 1 1 D e s t i n		ADEA	-----		
DBcc		Dn,label	0 1 0 1 C o n d 1 1 0 0 1 D d r D i s p l a c e x x x x x x x x	Dn,I	PC	-----		[d]
TRAPcc.s3	20	{#n}	0 1 0 1 C o n d 1 1 1 1 1 S i z (x x x x x x x x x x x x x x x x) (x x x x x x x x x x x x x x x x)	[t]	[t]	-----		[b] [d]
SUBQ.s		#d3,ea	0 1 0 1 I m m 1 S z D e s t i n	Q	AEA [k]	*****		

Bcc	[f]	label	0 1 1 0 C o n d D i s p l a c e (D i s p l a c e x x x x x x x x) (x x x x x x x x x x x x x x x x)	I	PC	-----	[e]
BRA	[f]	label	0 1 1 0 0 0 0 0 D i s p l a c e (D i s p l a c e x x x x x x x x) (x x x x x x x x x x x x x x x x)	I	PC	-----	[e]
BSR	[f]	label	0 1 1 0 0 0 0 1 D i s p l a c e (D i s p l a c e x x x x x x x x) (x x x x x x x x x x x x x x x x)	I	PC	-----	[e]
MOVEQ (.L)		#d8,Dn	0 1 1 1 D d r 0 I m m e d i a t	Q	Dn	-**00	
OR.s		ea,Dn Dn,ea	1 0 0 0 T d r D S z F e f a d r	DEA Dn	Dn AMEA	-**00	
DIVU.W/DIVS.W		ea,Dn	1 0 0 0 D d r T 1 1 S o u r c e	DEA	Dn	-***0	[v]
SBCD		Dn1,Dn2	1 0 0 0 D d r 1 0 0 0 0 0 S d r	Dn	Dn	*U*U*	
SBCD		–(An1),–(An2)	1 0 0 0 D a r 1 0 0 0 0 1 S a r	–(An)	–(An)	*U*U*	
PACK	20	Dn1,Dn2,#d16	1 0 0 0 D d r 1 0 1 0 0 0 S d r A d j u s t m e n t x x x x x x	Dn	Dn	-----	
PACK	20	–(An1),–(An2),#d16	1 0 0 0 D a r 1 0 1 0 0 1 S a r A d j u s t m e n t x x x x x x	–(An)	–(An)	-----	
UNPK	20	Dn1,Dn2,#d16	1 0 0 0 D d r 1 1 0 0 0 0 S d r A d j u s t m e n t x x x x x x	Dn	Dn		
UNPK	20	–(An1),–(An2),#d16	1 0 0 0 D a r 1 1 0 0 0 1 S a r A d j u s t m e n t x x x x x x	–(An)	–(An)	-----	

Instruction	CPU	Syntax	Instruction Code Map	SRC	DST	Condition Codes	Priv	Notes
SUB.s		ea,Dn Dn,ea	1 0 0 1 T d r D S z F e f a d r	EA [k] Dn	Dn AMEA	*****		
SUBA.s2		ea,An	1 0 0 1 D a r S 1 1 S o u r c e	EA	An	-----		
SUBX.s		Dn1,Dn2	1 0 0 1 D d r 1 S z 0 0 0 S d r	Dn	Dn	*****		
SUBX.s		–(An1),–(An2)	1 0 0 1 D a r 1 S z 0 0 1 S a r	–(An)	–(An)	*****		
User–defined			1 0 1 0					[w]
CMP.s		ea,Dn	1 0 1 1 D d r 0 S z S o u r c e	EA [k]	Dn	-****		
CMPA.s2		ea,An	1 0 1 1 D a r S 1 1 S o u r c e	EA	An	-****		
EOR.s		Dn,ea	1 0 1 1 S d r 1 S z D e s t i n	Dn	ADEA	-**00		
CMPM.s		(An1)+,(An2)+	1 0 1 1 D a r 1 S z 0 0 1 S a r	(An)+	(An)+	-****		
AND.s		ea,Dn Dn,ea	1 1 0 0 T d r D S z F e f a d r	DEA Dn	Dn AMEA	-**00		
MULU.W/MULS.W		ea,Dn	1 1 0 0 D d r T 1 1 S o u r c e	DEA	Dn	-***0		
ABCD (.B)		Dn1,Dn2	1 1 0 0 D d r 1 0 0 0 0 0 S d r	Dn	Dn	*U*U*		
ABCD (.B)		–(An1),–(An2)	1 1 0 0 D a r 1 0 0 0 0 1 S a r	–(An)	–(An)	*U*U*		
EXG (.L) (Dn)		Dn1,Dn2	1 1 0 0 S d r 1 0 1 0 0 0 S d r	Dn,Dn		-----		
EXG (.L) (An)		An1,An2	1 1 0 0 S a r 1 0 1 0 0 1 S a r	An,An		-----		

Instruction		Operands	Opcode	Source	Destination	Flags
EXG (.L) (Dn,An)		Dn1,An2	1 1 0 0 S d r 1 1 0 0 0 1 S a r	Dn,An		-----
ADD.s		ea,Dn Dn,ea	1 1 0 1 T d r D S z F e f a d r	EA [k] Dn	Dn AMEA	*****
ADDA.s2		ea,An	1 1 0 1 D a r S 1 1 S o u r c e	EA	An	-----
ADDX.s		Dn1,Dn2	1 1 0 1 D d r 1 S z 0 0 0 S d r	Dn	Dn	*****
ADDX.s		–(An1),–(An2)	1 1 0 1 D a r 1 S z 0 0 1 S a r	–(An)	–(An)	*****
ASR.s/ASL.s		#d3,Dn	1 1 1 0 C n t R S z 0 0 0 D d r	Q	Dn	*****
ASR.s/ASL.s		Dn1,Dn2	1 1 1 0 S d r R S z 1 0 0 D d r	Dn	Dn	*****
LSR.s/LSL.s		#d3,Dn	1 1 1 0 C n t R S z 0 0 1 D d r	Q	Dn	***0*
LSR.s/LSL.s		Dn1,Dn2	1 1 1 0 S d r R S z 1 0 1 D d r	Dn	Dn	***0*
ROXR.s/ROXL.s		#d3,Dn	1 1 1 0 C n t R S z 0 1 0 D d r	Q	Dn	***0*
ROXR.s/ROXL.s		Dn1,Dn2	1 1 1 0 S d r R S z 1 1 0 D d r	Dn	Dn	***0*
ROR.s/ROL.s		#d3,Dn	1 1 1 0 C n t R S z 0 1 1 D d r	Q	Dn	-**0*
ROR.s/ROL.s		Dn1,Dn2	1 1 1 0 S d r R S z 1 1 1 D d r	Dn	Dn	-**0*
ASR/ASL (.W)		ea	1 1 1 0 0 0 0 R 1 1 D e s t i n		AMEA	*****
LSR/LSL (.W)		ea	1 1 1 0 0 0 1 R 1 1 D e s t i n		AMEA	***0*
ROXR/ROXL (.W)		ea	1 1 1 0 0 1 0 R 1 1 D e s t i n		AMEA	***0*
ROR/ROL (.W)		ea	1 1 1 0 0 1 1 R 1 1 D e s t i n		AMEA	-**0*
BFTST	20	ea {offset:width}	1 1 1 0 1 0 0 0 1 1 D e s t i n 0 0 0 0 B i t o f f B i t w i d		CEA & Dn	-**00

Instruction	CPU	Syntax	Instruction Code Map	SRC	DST	Condition Codes	Priv	Notes
BFEXTU	20	ea {offset:width},Dn	1 1 1 0 1 0 0 1 1 1 S o u r c e 0 D d r B i t o f f B i t w i d	CEA & Dn	Dn	-**00		
BFCHG	20	ea {offset:width}	1 1 1 0 1 0 1 0 1 1 D e s t i n 0 0 0 0 B i t o f f B i t w i d		ACEA & Dn	-**00		
BFEXTS	20	ea {offset:width},Dn	1 1 1 0 1 0 1 1 1 1 S o u r c e 0 D d r B i t o f f B i t w i d	CEA & Dn	Dn	-**00		
BFCLR	20	ea {offset:width}	1 1 1 0 1 1 0 0 1 1 D e s t i n 0 0 0 0 B i t o f f B i t w i d		ACEA & Dn	-**00		
BFFFO	20	ea {offset:width},Dn	1 1 1 0 1 1 0 1 1 1 S o u r c e 0 D d r B i t o f f B i t w i d	CEA & Dn	Dn	-**00		
BFSET	20	ea {offset:width}	1 1 1 0 1 1 1 0 1 1 D e s t i n 0 0 0 0 B i t o f f B i t w i d		ACEA & Dn	-**00		
BFINS	20	Dn,ea {offset:width}	1 1 1 0 1 1 1 1 1 1 D e s t i n 0 S d r B i t o f f B i t w i d	Dn	ACEA & Dn	-**00		
cpGEN	20	[cp parameters]	1 1 1 1 C p i 0 0 0 D e s t i n C o p r o c e s s o r c o m m d			-----		[n]
cpScc(.B)	20	ea	1 1 1 1 C p i 0 0 1 D e s t i n 0 0 0 0 0 0 0 0 0 0 C pc o n d		ADEA	-----		
cpDBcc(.W)	20	Dn,label	1 1 1 1 C p i 0 0 1 0 0 1 D d r 0 0 0 0 0 0 0 0 0 0 C p c o n d D i s p l a c e x x x x x x x x	Dn,I	PC	-----		

cpTRAPcc.s3	20	{#n}	1 1 1 1 C p i 0 0 1 1 1 1 S i z 0 0 0 0 0 0 0 0 0 0 C p c o n d (x x x x x x x x x x x x x x x x) (x x x x x x x x x x x x x x x x)			-----	
cpBcc.s2	20	Dn,label	1 1 1 1 C p i 0 1 S C p c o n d D i s p l a c e x x x x x x x x (x x x x x x x x x x x x x x x x)	I	PC	-----	
cpSAVE	20	ea	1 1 1 1 C p i 1 0 0 D e s t i n		ACEA & –(An)	-----	X
cpRESTORE	20	ea	1 1 1 1 C p i 1 0 1 S o u r c e		CEA & (An)+	-----	X

[a] The S bit field in CHK is reversed from other instructions (0=longword, 1=word). This is because the longword format is an MC68020 feature (not originally designed).

[b] ILLEGAL is the only instruction pattern guaranteed to always be an illegal instruction. All other patterns are reserved for future expansion by Motorola. TRAPF has no effect in an MC68020 program (like a NOP), but in a MC68010 program will cause an illegal instruction exception. Hence, Motorola recommends putting a TRAPF instruction at the beginning of any MC68020 program that is not backwards compatible with the MC68010. If the program is ever run on the MC68010, it will not cause serious trouble.

[c] An immediate value of 0 is interpreted as 8 in ADDQ, SUBQ, and the shift instructions.

[d] Condition codes 0000 (T) and 0001 (F) are not available in Bcc and cpBcc. Note that BRA has a bit pattern corresponding to "BRT", and BSR has a bit pattern corresponding to "BRF". DBcc, cpDBcc, Scc, cpScc, and TRAPcc allow all condition codes.

[e] Certain instructions have extended functions in the MC68020. Bcc, BRA, BSR allow 32–bit displacements; CHK allows 32–bit extensions (CHK.W legal on MC68000, CHK.L legal on MC68020); CMPI, TST support PC relative addressing modes.

[f] Bcc, BRA, BSR allow 8–bit, 16–bit, and 32–bit displacements as follows:
MC68000—If the 8–bit displacement is 0, then a 16–bit displacement follows.
MC68020—If the 8–bit displacement is hex FF, then a 32–bit displacement follows.

[g] BKPT has evolved as follows:
MC68000—Not implemented.
MC68010—Generates a breakpoint bus cycle with address space bits 111 and 32–bit address 0.
MC68020—Generates a breakpoint bus cycle with the breakpoint vector on address lines A2, A3, A4, and zero on addressed lines A0, A1; a response is also generated, either a 16–bit instruction, or an illegal instruction exception.

[h] MOVEC supports more control registers on the MC68020 (see list). For a list of the control registers, see the explanation of the instruction code map columns preceding Table D–2.

[i] MOVE from CCR and MOVE to CCR are technically word operations. Both require word (even) addresses, but only move the CCR byte. In addition, MOVE from CCR clears the upper byte of the destination.

[k] Address registers are illegal in byte operations.

[m] Note that CAS2 allows data indirect addressing, that is, (Dn).

[n] cpGEN: the legal addressing modes and condition code changes are dependent on the coprocessor.

[p] MOVE from SR is not privileged in MC68000, but is in MC68010/MC68020. This is necessary in order for the MC68010 to support system emulations. If an emulating operating system is actually running in user state, it must not be aware that is not in supervisor mode. By trapping any MOVE from SR instructions, this can be accomplished.

[q] MOVES moves across different address spaces, so its addressing modes are correspondingly limited.

[r] Displacement also added to SP (RTD instruction).

[s] RTE properly returns from any exception. RTE pops 4 to 44 words from the SSP or ISP, restores the PC and SR, and (when appropriate) restores other internal processing registers. Note: bus and address errors on the MC68000/MC68008 generate a stack format which does not fit into the general RTE return scheme. In these cases, 4 words must be popped from the stack before doing an RTE.

[t] TRAP, TRAPcc, TRAPV generate exceptions, and affect several registers.

[v] The division commands formats are:

DIVx.W ea,Dn	DN(long)	/ ea(word)	→	Dn(word quot , word rem)
DIVx.L ea,Dn	Dn(long)	/ ea(long)	→	Dn(long quot)
DIVx.L ea,Dn1:Dn2	Dn1:Dn2(quad)	/ ea(long)	→	Dn1(long rem) , Dn2(long quot)
DIVxL.L ea,Dn1:Dn2	Dn1(long)	/ ea(long)	→	Dn1(long rem) , Dn2(long quot)

[w] Instructions starting with bits 1010 are reserved for user definition. They generate interrupts, and are variously called emulate, user–defined, illegal, and undefined instructions. On the MC68000 and MC68010, instructions starting with bits 1111 generate interrupts similar to the 1010 instructions, but on the MC68020 they are used for the co–processor instructions.

E

M68000 Resources

The following symbols to the right of a listing indicate the categories of items available from a supplier (note that many of the systems mentioned in this list are now becoming available in 68020 versions):

K	Kits
SBC	Single board computers
Sys	Complete systems
S	Software
X	Cross compilers
U	Unix (or Unix-related)
Chip	Second source manufacturer

Allen Systems K/SBC/X
2151 Fairfax Road
Columbus, OH 43221
(614) 488-7122

FX-688 SBC inc MC68008/6551 USART @ $350 inc 8K EPROM/2K RAM
Cross assemblers for Apple II/John B. Allen

Alpha Microsystems Sys/S/U
PO Box 18347
Irvine, CA 92714

AM-100L/AM-1000/ Work Stations and Multiuser Systems MC68000 under AMOS, PC-DOS and UNIMOS. $5,000 to $100,000+

Alycon Corporation S/Sys/SBC/U
8716 Production Avenue
San Diego, CA 92121
(714) 578-0860

REGULUS OS (Unix+)/A68KPM SBC with LSI-11 bus compatiblity
256K basic model @ $2900; APX extended proc @ $29,900
I/O processor @ $2,345

Apple Computers Sys/S
20525 Mariani Avenue
Cupertino, CA 95014

Macintosh/Big Mac/XL/Lisa
Laser printer uses 10MHz MC68010 + 1 Mb RAM + .5 Mb ROM

Arete Systems Corp. Sys/S/U
San Jose, CA
(408) 263-9711

Dual 68000/Unix engine: Model 1124/under Unix V or RM/COS

Atari Sys/S
1196 Borregas Ave.
Sunnyvale, CA 94086

MC68000-based 520ST personal computer @ $800. Built-in color, sound, 512K RAM, 8 MHZ CPU. Runs TOS™, GEM™ (Digital Research Inc.).

AT&T Sys/S/U
P0 Box 967
Madison Square Station
New York, NY 10159

PC7300 uses 68010/512K-1 floppy/10Mb hard/built by Convergent Technology/built in 1200 baud modem @ $4,000-7,000

Boston Systems Office S/U/X
469 Moody Street
Waltham, MA 02154
(617) 894-0760

Software development for most micros/DEC//UMDS-10 OS/UMDS-30

CCA Uniworks S/U
Four Cambridge Center
Cambridge, MA 02142
(617) 492-8860

CCA EMACS = Full screen text editor under UNIX
Elisp = extension language

Charles River Data Systems, Inc. Sys/S/U
983 Concord Street
Framingham, MA 01701
(617) 655-1800

Universe 68/05 32bit versabus/12.5 mh/MC68000 i/o proc
Universe 2203 VME/UNOS = realtime ext of UNIX V

Chromatics Sys/S
2558 Mountain Industrial Boulevard
Tucker, GA 30084

CGC 7900 Color Graphics Computer/under IDRIS OS

Codata Systems, Inc. Sys/S/U
(CONTEL CODATA)
285 N. Wolfe Road
Sunnyvale, CA 94086

UniSoft UniPlus+/CTS-300/Intel Multibus/MERLIN OS/ Model 3300=multi-user 84Mb @ $13,500/ 33 Mb @ $9,600/ 12Mb @ $7,600/

Commodore International Sys/S
1200 Wilson Drive
Westchester, PA 19380
(215) 431-9100

AMIGA MC68000-based business/home computer @ $1295
Built-in Graphics/Sound/Amiga DOS

Compupro, Inc. Sys/S
3506 Breakwater Court
Hayward, CA 94545

Wide range of CP/M-68K single/multi-user systems

Control Systems, Inc. S
1317 Central Avenue
Kansas City, KS 66102

UCSD 2.0 Pascal compiler/interpreter for M68000

Convergent Technologies Sys/S/U
Data Systems Division
3055 Patrick Henry Drive
Santa Clara, CA 95050
(408) 980-0850

$20,000 16-user MegaFrame with 68010 10MHz
MiniFrame starter at $5,000
Unix V/ cobol;fortran-77;basic;pascal;C
See also AT&T PC7300

Cromemco, Inc. Sys/S/U
280 Bernardo Avenue
PO Box 7400
Mountain View, CA 94039
(415) 969-4710

UNIX V/ System 100 with 4 Mb up to System 300 with 16 Mb

CYPHER SBC/K/S
Motel Computers, Ltd.
174 Betty Ann Drive
Willowdale, Ontario
M2N 1X6, Canada
(416) 221-2340

MC68000/Z80 SBC, kit or assembled/under CP/M88

Digital Research, Inc. S/U
PO Box DRI
Monterey, CA 93941

CP/M 68K = version of CP/M for M68000

DUAL Systems Corporation Sys/S/U
720 Channing Way
Berkeley, CA 94710
(415) 549-3854

Instrumentation/process control
Model 83/80 UNIX// 68KS-7;68KS-8 UNIX V7
UniSoft UniPlus+ on S-100

Educational Microcomputer Systems SBC/K/X/S
PO Box 16115
Irvine, CA 92713
(714) 854-8545

M68000 macro cros ass for IBM PC @ $199
SBC @ $695 16K EPROM/20K RAM/2xRS-232C/debug monitor

EFCIS Chip
(Thomson-CSF & French Atomic
Energy Commission)
45 ave de l'Europe
78140 Velizy-Villacoublay
France

M68000 second source

Emulogic, Inc. X/S
362 University Avenue
Westwood, MA 02090

ECL-3211 OS/ assm/basic/C/fortran/pascal

Enertec, Inc. S
19 Jenkins Avenue
Lansdale, PA 19446
(215) 362-0966

Micro concurrent Pascal for M68000/interpreter-kernel 3.2K

farbware S/X
1329 Gregory
Wilmette, IL 60091
(312) 251-5310

Xassmblr A68K/linker L68K/+LIB68K for CP/M and PC-DOS @ $200- 250
C source @ $700

Forward Technology Sys/S/U
2175 Martin Avenue
Santa Clara, CA 95050
(408) 988-2378

FT-68X has Xenix/10Mhz Multibus Grafics cntlr

Genrad/Futuredata S/X
5730 Buckingham Parkway
Culver City, CA 90230

Pascal cross compiler

Hemenway Associates, Inc. S
101 Tremont Street, Suite 208
Boston, MA 02108

Floating Point package/Pascal compiler

Heurikon Corporation SBC/U/S
3201 Latham Drive
Madison, WI 53713
(800) 356-9602
(608) 271-8700

Minibox = UniSoft UniPlus+/ HK68 = SBC with DR CP/M 68K
PolyForth/Regulus/6-slot Multibus

Hewlett-Packard Sys/S/U
19447 Pruneridge Avenue
Cupertino, CA 95014

HP 9826A/HP 9000/200/ HP-UX OS
Portable UNIX on HP Integral PC @ $4990 inc HP-UX,PAM,HP Windows

Hitachi America Ltd Chip
1800 Bering Drive
San Jose, CA 95112

Licensed second source M6800/68000
CMOS version expected soon/=HD68000 available in normal 64pin
DIP PLUS new flat-pack for low-power/low-space portables

Honeywell, Inc. Sys/S/U
Billerica, MA
(617) 671-2744

M68000-based Unisoft UniPlus+ port
Workstation = MicroSystem NX @ $8,895-9,500

IBC Sys/S/U
Integrated Business Computers
21621 Nordhoff Street
Chatsworth, CA 91311
(818) 882-9007

IBC Ensign = UniSoft UniPlus+ port/32 station multi-user/8Mb

IBM Sys/S
Instruments Division
Orchard Park
PO Box 332
Danbury, CT 06810

Model 9000 @ $5,695 basic = 128K RAM/128K ROM/VERSABUS compatible
IEEE-488 interface/ Optional 4x5mb or 4x10mb hard disk

ICL, Ltd. Sys/S
Putney Bridge House
London, England

Version of Sinclair QL/MC68008 with telephone/modem

Inner Access Corporation Sys/K/SBC/S
517K Marine View
Belmont CA 94002
(415) 591-8295

MultiUser-16 @ $9,995 OEM = 8 user/500K/40 Mb/Mirage OS/S-100
MC68000 processor board @ $695/MC68010 version @ $795
Matching I/O board @ $695

Interleaf, Inc. Sys/S

Tech Publishing System TPS-2000 on MC68010 @ $37,500+

Intermetrics, Inc. S/X/U
733 Concord Avenue
Cambridge, MA 02138
(617) 661-0072

Cross asm/pascal/c - for all M68000s
Runs on VAX/VMS/UNIX also Apollo/Sun

IPI Sys/SBC/S
Industrial Programming, Inc.
100 Jericho Quadrangle
Jericho, NY 11753

MTOS-68K//assm/C/pascal//8K single-user
MTOS-68KF - ROM for Omnibyte/Microbar MC68000 SBC

Lattice, Inc. S/U

Lattice C compiler for all M68000s

Lexidata Corporation Sys/S/U
755 Middlesex Turnpike
Bilerica, MA

Graphics system 8000/UniSoft UniPlus+ port

Manx Software Systems S/X/U
PO Box 55
Shrewsbury, NJ 07701
(800) 221-0440

C compilers/cross compilers all M68000-based UNIX systems

Mark Williams Company S/X/U
1430 West Wrightwood Road
Chicago, IL 60614
(312) 472-6659

Unix compatible multi-user, multi-tasking COHERENT OS (tm)
C-compilers cross/native for M68000/PDP-11/Z8000/8086

MDB Systems, Inc. Sys/S/U
1995 N. Batavia Street
PO Box 5508
Orange, CA 92667-0508
(714) 998-6900

Micro/32 runs under Regulus OS

Metacomco S
Monterey, CA

LISP 68000 for creating expert systems

MicroDaSys, Inc. Sys/S/U
1541 S. Manhattan Place
Los Angeles, CA 90019
(213) 731-1475

68K Miniframe runs XENIX /uses MC6809 MMU. Plans for VENIX (VM version)

Microfocus, Inc. Sys/S
2465 E. Bayshore Road
Suite 400
Palo Alto, CA 94303
(415) 856-4161

Animator Visual Programming/ COBOL debugging aids

Microsoft S/U/X
10800 NE 8th Street
Bellevue, WA 98004
(206) 426-9400

XENIX = version of UNIX v7/assm/basic/C/fortran 77/Cobol-74 for M68000 and 8086/8088

Microware Systems Corporation S/U
1866 NW 114th Street
Des Moines, IA 50322
(515) 224-1929

OS-9 = UNIX-like OS; runs on most M6809/68000s from ROM-based control systems up to medium-scale time-sharing systems. 16K ROMable written in M68000 assm. C/pascal/basic/cobol

Morrow Designs, Inc. Sys/S/U
600 McCormick Street
San Leandro, CA

TRICEP = $2,500 per user/4-8 users/UniSoft UniPlus+ port/UNIX v/ 512K+4CRTs+16Mb disk @ $10,495// with 32Mb disk @ $12,495

Mostek Corporation Chip
1215 West Crosby Road
Carrollton, TX 75006

Licensed second source

Motorola Microsystems Sys/K/S
3102 North 56th Street
Phoenix, AZ 85018

VERSAdos/structured Macro assm/pascal/fortran-77
Wide range of Software Development aids

Motorola Semiconductor Products, Inc.
Literature Department
PO Box 20924
Phoenix, AZ 85036

Books/tech lit

Motorola Semiconductors, Inc. Chip/S/X/K/U
3501 Ed Bluestein Boulevard
Austin, TX 78721
(512) 440-2122

EXORcisor- MEX68KDM Design module-MACSbug 8K monitor
VERSAbus/VMM-Versamodule monoboard micro
VME bus/subset of versabus

Multi Solutions, Inc. S/X
123 Franklin Corner Road, Suite 207
Lawrenceville, NJ 08648
(609) 896-4100

S1 OS on M68000 for DataMedia 932/IBM 9000/ NCR Tower/Compupro 68K/
Dual CPU/ IBC Ensign/ Stride/ SORD 68/ Pertec 3200/ FORCE
Wide range of Cross assemblers/compilers for M68000 and most micros

Network Research Corporation S
1101 Colorado Avenue
Santa Monica, CA 90401
(213) 394-9508

LAN software-interconnects M68000/DEC-VAXen/IBM-PC; more

OASYS Inc. S/X
60 Aberdeen Ave.
Cambridge, MA 02138
(617) 491-4180

Cross development tools/C and macro assemblers

Omnibyte Corporation SBC/K
245 W. Roosevelt Road
West Chicago, IL 60185

Multibus OB68K1 SBC

Oregon Software S/X
6915 S.W. Macadam Avenue
Portland, OR 97021
1(800) 874-8501
(503) 226-7760

Pascal-2 native/cross all M68000-based UNIX systems

Perkin-Elmer Sys/S/U
Oceanport, NJ

Wide range single/multi-user systems (UniSoft UniPlus+ port)

Pertec Computer Corporation Sys/S/U
Irvine, CA
(714) 660-0488

Model 3220 multiproc/5 stations/53 Mb @ $14,000

Phase One Sys/S
Suite 830, 7700 Edgewater Drive
Oakland, CA 94621
(415) 562-8085

OASIS OS on Intel 8086/8 and M68000/ 32-users

Phase Zero, Ltd. S/X
2509 N. Campbell Ave.
Suite 130
Tucson, AZ 85719

ASSEM68K Apple II/II+ (32K) to MC68000 cross assm. @ $95
MINOS 1.0 OS for Apple II(+/E) and dtack grounded 68000AP board gives direct m/c language control of MC68000

PIXEL Computers, Inc. Sys/S/U
260 Fordham Road
Wilmington, MA 01887

Pixel 80/10 MHz M68000 with UniSoft UniPlus+ port

Plexus Sys/S/U

Model P/35 and wide range UNIX workstations

Pyramid Sys/S
PO Box 7295
Mountain View, CA 94039

Wide range multiuser business/scientific systems

Radio Shack Computers Sys/S/U
A Division of Tandy Corporation
300 One Tandy Center
Fort Worth, TX 76102

Model TRS-16 Professional & Business PC

RDS S/U
Relational Database Systems, Inc.
2471 East Bayshore Road, Suite 600
Palo Alto, CA 94303

INFORMAX/File-it!/C-ISAM on most M68000-based UNIX systems

Relational Technology, Inc. S
2855 Telegraph Avenue
Berkeley, CA 94705
(415) 845-1700

INGRES - Relational Database Management for M68000-based UNIX systems

RELMS /X/S
Relational Memory Systems, Inc.
1650-B Berryessa Road
San Jose, CA 95133
(408) 729-3011

ICEBOX/SPICE software development systems
Wide range of Assemblers/Cross Assemblers for Intellec and iPDS

Rockwell International Chip
Electronic Devices Division
PO Box 3669, RC55
Anaheim, CA 92803

Licensed second source

Ryan McFarland Corporation S
609 Deep Valley Drive
Rolling Hills Estates, CA 90274
(213) 541-4828

RMCOBOL compiler for M68000-based UNIX systems

SBE, Inc. Sys/SBC/S/X
4700 San Pablo Avenue
Emeryville, CA 94608
(415) 652-1805

SBE350/300/250 multiuser systems run Regulus OS (see Alycon)/LEX68
Wide range of M68000-based SBCs and software
PROBUG for M68K10 or M68K12 or M68CPU (tm)
IEEE796 multibus SBC's/1Mb on board RAM

Signetics/Phillips Chip
811 East Arques Avenue
Sunnyvale, CA 94086

Licensed second source

Silicon Graphics Sys/S/U
Mountain View, CA

Graphics Workstation - M68000-based UNIX

Sinclair Electronics Sys/S
Cambridge, England

QL (Quantum Leap) MC68008 home computer under $1,000

Smoke Signal Sys/S/U
Westlake Village, CA
(818) 889-9340

UNIX desktop family = VAR/68K (MC68008 + Regulus os) $7,900- 25,000

Southwind Software, Inc. S
4520 E. 47th St. So.
Wichita, KS 67210
(316) 788-5537

IPT (Integrated Productivity Tools) for NCR Tower, 1632 and Plexus P/35

SRITEK, Inc. K/SBC/S/U
10230 Brecksville Road
Cleveland, OH 44141
(216) 526-9433

MC68000 Versabus/microcard to run XENIX on IBM XT @ $1995-$2995 including software

Stride Micro Sys/S/U
(formerly Sage Computers)
4905 Energy Way
Reno, NV 89502
(702) 322-6868

Stride 400 series/ multi-user/multi-OS/VMEbus @ $2,900-$60,000

Sun Microsystems, Inc. Sys/S/U
2550 Garcia Avenue
Mountain View, CA 94043
(415) 960-1300

Model 2/250 UNIX Workstation under $10,000 (10MHz 68010)
Range of multiuser VM systems eg Model 2/120 = 1Mb, Model 2/170 = 2 Mb
Graphics/10 Mb per sec Ethernet

Swift Computers, Ltd. S
England

Mirage OS for M68000-based multiuser systems

Symbiont Systems, Inc. Sys/S
PO Box 44652
Lafayette, LA 70504-4652
(318) 984-6545

Series 70/400 = multiuser 12MHz M68000 under MIRAGE OS

System Kontakt S/X
6 Preston Court
Bedford, MA 11730

Cross assm/pascal compiler - M68000 and DEC PDP-11

Technical Systems Consultants, Inc. S/X
1200 Kent Avenue
West Lafayette, IN 47906

UniFLEX/macro and cross assm/basic/C/pascal

Tecmar, Inc. K/S

M68000-based hard disc - links to Apple ImageWriter and modem
Daisy chains on AppleTalk LAN

TeleSoft S/X
10639 Roselle Street
San Diego, CA 92121

Pascal/ADA software development tools for M68000

Texas Instruments, Inc. Sys/S/K/U
PO Box 402430
Dallas, TX 75240
1(800) 527-3500

The Nu Machine = MC68010 10MHz UNIX
32 bit data/address 37.5 Mb per sec bandwith NuBus
with Multibus converter/ under Motorola System V/68 OS

UniPress Software, Inc. S/X/U
2025 Lincoln Highway
Edison, NJ 08817
(201) 985-8000

EMACS/MINIMACS full screen/multi-window editors for M68000 systems. AMSTERDAM compiler kit = C; Pascal compilers/cross compilers for M68000 and Intel 8086/8 running under UNIX

UNISOFT Systems S/X/U
739 Allston Way
Berkeley, CA 94710
(415) 644-1230

UNIX porting for over 90 microcomputers from 60 manufacturers
UniSoft UniPlus+ available on most M68000-based systems
ASM68 assemblers and cross assemblers for VAXen, etc.
IP/TCP networking/record and file locking

Victory Computer Systems, Inc. SBC/S/U
1610 Berryessa Road
San Jose, CA 95133
(408) 295-7370

UniSoft UniPlus+/VME bus SBC has M68000 + 256K dual-ported RAM/ OS=VRTX

Whitesmiths, Ltd. S/X/U
PO Box 1132
Ansonia Station
New York, NY 10023

C/pascal compilers for M68000-based UNIX and versados systems

Wicat Systems Sys/S/U
Orem, UT

UNIX workstations/multiuser systems under UniSoft UniPlus+/MCS OS/150WS

Xidak, Inc. S/X
530 Oak Grove Ave., Suite 101
Menlo Park, CA 94025
(415) 324-8745

MAINSAIL = applications software development language for M68000-based UNIX systems (and others)

F

ASCII Table — Numerical Conversions

DEC X_{10}	HEX X_{16}	OCT X_8	Binary X_2	ASCII
0	00	00	000 0000	NUL
1	01	01	000 0001	SOH
2	02	02	000 0010	STX
3	03	03	000 0011	ETX
4	04	04	000 0100	EOT
5	05	05	000 0101	ENQ
6	06	06	000 0110	ACK
7	07	07	000 0111	BEL
8	08	10	000 1000	BS
9	09	11	000 1001	HT
10	0A	12	000 1010	LF
11	0B	13	000 1011	VT
12	0C	14	000 1100	FF
13	0D	15	000 1101	CR
14	0E	16	000 1110	SO
15	0F	17	000 1111	SI
16	10	20	001 0000	DLE
17	11	21	001 0001	DC1
18	12	22	001 0010	DC2
19	13	23	001 0011	DC3

DEC X_{10}	HEX X_{16}	OCT X_8	Binary X_2	ASCII
20	14	24	001 0100	DC4
21	15	25	001 0101	NAK
22	16	26	001 0110	SYN
23	17	27	001 0111	ETB
24	18	30	001 1000	CAN
25	19	31	001 1001	EM
26	1A	32	001 1010	SUB
27	1B	33	001 1011	ESC
28	1C	34	001 1100	FS
29	1D	35	001 1101	GS
30	1E	36	001 1110	RS
31	1F	37	001 1111	US
32	20	40	010 0000	SP
33	21	41	010 0001	!
34	22	42	010 0010	’’
35	23	43	010 0011	#
36	24	44	010 0100	$
37	25	45	010 0101	%
38	26	46	010 0110	&
39	27	47	010 0111	‘
40	28	50	010 1000	(
41	29	51	010 1001	)
42	2A	52	010 1010	*
43	2B	53	010 1011	+
44	2C	54	010 1100	’
45	2D	55	010 1101	-
46	2E	56	010 1110	.
47	2F	57	010 1111	/
48	30	60	011 0000	0
49	31	61	011 0001	1
50	32	62	011 0010	2
51	33	63	011 0011	3
52	34	64	011 0100	4
53	35	65	011 0101	5
54	36	66	011 0110	6
55	37	67	011 0111	7
56	38	70	011 1000	8
57	39	71	011 1001	9
58	3A	72	011 1010	:
59	3B	73	011 1011	;
60	3C	74	011 1100	<
61	3D	75	011 1101	=

DEC X_{10}	HEX X_{16}	OCT X_8	Binary X_2	ASCII
62	3E	76	011 1110	>
63	3F	77	011 1111	?
64	40	100	100 0000	@
65	41	101	100 0001	A
66	42	102	100 0010	B
67	43	103	100 0011	C
68	44	104	100 0100	D
69	45	105	100 0101	E
70	46	106	100 0110	F
71	47	107	100 0111	G
72	48	110	100 1000	H
73	49	111	100 1001	I
74	4A	112	100 1010	J
75	4B	113	100 1011	K
76	4C	114	100 1100	L
77	4D	115	100 1101	M
78	4E	116	100 1110	N
79	4F	117	100 1111	O
80	50	120	101 0000	P
81	51	121	101 0001	Q
82	52	122	101 0010	R
83	53	123	101 0011	S
84	53	124	101 0100	T
85	55	125	101 0101	U
86	56	126	101 0110	V
87	57	127	101 0111	W
88	58	130	101 1000	X
89	59	131	101 1001	Y
90	5A	132	101 1010	Z
91	5B	133	101 1011	[
92	5C	134	101 1100	\
93	5D	135	101 1101	]
94	5E	136	101 1110	∧
95	5F	137	101 1111	—
96	60	140	110 0000	`
97	61	141	110 0001	a
98	62	142	110 0010	b
99	63	143	110 0011	c
100	64	144	110 0100	d
101	65	145	110 0101	e
102	66	146	110 0110	f
103	67	147	110 0111	g

DEC X_{10}	HEX X_{16}	OCT X_8	Binary X_2	ASCII
104	68	150	110 1000	h
105	69	151	110 1001	i
106	6A	152	110 1010	j
107	6B	153	110 1011	k
108	6C	154	110 1100	l
109	6D	155	110 1101	m
110	6E	156	110 1110	n
111	6F	157	110 1111	o
112	70	160	111 0000	p
113	71	161	111 0001	q
114	72	162	111 0010	r
115	73	163	111 0011	s
116	74	164	111 0100	t
117	75	165	111 0101	u
118	76	166	111 0110	v
119	77	167	111 0111	w
120	78	170	111 1000	x
121	79	171	111 1001	y
122	7A	172	111 1010	z
123	7B	173	111 1011	{
124	7C	174	111 1100	¦
125	7D	175	111 1101	}
126	7E	176	111 1110	~
127	7F	177	111 1111	DEL

Index

MORE FROM SAMS